*L.A. Maritime Institute and
the Port of Los Angeles*

Partners in the
TopSail Youth Sail
Training Program

www.portoflosangeles.org

Los Angeles Maritime Institute
www.LAMItopsail.org

⟆ GREENPORT HARBOR ⟅
LONG ISLAND, NEW YORK

Photo: Gil Amiaga

An authentic, working deep water port
surrounded by seaside farms & vineyards...

Official 2004 TALL SHIPS CHALLENGE® Atlantic Coast Port

Tall Ships 2000® Cruise Port

Americas' Sail Host-1995 & 1998

Visit Mitchell Park & Marina.
Deep water dockage, vintage carousel, amphitheater
and boardwalk—all in the heart of the village!
Easy walk to stores, galleries, beach,
hospital & Historic District.

Special arrangements made for visiting tall ships.

Services available include hauling, shipbuilding,
welding, engine repair & hardware.

For more information contact:
Mayor David E. Kapell, Village of Greenport
236 Third Street, Greenport, New York 11944
631-477-3000 • FAX 631-477-1877
or hail the harbormaster on VHF channel 9

Yorktown, Virginia

Riverwalk Landing

Deep water port rejuvenates 18th century village.

New port opening spring 2005 on the shores of the York River in historic Yorktown, Virginia. Only minutes from the Chesapeake Bay, Riverwalk Landing offers deep water dockage, ice machine, pump-out, private showers and locker room for crew, floating docks at the foot of the new development to accommodate ships from 20' to 400' and ample parking. Also featured at Riverwalk Landing are specialty shops, an upscale restaurant, an outdoor performance venue for events and free parking. Easy walk to the historic village, shops, galleries, beach and restaurants and just 12 miles from Williamsburg.

——— For More Information: ———
Kristi Olsen, York County Tourism and Events
P.O. Box 532, Yorktown, VA 23690
757-890-3500
or contact the dock master at Coastal Properties
cpm@erols.com or 410-269-0933

www.riverwalklanding.com

Look what's *blowing* into town...

2003 ASTA Port of the Year!

TALL SHIPS®
CHICAGO 2006

August 3-9

Chicago River, Lakefront and Navy Pier®

For more information visit
www.cityofchicago.org/specialevents

MAYOR'S OFFICE OF
SPECIAL EVENTS
CHICAGO
RICHARD M. DALEY, MAYOR

CHICAGO
PARK
DISTRICT
come out
and play

City of Chicago
Richard M. Daley, Mayor

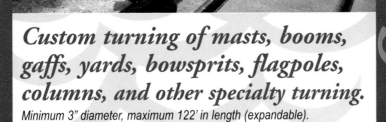

Jordan Harrison
Insurance Brokers, Inc.

Marine Insurance Professionals

Innovative & Comprehensive Solutions

For Licensed Marine Professionals
and their Vessels

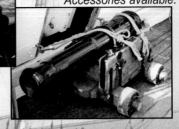
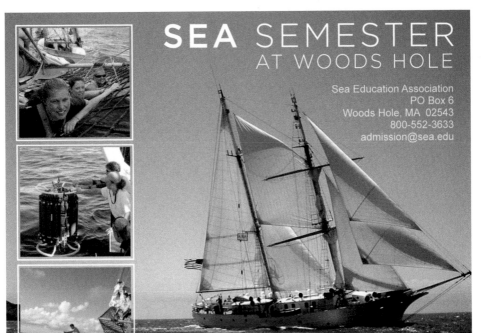

Develop
A New
image
for your business.

ASTA

The official design agency of the
ASTA organization

advertising

marketing

direct mail

brand identity

website design

packaging

ARTINIUM

3 Davol Square
Providence, RI

401•454•5297
www.artinium.com

photo by Voytec Wacowski

American Sail Training Association

The mission of the American Sail Training Association is to encourage character building through sail training, promote sail training to the North American public, and support education under sail.

This Book is Dedicated to
the Memory of
Exy and Irving Johnson

TALL SHIPS CHALLENGE®
RACE SERIES

photo by Volker Corell

2005 PACIFIC COAST

June 23-26	Victoria, British Columbia, Canada
June 27-28	RACE 1: Victoria to Tacoma
June 30-July 4	Tacoma, Washington, USA
July 7-10	Vancouver, British Columbia, Canada
July 12-15	Port Alberni, British Columbia, Canada
July 16-20	RACE 2: Port Alberni to Oregon
Aug 5-8	Channel Islands Harbor, Oxnard, California, USA
Aug 9-11	RACE3: Oxnard to Los Angeles
Aug 11-14	Los Angeles, California, USA
Aug 15-17	RACE 4: Los Angeles to San Diego
Aug 17-21	San Diego, California, USA

2006 GREAT LAKES

2007 ATLANTIC COAST

Set Sail With The Challenge!
Contact ASTA Today!

American Sail Training Association
240 Thames Street-PO Box 1459, Newport, RI 02840 USA
401-846-1775 asta@sailtraining.org
www.tallships.sailtraining.org

TALL SHIPS
CHALLENGE

Adventure + Education = Sail Training

photo by Mitec Wacowski   photo courtesy of SALTS

Table of Contents

The mission of the American Sail Training Association is to encourage character building through sail training, promote sail training to the American public, and support education under sail.

Published by:

American Sail Training Association (ASTA)
PO Box 1459, 240 Thames Street
Newport, RI 02840 USA
Phone: (401) 846-1775
Fax: (401) 849-5400
E-mail: asta@sailtraining.org
Website: www.tallships.sailtraining.org

Acknowledgments

Many of the photographs in this edition of *Sail Tall Ships!* were supplied by:

Thad Koza
Tall Ships Photography
24 Mary Street
Newport, RI 02840 USA
Phone: (401) 846-5274

MAX
Bywater Lodge-Pierside Marine
Lymington, Hants SO41 5SB
UNITED KINGDOM
Phone: + 44 (0) 1590 672047

Benson Lee
Maritime Photography
PO Box 282996
San Francisco, CA 94128
Tel: 415-585-1805

Registered Trademarks

The following registered trademarks and service marks are owned by the American Sail Training Association:

Tall Ships®
Tall Ships are Coming!®
Tall Ships 2000®
TALL SHIPS CHALLENGE®

Sail Tall Ships! A Directory of Sail Training and Adventure at Sea, 16th edition

Directory Team

Compiled and edited by Lori A. Aguiar, ASTA Program Manager
Design by Darren Marinelli, Artinium Design, 3 Davol Square, Providence, RI 02903
Consulting by Pucino Print Consultants, 631 Fletcher Road, North Kingstown, RI 02852
Printed in Canada by Dollco Printing

ISBN 0-9636483-9-X
Cover photo: *The Picton Castle*, Photo by Captain Daniel Moreland

Foreword █ By Peter A. Mello

Welcome Aboard!

Books like this one serve several purposes. First, they allow us to dream about things we have not yet experienced. Second, they allow us to learn about the possibilities of changing lives, including our own. Third, they guide us through the process of making those dreams come to life. Finally, they offer us the opportunity to become part of a community that seeks out adventure and a better appreciation of our rich maritime heritage.

Whether you have been to sea on a tall ship or not, SAIL TALL SHIPS! will introduce you to new vessels, ideas, dreams, experiences and friends.

Dream - Four years ago the Michigan Maritime Museum undertook the daunting task of designing, building, launching and operating a replica tall ship. This fascinating story of how their dream became a reality can be found on page 58.

Beautiful images of tall ships cause us to dream and in the center of the book you will find the wonderful work of renowned maritime photographer Benson Lee. We also take pleasure in introducing you to some of the majestic ASTA member vessels that will be taking part in our 2005 TALL SHIPS CHALLENGE® Series. While we often think of tall ships as being from the past, all of these wonderful images are of sail training vessels today!

Learn- In his essay "Fair Winds – Tall Ships Set Sail for Adventure" (adapted with permission from Alaskan Airlines Magazine), Paul Frichtl writes about an adventure he embarked on with his 16 year old son Kyle on the schooner *Maple Leaf*. Intergenerational life long learning experiences like this can be found on ASTA member vessels all across the globe.

In his essay Around the Word Adventure, Erik Pickhardt shares his adventures and experiences on his 12-month circumnavigation on board the *Picton Castle*. Erik shows us why sail training is a life changing experience for young trainees.

Sail - SAIL TALL SHIPS! will help you chart a course to your adventure at sea. Sail training experiences are valuable for "youth of all ages" and voyages of any duration and distance. Whether you are a K-12 teacher scouting field trips for the day, a college junior away for a semester at sea, a couple celebrating an anniversary on an adventure-travel sailing expedition, a family on a weekend excursion on a Maine windjammer or an older adult on an Elderhostel Adventures Afloat program, this book contains the information to make your experience successful and to create memories that will last for a lifetime.

Join - Finally, we encourage you to become part of an incredible community of tall ship sailors, professional sail trainers, sail trainees, marine educators, tall ships enthusiasts and others that support the ASTA mission. You don't have to work or have ever sailed on a tall ship to join. If you enjoy this book you are automatically eligible to be a member. All of the information that you will need to join ASTA today, can be found at the end of this book. Your membership supports ASTA youth education, leadership development and maritime heritage preservation programs. We look forward to having you as our crew member for this exciting and worthwhile voyage. Please don't hesitate!

So we hope you dream, learn but most importantly SAIL TALL SHIPS!

Peter A. Mello, Executive Director

2005 Board of Directors

Officers

Chairman – Captain Michael J. Rauworth, Esq. – Boston, MA
Vice Chairman – Mr. Jeffrey Parker – McLean, VA
Vice Chairman – Captain Doug Prothero – Halifax, NS, Canada
Treasurer – Mr. Dexter Donham – Dover, MA
Executive Director – Mr. Peter A. Mello – Mattapoisett, MA

Class of 2007

Mr. Michael Brown – Jamestown, RI
Captain Deborah Hayes – Newport, RI
Mr. James Kerr, Esq. – New York, NY
Mr. Dan Stetson – Dana Point, CA
Captain Christopher Rowsom – Baltimore, MD

Mr. Robert Frost – White Plains, NY
Ms Karen Helmerson – New York, NY
Captain Ken Neal-Boyd – San Francisco, CA
Mr. F. C. "Bunky" Wichmann – Charleston, SC

Class of 2006

Mr. Christopher Cloud – New Haven, CT
Mr. Richard Hawkins – Hyannis, MA
Ms Meghan Wren – Port Norris, NJ
Captain Joseph Maggio – Coconut Grove, FL

Captain James Gladson – San Pedro, CA
CAPT Ivan Luke, USCG – Newport, RI
Mr. Greg Child – Fort Lauderdale, FL

Class of 2005

Mr. Eric R. Dawicki – Fairhaven, MA
Mr. Pierre Manigault – Charleston, SC
Mr. Jed Pearsall – Newport, RI
Mr. Barclay "Tim" Warburton IV – Newport, RI
Captain William Pinkney – Chicago, IL
Ms Nicole McLoughlin – Scarborough, ONT, Canada

Mr. Graham Green – San Francisco, CA
Mr. Herb McCormick – Newport, RI
Ms Alix Thorne – Georges Mills, NH

National Advisory Board / Commodores Council

Mr. Henry H. Anderson, Jr. – Newport, RI
Ms Beth Bonds – Mt. Pleasant, SC
Mr. Chuck Fowler – Olympia, WA
Ms Nancy H. Richardson – San Pedro, CA
Captain Walter Rybka – Erie, PA
Ms Pamela Dewell – Kinnear, WY
VADM Thomas R. Weschler, USN (Ret.) – Newport, RI
CAPT David V. V. Wood, USCG (Ret.) – Newport, RI

Captain Richard Bailey – Wellfleet, MA
Mr. Bart Dunbar – Newport, RI
Mr. Thomas Gochberg – New York, NY
Mr. Nigel Rowe – Gosport, Hants, UK

ASTA Crew

Ms Lori A. Aguiar – Program Manager
Mr. Nicholas M. Baker – Operations Assistant
Mr. Steven H. Baker – Race Director
Mr. Michael A. Jehle – Development Director
Ms Adria M. Lande – Education Coordinator
Mr. Peter A. Mello – Executive Director

A Brief History of the American Sail Training Association

In the summer of 1972 Barclay Warburton III, of Newport, Rhode Island, his two sons, and several friends, sailed his brigantine *Black Pearl* across the Atlantic to participate in a tall ships race from Cowes on the south coast of England to Malmo in Sweden, organized by what was then known as The Sail Training Association. He was so inspired by the enthusiasm and spirit he saw in that international gathering of tall ships and young people that he set out to create a similar organization in order to bring the same kind of spirit to the United States, and through his efforts the American Sail Training Association was founded the following year. ASTA soon became the first national association to formally affiliate with what eventually became known as the International Sail Training Association.

The Tall Ships Races in which the *Black Pearl* took part had first been held in 1956, when a London solicitor, Bernard Morgan, had the idea of bringing what he imagined to be the last of the world's great square-riggers together for a race as a sort of last hurrah—a farewell salute—for the Great Age of Sail. A committee was formed, and with the support and assistance of the Portuguese Ambassador in London, a race was organized from Torbay, on England's Cornish coast, to Lisbon. Five square-rigged schoolships entered the race: Denmark's *Danmark*, Norway's *Christian Radich* and *Sorlandet*, Belgium's *Mercator*, and Portugal's first *Sagres*.

The event proved to be anything but a funeral procession, however, and it has since grown into an annual series that would astonish its original organizers. Today, hundreds of tall ships from around the world come together annually for friendly competition in international and regional Tall Ships Races organized by Sail Training International in Europe and national affiliates such as ASTA. These races, along with waterfront festivals in designated start and finish ports, bring together the ships and young people of most European countries, Russia and the former Soviet states, the Americas, and the Pacific Rim. The key elements uniting these events are an emphasis on youth—from the beginning, tall ship racing rules have required that not less than half those onboard participating vessels be between 15 and 25 years of age—and a formula for rating participating vessels which allows vessels ranging in size from the largest square-riggers down to yachts of 30 or more feet in length.

The mission of the American Sail Training Association is to encourage character building through sail training, promote sail training to the North American public, and support education under sail.

The American Sail Training Association's efforts in its first decade were primarily focused on organizing tall ships races on the European model, but from the mid-1980s to the mid-1990s it worked on a multitude of activities broadly aimed at promoting sail training and supporting education under sail in North America. Thus at the beginning of the 21st century, the American Sail Training Association has evolved into an organizer of tall ships races, a strong industry association for the growing numbers of vessels involved in providing opportunities for people of all ages to take part in deep water sailing experiences and a public charity which makes sail training more available and affordable for young people.

With an organizational membership of over 250 vessels, the American Sail Training Association serves as a forum for information exchange, professional development, and program standards. Through such initiatives as the Council of Educational Ship Owners, which worked successfully for the passage of the Sailing School Vessels Act of 1982 and the Sailing School Vessels Council, founded the following year, ASTA has continued to work with the US Coast Guard and other agencies to create and maintain a friendly regulatory climate for the development of sail training.

Safety at sea has been an enduring emphasis, and in conjunction with the Australian bicentennial gathering of tall ships in Sydney in 1988, a group of ASTA members organized the first international discussion on safety standards and practices, and equipment for sail training programs. Since 1992, ASTA has organized a biennial Safety Forum, which regularly draws professional sail trainers from around the world. Also in the 1980s, ASTA developed the concept of the Sail Training Rally; a competition among crews both at sea and ashore, which provides trainees with an opportunity to demonstrate their seamanship skills in a friendly but competitive format. During shore side events, the general public can observe the sort of teamwork and maritime skills that are learned on board sail training vessels at sea.

Over the years, the American Sail Training Association has undertaken many other projects to meet the needs of a rapidly growing sail training community. These include a variety of publications including SAIL TALL SHIPS! A Directory of Sail Training and Adventure at Sea, an Annual Conference on Sail Training which attracts international interest and participation, a Billet Bank to assist vessels in finding qualified crewmembers, and vice versa, a growing program of scholarships and grants to support trainees, vessels, and professional crew, and a constantly expanding website. In 2001, building on the spectacular success of Tall Ships 2000®, ASTA launched its most ambitious project to date—the TALL SHIPS CHALLENGE® Series, an annual series of tall ships races and maritime port festivals that informs the general public about tall ships, our maritime heritage and the incredible power of sail training to change lives.

Captain Irving and Exy Johnson--extraordinary people at home at sea with a tremendous zest for life- what the Johnsons did is enough to merit the record books... but how they did it is even more inspiring.

2005 marks the 75th Anniversary of Irving Johnson's incredible filming of Around Cape Horn aboard the great square-rigger *Peking*. Plus, with Exy Johnson's passing in 2004, we are reminded to honor the memory of her wonderful inspiration and their remarkable legacy as a couple. "The pleasure of being afloat is ever with us, under sail or power. Voyaging is our life's work..." said Exy of their 'retirement' after sailing more miles than astronauts to the moon and back!

In the Wake of Captain Irving and Exy Johnson...

By Nancy Richardson

When conferees were asked at an ASTA Conference "how were you inspired into sail training?" over half wrote 'Irving Johnson' and/or *Yankee*. At the same time, more than half of the rest mentioned that first generation of inspirees...and so on as we sail into the future in their wake. With quotes from shipmates, as well as Irving and Exy's own words, here are insights on why the Johnsons are universally revered as the premier pioneers of sail training.

"It is not only the remarkable statistics of their singular accomplishments that bring us together. We are all familiar with their unprecedented seven circumnavigations, the endless miles carefully planned and completed in the canals and waters of Europe, and the adventurous cruising along the New England coastline. The lives of these two extraordinary people are most unusual and noteworthy for all these tangible and well known accomplishments. However, this well-deserved tribute is more a natural outgrowth of the deep feelings we all share for the manner in which the Johnsons have touched and enriched our own lives as a result of the opportunity to know them as shipmates and friends. Whether one sailed for a week as a young Girl Scout on *Yankee* or as a canal hand on the lovely ketch in Europe, perhaps traveled with them vicariously by way of their many exciting writings and lecture films, or were actually lucky enough to spend 18 months voyaging around the world with them, the rare privilege to have these two people in any part of our lives has most certainly contributed to the sum total of our productive and pleasant experiences, and stimulated each one of us in a most astounding way.

The lessons of life taught by them personally, or by way of meeting the enormous challenges of life at sea under their direction, are ones that have influenced each of us and provided an unusual life experience from which to draw strength, help, or just pure pleasure at being alive and able to make the most of what life has to offer in its various stages. Going to sea with the Johnsons meant an opportunity to benefit by Irving's natural ability to teach and instill self-confidence, and Exy's warmth and appreciation for each person's precious individuality. Each crew, large or small, developed a spirit of cooperation and a sense of independence."

Written for the program of the Yankee reunion at National Geographic in 1976, by Lydia Edes Jewell, 6th World Voyage

PREPARATION, LEADERSHIP AND TEAMWORK

"And regarding Exy, my favorite memory was in '99 when we had a ceremony aboard EAGLE to cut the first plank for the two Johnson namesake vessels in LA. It was supposed to be a ceremonial thing and you had a handsaw and miter box set up with a piece of wood in it, and the idea was for her to make a few strokes of the saw and then get on with the reception. Well, we didn't figure Exy's tenacity into the equation... She started sawing and wouldn't quit! As I recall it was a piece of hard wood about 2 inches thick and she was bound and determined to saw it all the way through. She was frail and not the heartiest looking lady physically, but she didn't know that and kept sawing away like a lumberjack. We finally had one of the young guys take over for her and finish the cut lest we risked having the guest of honor collapse during the ceremony!"

CAPT Ivan Luke, USCG
Former CO, USCG Barque EAGLE

"What Captain Johnson did for us, via that short film, was to connect whole generations of Coast Guard sailors learning about the sea aboard EAGLE with their heritage... Connect them with a time past when it was very much man against the sea. A time before multiple layers of technology insulated us from the environment. With Irving's help we strove to remind cadets, officer candidates and crew that going to sea remains a challenging profession where preparation, leadership and teamwork will always be important. Irving's singularly concise and engaging way of telling his story, coupled with some unbelievable amateur video did more to make the point in a half hour or so than a thousand hours of lecture could ever do. And his dry Yankee wit was second to none!"

Captain Ivan Luke, former CO, USCG Barque EAGLE, writing about the impact of the Peking Around the Horn film.

ATTENTION TO DETAIL

When asked for advice, Irving invariably said, "pay attention to detail" and he applied it everywhere, at sea and ashore. The Johnsons held themselves to the highest standards and sailed with high expectations of others, saying "If you're going to do something, do it right (and don't wait too long.)" Irving carried learnings from *Peking's* Captain Jurs all his life. He said that with Jurs "it was never a case of 'good enough!'"

SHIPMATES

Of his shipmates around Cape Horn, Irving said, "there is some remarkable force that makes ordinary men surpass themselves in feats of strength, effectiveness, and daring... almost a complete disregard of self when the ship badly needed something done..." He went on to marvel at the "incredible use of human hands" aboard *Peking*. Others were quick to recognize Irving's own remarkably strong hands and grip. With just his handshake you felt his grasp up to your elbow!

"Irving had the sea skills and Exy had the people skills, and they complemented each other throughout their lives and life together. She was a linguist, able to relate to people on their many foreign shores. Irving and she were powerful people, as gentle as they were strong. No soft touch, Irving's discipline held us together...with no loss overboard and no crew break up, even in Tahiti!"

"While Irving was the consummate captain, Exy was the perfect hostess, cruise-director, translator and guide, in addition to her usual functions as helmsman, accountant, social and business correspondent and writer. "

SHIPS

Their three ships named *Yankee* were strong and simple, sailed smartly and safely. "*Yankee* had more than strength and beauty. She was ideally suited to our purpose. We wanted a home and a ship that amateurs could sail." In fact, Brigantine *Yankee* was so beautiful it was one of National Geographic's first cover pictures, and was reproduced more often than any other NG photo for years!

At Sea Education Association, Irving and Exy were trusted advisors from the beginnings, with each ship an evolution, purpose-designed in a succession from *Yankee*. And, of the program, Exy wrote "Molding the lives of young people by taking them to sea is something that cannot be accomplished in any other way."

"Starting with the schooner. The North Sea pilot ships did not have yards, they were just fore and aft rigged. They did not tend to go very far, but just go back and forth to pick up and deliver pilots. Father knew that we would be sailing in the tropics with the (fair) trade winds so he added a yard with a foresail below. The raffee above was an easy sail to set with a six foot long club that came down to the deck. In those days, topsail schooners were fairly common. If you ignored the foresail and the raffee, it was an ordinary schooner which could be easily handled with a small crew.

By the time of the brigantine, things had changed a bit. Father had had a lot of experience sailing in the tropics and knew that the squaresails really pulled a lot in the trade winds. Increasing their area would help. Also, operating square riggers were as rare as hen's teeth. The three yards and squaresails (with the two studdingsails for pictures) really made the brigantine stand out. It was great for photos, great for publicity, as well as useful. The topsail was small and heavy duty, it was one of our "lowers", and could be used in heavy weather. The topgallant (it was shaped like a topgallant, although it was rigged like an upper top-sail, but certainly Father liked the name topgallant better) was beautiful with the private signal on it (also great for photos). I doubt that the curtain track on the bottom of the fore yard was an original idea of my father's, but certainly it was uncommon and untraditional. Father made the foresail head only two thirds of the length of the yard, because the lee-ward third was always blanketed anyways. Less sail with the same amount of pulling power. Again, if you ignored the squaresails, it was an easily handled schooner with a small mainsail. On the world cruises we always had a large crew, so the extra work of the squaresails was not a problem. During the summers with the Girl Scout Mariners, we would take in the squaresails earlier because we were short handed (of those who could work aloft). One interesting trick that my father used when a squall came up was to temporarily slack the fisherman peak halyard and sheet. The sail would lie against the leeward yardarms and the pressure would be off the maintopmast. After the squall we would just tighten up and we avoided all the work of dousing and resetting the sail.

The ketch was designed to be handled by two people, one at the helm. 400 sq ft is about the largest sail that one person can handle in a breeze. My father figured that he could handle a bit more, so the mainsail was 450 sq ft. He figured that the "guests" would not always be sailors able to help and he did not want to need to have another crewmember. The red and white headsail was one of the first, also great for photos and publicity. The mule was a great sail, but very uncommon. The luff was set on the main backstay and it sheeted to the top of the mizzenmast. One could both tack and jibe under that sail alone. Being up high it really pulled well and was easy to handle. Father was very pleased with it. Of course the ketch had many other unusual features: folding masts, twin centerboards, three foot wide keel, interior circulating engine cooling, etc.. My father really enjoyed the year and a half on the seventh world voyage that he spent designing it. Rod Stevens, who drew the lines, said that she was the stiffest yacht that he ever designed. The mainmast was enormous in circumference." - Robert Johnson

SAILING THE SEAS

The fact that they sailed with youth crew makes their record of seven circumnavigations even more notable. Together with their crews of youth-of-all-ages, they were passage and friend-makers, exploring remote anchorages and encountering new peoples, like the bungee-vine-jumpers in the New Hebrides. In WWII, Irving's knowledge of strategic anchorages in the Pacific led to his commanding a Navy survey vessel.

They reveled in sharing their exuberance under sail. Exy's determination and enthusiasm were unbounded, and there are numerous times others worried while she climbed aloft, even into her late 80s. She thought of her life as "uncommonly lucky, and blessed at having a husband I could love all the time!" Under sail, Irving became energized and alive. He belonged to

Carefully balancing the crew of teenage boys with a few college-age young women to add maturity and social graces, Irving and Exy chose youth crew from those who understood that it was not "time out from school" but rather time IN for real life. . . similar to Captain Jim Gladson's mantra "School is where the kids are!" for LA Maritime Institute's Topsail Youth program aboard the twin brigantines proudly named after Irving and Exy.

Captain Jim Gladson with Exy Johnson

the sea. Though not very tall, his strength was legendary, and he moved on deck – glided is a better word – with a certain grace... Ever challenged and challenging, Irving described the exhilaration of being at the helm in a storm – "like being an attempt to keep the ship on the head of a pin!"

If Irving hated anything, it was having to take in sail. About the 'A-number-one storm' he wished for around Cape Horn he wrote, "But what is there to read about if you have a smooth sea?" Years later, on a cruise-ship tour to Antarctica, Irving was glad for the chance calm landing to get a little piece of Cape Horn to carry on his keychain.

At the 2002 launching of LA Maritime Institute's twin brigantines, when naming Exy Johnson, Exy said she felt "a sense of immortality in this ship since she will carry young people in my name."

BOOKS: By Irving Johnson:
The Peking Battles Cape Horn, Sea History Press, NMHS,1977
(Round the Horn in a Square Rigger, pub. by Milton Bradley,1932)
Shamrock V's Wild Voyage Home, pub. by Milton Bradley,1933

By Irving and Electa Johnson:
Westward Bound in the Schooner Yankee, pub. by W.W. Norton,1936
Sailing to See, pub. by W.W. Norton, 1939
Yankee's Wander World, pub. by W.W. Norton,1949
Yankee Sails Across Europe, pub. by W.W. Norton,1962
Yankee Sails the Nile, pub. by W.W. Norton,1966

By Irving and Electa Johnson and Lydia Edes
Yankee's People and Places, pub. by W.W. Norton,1955

Numerous articles and specials for National Geographic

Videos: Around Cape Horn in Peking, Mystic Seaport
          Irving Johnson: High Seas Adventurer, Mystic Seaport

Just as Irving was always 'full-bore and never halfway on anything,' Exy certainly echoed his 'Full Steam Ahead' philosophy.   When asked what his wife thought of all the sailing Irving replied "It was her idea."

LEAN FORWARD INTO LIFE

Peter Stanford (NMHS President emeritus) wrote in the foreword to *Peking Battles Cape Horn*: "Years ago, Captain Johnson was the guest of honor at the dinner of the American Sail Training Association held at Mystic Seaport. He talked of what he had learned in his seafaring, beginning with the ever memorable voyage in *Peking*. There was laughter and cheering, and all hands came to their feet, as one person, when he'd done. There was rapt silence among those sailing skippers, however, when he spoke of scenes from the voyage, battling for life off Cape Horn…' that taught me something,' said Captain Johnson to his hushed audience. 'It taught me to lean forward into life.' "

Irving M. Johnson 1905-1991, from Hadley, Massachusetts
Electa Search Johnson 1907-2004 from Rochester, NY
          Smith College 1929; University of California, Berkeley 1930
Met on Trans-Atlantic voyage aboard Schooner WANDER BIRD, 1931
Married 1932
Life stages – by cycles with Ships
1932-1958
          Seven 18-month-long world voyages with youth crew
          In between, 18 months at 'home', with winters spent lecturing, writing, film editing; and
          summers cruising in New England waters with Girl Scout Mariners
          (more than 2000 over the years!)

Yankee-Mariner Alumni Search

"Shipmates go their various ways and don't often meet again, but when they do, what memories!"

My own story goes back to my Brownie days, when Girl Scout Mariners in Maplewood, NJ sold my mother tickets to see 'Skipper' Johnson lecture about YANKEE around the world—from then on I wanted to be a Mariner and sail tall ships! Close to 100 ships later, my greatest blessing is the countless shipmates who have become friends, sharing Irving and Exy as our heroes.

Now we're looking for YANKEE-Mariner alums and are planning a reunion at LA Maritime Institute with our twin brigantines IRVING JOHNSON and EXY JOHNSON. Contact Nancy Richardson at nancy@sailtraining.org or write or call me at LAMI, Berth 84, San Pedro, CA 90731; 310-833-6055

June 6-10, 2004	**Race 1:** Miami to Jacksonville
June 10-13, 2004	Jacksonville, Florida, USA
June 14-17, 2004	**Race 2:** Jacksonville to Charleston
June 17-20, 2004	Charleston, South Carolina, USA
June 22-29, 2004	**Race 3:** Charleston to the Entrance to Delaware Bay
July 1-4, 2004	Philadelphia, PA and Camden, NJ, USA
July 8-11, 2004	Greenport, New York, USA
July 13-14, 2004	**Race 4:** Long Island to entrance to Narragansett Bay
July 15-20, 2004	Newport, Rhode Island, USA
July 21, 2004	**Race 5:** Wickford, RI to Fishers Island, NY
July 22-25, 2004	New London, Connecticut, USA
July 25-29, 2004	**Race 6:** New London to Halifax
July 29-Aug. 2, 2004	Halifax, Nova Scotia, Canada
Aug. 3-10, 2004	Additional Nova Scotia ports during Acadian 400th Anniversary
Aug. 12-15, 2004	Saint John, New Brunswick, Canada

The TALL SHIPS CHALLENGE® Race Series began in 2001 on the Great Lakes. Thirty vessels from 6 countries, and 1000 sail trainees and cadets participated in the races, sail training rallies and port festivals in seven US and Canadian ports. Detroit and Windsor celebrated their 300th Anniversary; additional ports were Kingston and Port Colborne, Ontario; Cleveland, Ohio; and Bay City and Muskegon, Michigan.

The 2002 series was sailed on the Pacific Coast of North America: Sixty vessels from seven countries participated in the series which included port festivals in Richmond, British Columbia; Seattle, Washington; San Francisco and Los Angeles, California. Races were sailed from the mouth of the Strait of Juan de Fuca to San Francisco and then on to Los Angeles. More than 1200 sail trainees enjoyed the experience.

The 2003 series was again on the Great Lakes: Twenty-seven vessels from India, the Netherlands, the British Virgin Islands, the US and Canada participated. Port festivals were held in Cleveland and Toledo, Ohio as part of the Ohio Bicentennial; Chicago; Muskegon and Bay City, Michigan; and Sarnia, Ontario. Four races were held between

ARE YOU READY...

ports and more than 1000 trainees enjoyed the races and cruises aboard vessels in the fleet. Millions of spectators came to the city waterfronts to see the vessels and talk with their crew/trainees to learn about life under sail and the opportunities to sail on ASTA member vessels.

The 2004 TALL SHIPS CHALLENGE® Race Series brought vessels together from ten different countries: Belgium, Brazil, Canada, the Cook Islands, Mexico, Poland, Romania, the United Kingdom, the United States, and Uruguay. Across 2,300 nautical

Grand Nellie

Tenacious

Cuauhtemoc

Pride of Baltimore II

miles these traditional sailing vessels tested their crews in friendly competition. The sailors aboard proudly displayed their ships to fascinated crowds in a dozen ports between race segments. Under blistering Florida sunshine and through impenetrable Nova Scotia fog, the ships' crews led their trainees in every aspect of running the vessels. Hand in hand with learning the ropes, the ships promoted team effort, responsibility, and personal development.

Of the nearly 40 vessels participating in the series, thirteen ships competed in the races, starting in Miami, Florida and finishing in Halifax, Nova Scotia. Using the Racing and Sailing Rules from Sail Training International, ASTA established a Youth Sail Training Division, requiring fifty percent or more of each vessel's crew to be between the ages of thirteen and twenty-five, and also added a Cruising Division, designed for vessels unable to meet the age criteria for the Youth Division.

The ships' diverse trainees took part in a great adventure sailing up the Atlantic coast. The schooner *Grand Nellie*, with a crew of fourteen and fifteen year old boys from the southeastern US, earned first place in the Youth Sail Training Division with the best overall standing, an unbeatable five first place finishes in six races. The *Tenacious*, of the UK, made their first voyage to North America. The accessibility of the ship and the enthusiasm of the crew sparked interest in sail training for the physically disabled in every port they visited. A fleet of impressive sailing ships from the navies of the world showed that training under sail is still highly valued in the age of motor vessels.

Ships crossed the starting line for Race One between Miami, Florida and Jacksonville, Florida, on June 7. After three hot and sunny days of sailing the Florida coast, the *Grand Nellie* took first place in the Youth Sail Training Division, followed closely by the Mexican naval training ship *CUAUHTEMOC* The teamwork of the physically disabled and able-bodied crew of the *Tenacious* brought them a first place win in the Cruising Division.

Race Two, between Jacksonville, Florida and Charleston, South Carolina, from June 10 - 13, again saw *Grand Nellie* win first place in the Youth Sail Training Division. The 1812 era replica *Pride of Baltimore II* took first in the Cruising Division.

Race Three, July 17 – 20, was set between Charleston, South Carolina, and the entrance of the Delaware Bay. The skilled crew of the *Grand Nellie*, sailed to victory in the Youth Sailing Division, beating the valiant effort of the Romanians on the naval sail training ship *MIRCIA*. A new participant, the colorful naval sail training ship *CISNE BRANCO* from Brazil, won the Cruising Division.

Following a weekend of perfect weather Race Four began in Greenport, Long Island on July 13 in challenging conditions that prevented some vessels from starting. At race's end the following day in Narragansett Bay, Rhode Island, the Polish barquentine *Pogoria* won the Youth Sail Training Division. *Pride of Baltimore II* won for the second time in the Cruising Division.

Race Five, for Class B and C vessels, began on a windless day in Wickford, RI and finished off Fishers Island, New York. The two consistent leaders of this year's series, the *Grand Nellie* and *Pride of Baltimore II* persisted for first place finishes in the Youth and Cruising divisions respectively.

The final and longest race of the series, Race Six, July 25 - 29, stretched from New London, Connecticut up to the spectacular waterfront of Halifax, Nova Scotia. The USCGC Barque *EAGLE* came back strong, taking first place in the Youth Sail Training Division followed by the *Grand Nellie*, in second place. The *Tenacious* lived up to its name, winning first place for the Cruising Division.

The last majestic tall ships unfurled their sails, cast off dock lines, and set a course for home as the 2004 TALL SHIPS CHALLENGE® Race Series wrapped up in Saint John, New Brunswick on August 16.

The 2004 TALL SHIPS CHALLENGE® was a triumph in many ways. Whether a vessel won or lost, the ships' crews demonstrated exemplary team effort, camaraderie, and discipline. A great sailing adventure from start to finish, the TALL SHIPS CHALLENGE® continues the tradition of sailing ships from different countries competing together in the spirit of friendship.

Thanks to the vessel operators, crews, trainees, port organizers, event volunteers, ASTA interns, board and staff, and the US and Canadian Coast Guards for all their hard work in a very successful series on the Atlantic Coast.

Mircea

Cisne Branco

Pogoria

USCG Eagle

The 2005 TALL SHIPS CHALLENGE, Race is a series of sailing races, cruises, crew rallies and maritime festivals organized by the American Sail Training Association in conjunction with seven US and Canadian ports on the Pacific Coast of North America.

Nearly 60 traditionally-rigged sailing vessels from Canada, the US, Mexico, New Zealand, Russia and other countries are expected to take part. They are crewed by young people (either civilians or cadets) ages 13 - 25 who are engaged in sail training programs under the supervision of captains and professional crewmembers.

The maritime festivals in each host port give visitors a chance to board the vessels and meet the crew and trainees and learn about the many varied opportunities to sail and travel on ASTA member vessels. All seven host ports are planning a full program of cultural events, nautical displays and crew competitions – crewmembers and visitors will have plenty to do and see.

FOR THE CHALLENGE?

Racing is one of the most important components of the series. Historically, when two or more sailing vessels are found to be heading in the same direction, an impromptu race almost always ensues. The crews pay closer attention to the other ships and to the trim of their own sails in hopes of outdoing their counterparts.

To take advantage of this natural competitive spirit and the heightened awareness and enthusiasm racing brings out in the young crews, four races are planned during the 2005 TALL SHIPS CHALLENGE® Series. Race legs will take the ships from Victoria, BC to Tacoma, WA;

Port Alberni, BC to Oxnard, CA; Oxnard to Los Angeles; and Los Angeles to San Diego. But how can you compare the racing of a 60-foot sailboat with a 240-foot sailing ship carrying 10 times as much sail area? A special rating system developed in the European tall ships races is used to assign vessels of any size a relative performance factor. This gives all vessels an equal chance of winning if they are sailed well. Before the series starts, six pages of hull, rigging and sail measurements for each vessel are submitted to Sail Training International headquarters in England. They compute Time Correction Factors (TCFs) for each vessel using a program that has been fine-tuned over many years of competition. After each race, the ASTA Race Committee multiplies the time it takes for a vessel to complete the course – its elapsed time – by its TCF in the race to determine the corrected time; corrected times are then compared to determine final standings.

Safety at sea is critical and each participating sailing vessel has been inspected and certified for its intended use either by a national maritime authority (the Coast Guard in the US) or by an internationally-endorsed society. At the beginning of the season, the safety

TALL SHIPS CHALLENGE.

June 23-26	Victoria, British Columbia, Canada
June 27-28	**Race 1:** Victoria to Tacoma
June 30-July 4	Tacoma, Washington, USA
July 7-10	Vancouver, British Columbia, Canada
July 12-15	Port Alberni, British Columbia, Canada
July 16-20	**Race 2:** Port Alberni to Oregon
Aug. 5-8	Channel Islands Harbor, Oxnard, California, USA
Aug. 9-11	**Race 3:** Oxnard to Los Angeles
Aug. 11-14	Los Angeles, California, USA
Aug. 15-17	**Race 4:** Los Angeles to San Diego
Aug. 17-21	San Diego, California, USA

equipment on each vessel is double-checked by the ASTA Race Committee and any discrepancies are remedied prior to the first race.

While underway, racers use VHF or SSB radio to keep in contact once or twice daily with the race communications officer on the escort vessel and often with the ASTA race office by satellite-assisted email. Positions are noted and posted on ASTA's "Follow the Fleet" website so that friends and family can follow the sailors' progress. When the series starts, it is likely that not every trainee berth will have been spoken for and interested youth are encouraged to apply to sail in a race or cruise between host ports.

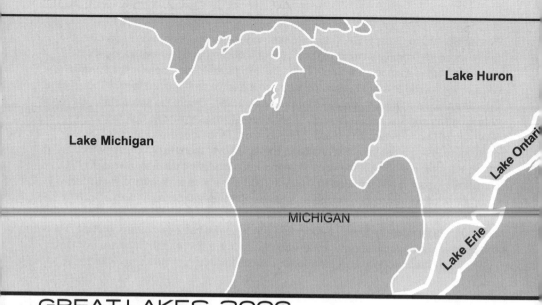

Lake Huron

Lake Michigan

Lake Ontario

MICHIGAN

Lake Erie

GREAT LAKES 2006

2006 TALL SHIPS CHALLENGE® Race Series Great Lakes
(for vessels under 35.5m rig height)

July 20-23, 2006   Bay City, Michigan, USA
July 27-31, 2006   Green Bay, Wisconsin, USA

Additional tentative host ports are: Cleveland, OH; Chicago, IL; and Detroit, MI / Windsor, ON, Canada

2006 TALL SHIPS® World Peace Cup

April 20-25, 2006   Antigua

in conjunction with the Antigua Classic Yacht Regatta

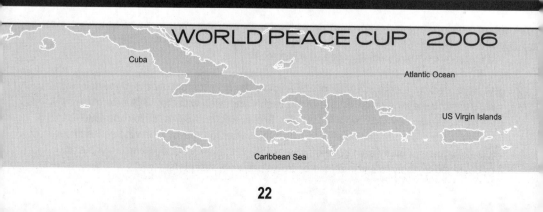

WORLD PEACE CUP 2006

Cuba

Atlantic Ocean

US Virgin Islands

Caribbean Sea

What did you do on your summer vacation?

From the Logs of the ASTA 2004 Summer Interns

By ASTA 2004 Summer Interns

Each summer during the TALL SHIPS CHALLENGE® Race Series, the American Sail Training Association offers a team of young people the opportunity to serve as interns with the ASTA Race Team. Throughout the course of the summer series, the interns assist the race director, work in the race office, man the ASTA information booths, interact with the participating vessels and their crews and trainees, the port organizers and volunteers, and represent ASTA to the hundreds of thousands of people who come out to see the tall ships. And of course, sail! Long days and hard work are a part of the job – but so are enduring friendships and memories that will last a lifetime. Since the first TALL SHIPS CHALLENGE® Series in the summer of 2001, young people from as far away as Japan and the United Kingdom, as well as Canada and the United States have had the chance to experience the CHALLENGE from this unique perspective.

25

Elizabeth Brin

Thursday, June 10, 2004

Day 3 of our stay in Jacksonville, Florida. It's sunny, hot, and borderline raining (for those of you who didn't see the 5:30 local Jacksonville news, Jacksonville was smack in between two hard core rain and thunder storms, but luckily in the clear). The spirits are high and energy is moving as we are all getting ready for the next couple days of festivities to begin.

My name is Elizabeth and I attend Bates College where I am a Studio Art major. I have studied abroad in Ghana and Florence. I love water of all sorts and am excited to be spending my summer traveling with ASTA exploring the East Coast by land and by sea!

Looking out of the window of my 15th floor room I can see the ships lined up on the docks with their flags flying from their rigging. Crazy to think that by tomorrow I will not only be looking at all of the ships lined up, but also staring directly at the masts of the *Eagle*, one of the biggest tall ships participating in this CHALLENGE. The past few days have consisted of a lot of packing, unpacking, loading, unloading, running around, waiting around, and basically getting all of the work done before the FUN begins, but that time is finally upon us. Although tedious at times, the work has definitely created a stronger bond between the interns and the staff members, which will not only help ASTA run more smoothly throughout the summer, but help the whole operation be a good and fun experience for all of us.

By 1:00 this afternoon the ASTA booth was set up, the wind had picked up and we were ready to work. Hurrah!! While waiting for some booth material to be picked up I had the lucky opportunity of watching the *Pogoria* and the *Pride of Baltimore II* come into port.

Elizabeth answers a question while working in the ASTA info booth.

What an incredible experience. The view of the ships was truly awe-inspiring. Struck by the same beauty that I saw, many people came up and asked me what this event was all about. Telling them all I could about the races that are happening they gladly listened and inquired how they could have a chance to participate. The whole air about this port seams to be of intrigue and excitement. I can't wait until the festivities get under way and then we are off to our next destination, via ship I hope.

My name is Jessica (Jess) and I am 21 years old. I am a recent graduate of Fairfield University with a bachelor's degree in communications. I love traveling and meeting new people and I can't wait for my adventure to begin as a part of the ASTA crew! Sailing on the tall ships will be a completely new experience for me and will surely bring new opportunities and challenges. I can't wait to get started!

Friday, June 24, 2004

On the longest race leg so far the TALL SHIPS CHALLENGE® fleet is pressing north towards the Delaware Bay. The ships paraded out of Charleston under overcast skies on Monday, passing flocks of 420s racing in the Harbor. Starting with a fair breeze the ships emerged from the haze and charged across the starting line. The crew of the *Grand Nellie* strategized well and crossed the line first, followed by an impressive series of ships – *Cisne Branco*, *Zenobe Gramme*, *Tenacious*, *Pogoria*, and *Mircea*. The *Eagle* and *Cuauhtemoc* started the race with the other ships but then diverged to visit a few other ports before they rejoin the CHALLENGE fleet in Newport, RI. Don't forget to check out the map of daily positions of the racing fleet. You can envision the tactics and strategy of each vessel as they try to take advantage of the wind and currents.

With their clouds of sail the tall ships are easy to spot, but there's something a little smaller you can be looking for as well... The crew if the Belgian ship *Zenobe Gramme* has made a tradition of setting off a message in a bottle every Sunday, no matter where in the world they are sailing. Keep your eyes peeled around the Delaware Bay, you may find an international note washed up on the beach!

We're certainly sad to leave a city as charming as Charleston – but we can't wait to see what Camden and Philadelphia have lined up for the 4th of July weekend.

Elizabeth (back) and Jess (front) watch the start of a race leg from the race committee boat

Rob Simmons

Saturday, July 9, 2004

The first rays of morning sun light glinted of the calm waters of the Delaware River, as I began my voyage aboard the *Grand Nellie*. There is nothing quite like the spectrum of colors from a sunrise coming off the water when you first wake. So surreal that one may think they are still within throws of a dream, as opposed to the reality of a very early morning aboard a sailing vessel filled with the sounds of young sail trainees and the ubiquitous eyes of Captain Jeff, and first mate Kyle.

From the moment I boarded the schooner *Grand Nellie*, and saw the crew of primarily fifteen year old young men, I knew I was in for a unique experience. Primarily from the south, generally in their first year of high school, they were very able and willing to run the ship in all areas of necessity. From raising the sails, to cooking dinner, to standing the midnight to four watches, they were all a tremendous asset to the ship, and taught me a great deal about the ways of a sailing vessel. They were learning at fifteen, what someone five years there elder would be learning at the Maritime Academy. It was very impressive to see that these young men had both the attention and focus necessary to help operate a ship.

Hello, my name is Robert Simmons. I am currently a third year student at the Massachusetts Maritime Academy. I have over 100 days spent at sea on Academy training cruises and am looking forward to applying my unique skill set within the American Sail Training Association organization.

Summer intern Rob with the young trainees of the *Grand Nellie*

28

Having been to sea before on Massachusetts Maritime Academy's training ship I thought I knew what to expect. I quickly realized that the differences between a 75 foot sailing vessel and a 550 training ship can be daunting. Every wave and swell no matter four feet, or ten is felt with far more distinction on a smaller vessel than when aboard the larger ship I was accustomed too. This manifested itself in about 12 hours of being sea-sick, upon leaving the calm waters of the Delaware River, and into the less hospitable north Atlantic. After this acclimation period of being back at sea, the remainder of the voyage was extremely enjoyable and relaxing. Traveling under sail is one of the most relaxing things I have experienced. No coarse sounds of a motor, just the rustling of the sails being pushed by the wind and conversation between the members of the crew.

I was not sure what to expect of the village of Greenport, but I was pleasantly surprised. A small quaint town, it has a very easy going atmosphere reminiscent of a town on Cape Cod back around the area I am from. The people I have met here have been very accommodating and friendly other than an occasional jab about my Boston Accent and Red Sox hat. If ever the chance I would recommend a trip to Greenport for a relaxing long weekend, especially for boaters as the marina and docking facilities here in Greenport are exceptional. One surprise was the absence of any kind of fast food restaurant. Every place to eat is more or less a family run establishment, and all that I have been to have been excellent.

The arrival in Greenport also marked the obvious transition between the sailing life, and working as an ASTA Intern member. It was kind of sad to leave the *Grand Nellie* and her crew behind, but it was good to press on with my summer voyage and see different people and places. I look forward to continuing my sailing experience on another vessel, and arrival at other ports.

Grand Nellie **and the crew
(front)** *Cuauhtemoc* **(back)**

Rebecca McNeill

July 14, 2004

Sometimes in life you have to do things that are hard; things that aren't that fun and things that take a huge effort and commitment but yield great reward. I learned this from my experience sailing on the *Tenacious*. Initially I could not imagine what would inspire a group of Brits to spend their holiday working on a tall ship. In order to get the whole experience of being a tall ship crew member they haul line (which they call rope), participate in watch (which involves hours of sitting and getting up at ungodly hours), climb aloft (it's called peer pressure) and clean ship everyday (they actually call it happy hour). What could anyone possibly be getting out of this? As it turns out, you get quite a lot out of it.

My name is Rebecca and I am an ASTA summer intern! I recently graduated with a degree in English and Sociology from University of Vermont. I enjoy music, reading, writing and outdoor activities such as skiing. I'm really excited to be out on the water this summer as part of the ASTA race team. I decided to join the team so I can travel to interesting places, learn about the history of the tall ships, and sail!

My experience on *Tenacious* began with an orientation the day before we set sail. The first mate Simon, a rough talking Scottish man from the Royal Navy, began by explaining our duties as voyage crew. The British have a way of being completely serious when necessary while retaining humor and fun. Everyone seemed ready to get to work with a smile. The first order of business was to climb aloft if you planned on being able to set sails etc. while at sea. This was very daunting to me seeing as I chickened out climbing aloft on the *Eagle*. I meet with my watch group, the forward port. Our watch leader, Richard, informed us we would be climbing the foremast. I don't think I could have climbed aloft, for the first time, on any other ship. My group, who ranged in age from 16 to 70 something, all seemed just as nervous as I. Because of our shared trepidation and the reassuring words of my watch leader, who offered to go up and be by my side, I was able to attempt a climb. Shaky, but determined, I began the ascent. Reaching the transition from the first ladder to the small scary looking one that lead up to the first platform, I froze. "I can't do this," I said as my arms shook and legs quivered. The third mate, Roger, seeing my distress came to my aid and coaxed me through it. Without his help I never would have made it up. John, a volunteer who's been part of the crew for a while and knows what he's doing, coached me up a rope ladder leading to the yardarm. "Stepping on starboard," I said in a nervous voice. Finally, I had made it. Climbing down was much easier and I was determined to do it again. The voyage crew knew how nervous I'd been and even though we had just meet there were hugs and words of praise and encouragement from everyone. I really felt as though I'd accomplished something....

I really knew the feeling of helping others as part of a team being on board the ship. On the *Tenacious* I was inspired to help others constantly. The ship consists of handicapped voyage crew as well as the able bodied. When you see someone struggling the best thing is to offer help and although they might refuse, being able to offer assistance to someone in need is one of the best feelings I've ever had. I also, to my own amazement, heard myself volunteering to go aloft and set sail. It was actually fun although I don't think I'll ever get over being nervous to do it. In my watch group I meet two disabled crew members, Kate and James. Kate made me smile with her irreverent humor and coordinated outfits. James made my heart melt with his offers to be my eyes on look out duty when I was tired. He is one of the nicest people I've encountered in life. I snapped a picture of him, being lookout on the starboard side as the sun is rising, that I will treasure. The permanent crew had the patience of saints, working with people of all abilities. I came to believe that the first mate despite his gruff speech is a softie underneath. The captain, who called everyone under the age of twenty "boy" regardless of gender, was hysterical with his nightly chart readings. And the second and third mate always had a hug and a smile for anyone looking down.

Every morning after a hearty breakfast ("Cereal and hot breakfast? Yes please!") it was time for happy hour. You would be surprised at how happy everyone was to scrub the decks, polish, vacuum, mop and clean toilets. I think since we all had to do it and we were working together to make the ship a better place to live, everyone was happy to do

Rebecca aloft on the *Tenacious*

it. Even cleaning heads, which I actually volunteered to do at one point, wasn't that bad. Besides, after happy hour the cook and mess men rewarded us with a wonderful British tradition called "smoke oh". Each day, at ten a.m. and three p.m., biscuits, cakes, brownies, flapjacks (oatmeal cookie type things) cookies, shortbread or perhaps scones are served along with tea, coffee and squash (squash is like Gatorade). This was definitely something to look forward to as we cleaned.

If you don't have watch in the afternoon it's free time. One day I took advantage of the opportunity to climb higher aloft, to the second platform, for an amazing view. The water was calm during our voyage and everyone spent a majority of their rest time on the deck enjoying the weather and good conversation. The dinners were amazing. On most nights, knowing I had watch in the middle of the night, I usually went to bed with a wonderfully full stomach after enjoying the sunset. Watch from 4 am to 8 am was amazing because we witnessed a beautiful sunrise at sea.

Tenacious did a harbor tour of New York City towards the end of our journey. Many of the voyage crew had never seen NYC and although I've been many times, I certainly hadn't come through the harbor on a tall ship. As we approached the city people were awed by the tall sky scrapers and the Statue of Liberty. I was a sunny day with no clouds. On lookers from other ships passed us by and waved, clearly impressed by the site of *Tenacious* coming through the harbor. We anchored across from an amazing view of the skyline and the Statue of Liberty; that night looking across the harbor at all the lights I felt incredibly lucky for such a view. We departed from NYC and made our way towards Greenport, Long Island. I had the privilege of being on mess duty. Surprisingly, it was very fun. The cook and cook's assistant required a lot of energy and stamina from their "mess men" but they were funny and charming. Even washing dishes was fun! I volunteered for an extra mess duty. I love food and I enjoyed serving everyone. The voyage crew, having done mess duty themselves, was very appreciative and thankful. During some of mess duty we participated in bracing stations. It was incredible to see members of the crew, in wheelchairs, hauling line and doing everything the able bodied crew did.

Once we arrived in Greenport I was sad to know I'd be leaving the *Tenacious*. However, I soon learned I'd be working on the ship while in port which I looked forward to. The day we arrived, the disabled crewmembers were given the opportunity to be hoisted aloft. I can't imagine their courage, putting their lives in our hands as we pull them up by rope. Everyone worked together and they all made it up safely. I witnessed James, from my watch, climb to the first platform on his own while everyone cheered below. James is confined to a wheelchair but he has partial use of his legs for brief periods of time. I had never seen anyone with such a barrier overcome an obstacle such as that; it was emotional and inspiring.

The next few days were tiring, harbor watch, cleaning, manning the gangplank, answering questions, and yet I enjoyed it all. Having had the incredible experience on the *Tenacious* I really wanted to share it with people and let them know about their amazing sail program. The experience ended with a voyage crew dinner at a nearby restaurant. I cried knowing I might never see these people again, and because I felt so lucky to have had this experience. I have to say, perhaps the ASTA interns shouldn't be allowed on the *Tenacious,* because once you're on you never want to leave.

Brooke James

July 21, 2004

Aboard the 75-foot schooner *Grand Nellie* on Wednesday morning, the race to New London, CT began. As we sailed past the *Pride of Baltimore II* with the "Ride of the Valkyries" blaring from our stereo, I quickly realized how the friendly competition created by the TALL SHIPS CHALLENGE® is such an exciting experience for the participating vessels.

My name is Brooke James and I am a student at St. Lawrence University. I will be graduating in 2006 with a BA in Psychology and Global Studies. I am excited to be joining the ASTA office as a summer intern. The internship with ASTA is ideal because it fosters my career interests and lifelong dream of working with sailing ships. My love of life and its many gifts is a product I wish to promote to others and I believe the internship with the ASTA requires just that.

This was my first time participating in the TALL SHIPS CHALLENGE® Race and I was overwhelmed with the power of sail training. I was amazed at the ability of such young people (a crew of five 14 year old boys) to understand the many aspects of sailing, and to seek knowledge in every new encounter. Our journey involved moments of beautiful sunshine and sunburns, deep fog, rolling swells and perfect sailing. A little bit of everything for my short 3 days of sailing. The arrival of the Parade of Sail to New London was somewhat foggy, but ended in the wonderful regrouping of 13 tall ships along State Pier. The weather and live music have created an upbeat atmosphere, and short lines have allowed visitors to easily tour all of the ships in one day. We can already tell it's going to be another great tall ships weekend here in New London before the ships head up to Halifax on Sunday evening.

Kevin Morrissey

Monday, August 2, 2004

To say the city of Halifax Nova Scotia came to life this weekend would be an understatement. In my entire experience with ASTA, this port festival has drawn some of the largest crowds I have ever seen. Not only did the people flock to the piers, but so did the ships. There are about 40 here, which really does make Halifax the largest Atlantic Coast Event.

On what was to be my final leg of the series, I was given the incredible opportunity to sail on the 75-foot schooner *Grand Nellie*. As most of you have read throughout the summer, her crew consisted of five teenage boys, who have endured, and truly matured over the past 9 weeks. As I arrived in Charleston in June, Captain Jeff and the *Grand Nellie* team were some of the first people I met. I was able to socialize every now and then, but until this past week, my experience on board the actual boat allowed me to grow quite close with everyone. In fact I would most definitely say that my trip really gave me the full understanding of what sail training is, and should be about.

We experienced great wind as we left New London on Monday, however, that was about all we would see over the next 4 days. Unfortunately the weather was gloomy, and we

My name is Kevin and I am from Nashua, NH. I am currently a cadet and midshipman in the Navy Reserves at MA Maritime Academy on Cape Cod. My love for the ocean and the ships that sail on it goes back to my childhood years. My first experience sailing was on the USCG Barque Eagle while attending the US Coast Guard Academy in 2000. I am extremely excited to be participating with ASTA this summer and I look forward to learning a lot and meeting new people from around the world.

USCG Barque *EAGLE* in Halifax, Nova Scotia

Crowds come out to see the ships in Halifax, Nova Scotia

had to motor the rest of our 400-mile journey up to Canada. Being a New Englander myself, I was more than understanding in regards to not being able to change the weather. As my father Dennis has always taught me, "Control the controllable," and that is exactly what we did.

I was able to work closely with the boys day in and out. As a current cadet at Mass Maritime Academy, I am required as a Marine Transportation cadet to take courses such as Celestial Navigation, and seamanship. Some of these young men could perform tasks, and had increased their knowledge and skill to a level which could be comparable. That is not only a positive reflection and a quality of hard work and dedication on the boys part, but also goes to show how talented and truly amazing the *Grand Nellie's* permanent crew and captain are.

In conclusion let me just finish by saying thank you. Thanks to the ASTA team for the opportunity I was given this summer to participate in the TALL SHIPS CHALLENGE® Series. Thanks to all of the crews of the many ships I was honored to sail on over the past couple of months. I have met many wonderful people over my short time here, some I will certainly be friends with for many years to come. So as I head home to New Hampshire on Monday after the parade of sail, I am thankful for being able to sail and enjoy these great ports of call and mostly because of what I learned about others, and even myself. The USCGC *Eagle* was my first tall ship sailing experience, and as special as she is to me, and probably still my favorite, my wealth of knowledge and respect for the many others I was able to board and sail this summer gave me a much wider and clearer vision for the sail training experience. It was an honor. Fair winds and following seas to you. Thank you all.

Awarded to an individual who has dedicated his/her life's work to getting people to Sea under sail and who has worked to preserve the traditions and skills of sail training.

The American Sail Training Association's
2004 Sail Training Awards
Lifetime Achievement Award

2004 Lifetime Achievement Award
Recipient Rafe Parker

"With over twenty years at the helm, Rafe Parker came to personify the spirit and excellence of SEA with the leadership that he provided. Under his command, SEA built two new ships, moved to a new campus and built the Madden Center, expanded the number of educational programs, achieved full enrollment, and developed many new initiatives, including our operations in the Pacific. He developed a network of affiliations with major colleges and universities all over the country and built a national reputation for SEA. He took the vision of SEA's founder, Cory Cramer, and carried it forward to outstanding new levels." (Photo: Current President of SEA, John Bullard (left), presents retired President, Rafe Parker (right), with the ASTA 2004 Lifetime Achievement Award)

Edmund B. Cabot, Chair, Sea Education Association Board of Trustees

Sail Trainer of the Year

Awarded to an ASTA member (may be either a Captain, crew member, volunteer, board member, etc.) whose contribution has been the demonstration of leadership by means of empowerment and inspiration.

Sail Trainer of the Year 2004
Terry Davies

Terry Davies is the CEO and Founder of the "Class Afloat" Program aboard *Concordia*. Kate Knight, a teacher from *Concordia* believes that "his commitment to youth and to the tall ship community is honorable, and he has truly helped to develop global citizenry and to equip our youth with the tools to be the leaders of the 21st century". (Photo: Terry Davies (left) accepts the 2004 Sail Trainer of the Year Award from Nancy Richardson (center) and Alice Cochran (right).)

Sail Training Program of the Year

Awarded to program which significantly contributes to the development of seamanship, navigation skills, teamwork, and leadership skills. Program must be offered by an ASTA member USCG (or national equivalent) inspected vessel. Must be offered by certified/ qualified personnel. Must have clear training goals and curriculum which is compatible to the ASTA syllabus and logbook. Students must have the opportunity to demonstrate knowledge at sea. (They can't be given a program and remain as passive passengers.)

2004 Sail Training Program of the Year
Ocean Classroom Foundation's "Camp Schooner Discovery" aboard the Harvey Gamage

Camp Schooner Discovery is a one week program for young cancer survivors from the Hole in the Wall Gang Camp. The camp was described by Alix Thorn, as "a stimulating and exciting experience for them (participants) and one which encompassed all of the goals of Sail Training Programs as supported by ASTA - leadership skills, confidence building, working together as shipmates, and in particular, stretching them to participate in new and occasionally even frightening endeavors. It also gave them a chance to "leave their cancer at sea" as one of the participants remarked in a letter that I received from him."

Sea Education Program of the Year

Awarded to a program offered by a current ASTA member which significantly contributes to the educational credibility of program under sail. The Program must be offered in conjunction with a school, school system, school group or other recognized educational institution and must have a clear curriculum of educational goals which are compatible with curriculum goals of traditional schools. The program must have qualified instructors on a certified vessel.

ASTA 2004 Sea Education Program of the Year
The New York Harbor School Program
aboard the Lettie G. Howard

The New York Harbor School Program is a year-round program created through the partnership and collaboration of South Street Seaport and the New York Harbor School. It is a multi-faceted program combining sailing on the schooner *Lettie G. Howard*, boat building, and estuary ecology.

"As a captain in the sail training world, I have been involved with numerous sail training programs and I truly consider the NY Harbor School to be a model program for sail training organizations nationwide." *-Captain Austin Becker*

(photo: Education Coordinator, Adria Lande (right) and chair of the Sail Training and Education Committee, Meghan Wren (left) present the captain and crew of the *Lettie G. Howard* and representatives from the New York Harbor School with the 2004 Sea Education Program of the Year Award.)

Port City of the Year

Awarded to a city/municipality which demonstrates significant support of ASTA, an ASTA Member Organization, or furthers public recognition of sail training.

ASTA Port City of the Year 2004
Halifax, Nova Scotia, Canada

For the exemplary planning and execution of the 2004 TALL SHIPS CHALLENGE® Series visit to their port city, Halifax, Nova Scotia has been named the ASTA 2004 Port of the Year. There was stiff competition from the other host ports, with Jacksonville's engaging crew activities, Charleston's southern hospitality, Philadelphi and Camden's big-city excitement, Greenport's small-town friendliness, Newport's experienced ship liason officers, New London's environmental focus, and St. John's enthusiastic volunteers. The 2004 ports have set the bar high for the future! Results were determined by surveys completed by vessel captains and crews participating in each port festival, and by event information and assessments provided to ASTA by the host ports.

(Race Director, Steve Baker and board member, Jeff Troeltzsch present representatives from the port of Halifax with the 2004 Port of the Year award.)

Awarded to the Top Finishing ASTA Member Vessel in the TALL SHIPS CHALLENGE®
Atlantic Coast 2004 race series

GRAND NELLIE
(Photo: Race Assistant, Sarah Austin,
presents Captain Jeff Troeltzsch of the
Grand Nellie with the Perry Bowl.
Under Captain Jeff, the *Grand Nellie*
also took the Perry Bowl during the
TALL SHIPS CHALLENGE® races in
2001 in the Great Lakes)

The ASTA Award

Awarded to the vessel best promoting international friendship and understanding during
the 2004 TALL SHIPS CHALLENGE® (as voted by participating ships)

TENACIOUS
(Photo: ASTA Chairman Mike
Rauworth (left) and ASTA Race
Director, Steve Baker, present Mr.
Simon Catterson and Mr. Andy
Spark (right) of the Jubilee Sailing
Trust, operators of the *Tenacious,*
with the 2004 ASTA Award.)

Special Recognition Award

For outstanding service in support of the ASTA TALL SHIPS CHALLENGE® Race Series

Steve Luthultz
(Photo: ASTA Executive Director, Peter A. Mello (left) and ASTA Program Manager, Lori Aguiar (center) present Steve Luthultz with an ASTA Special Recognition Award)

Volunteer of the Year 2004

For outstanding service and dedication in support of the ASTA mission.

Ms Cathy Spencer

**Congratulations to the Winners of the
American Sail Training Association
TALL SHIPS CHALLENGE® Atlantic Coast 2004 Special Awards**

Exceptional Sail Training
USCGC *EAGLE* and *Grand Nellie*

Traveled the Farthest to Compete
MIRCEA
(From their homeport of Constanza, Romania)

Cook Longest at Sea
Unicorn

Special Recognition Award
Grand Nellie
(Recognizing her as the only vessel to complete the entire
CHALLENGE, participating in every leg of the Race Series.)

The Sail Training Experience

Photo by Brian Falconer courtesy of Maple Leaf Adventures

My 16-year-old son Kyle and I are aboard the tall ship Maple Leaf, and we've motored out of Victoria on a brilliant morning...

Fair Winds -
Tall Ships Set Sails For Adventure

By Paul Frichtl

(Reprinted with permission from the August 2004 issue of Alaska Airlines Magazine)

Maple Leaf

Hand over hand, Kyle and I pull furiously on a thick, braided line. The mainsail rises up the mast, and a huge, red maple-leaf insignia begins to emerge from the sail folds that lap over the boom. As the sail continues to rise, it luffs in a light breeze, the first mate at the wheel not yet allowing it to take wind. With just a few more feet to raise, the sail gets very heavy, and stretching the last bags out of the cloth suddenly becomes a tough job. Kyle loops the line around a belay pin to get some friction, and I reach up the line as far as I can. Using all my weight, I pull down, and as I release the pressure, Kyle cinches the line around the mahogany pin. We've gained only a couple of inches, so again and again I tug the line downward and Kyle takes in inches of slack until the captain calls it good. Four more sails to go.

My 16-year-old son Kyle and I are aboard the tall ship *Maple Leaf,* and we've motored out of Victoria on a brilliant morning. We're on a day cruise with staff and volunteers from the Maritime Museum of British Columbia, sailing up the inside coast of Vancouver Island to Sydney. From there the *Maple Leaf* will continue north to begin her summer season of adventure sailing tours along the coast of British Columbia and Alaska.

The breeze has been cool, but Kyle and I are working up a sweat. It's both refreshing

47

and gratifying as we look up and see the sails rising through the rigging, casting a light shadow over our toil. Other guests step up to grab lines, and one by one, the sails spread out above us. Satisfied that the sails are set properly, Captain Kevin Smith calls for his first mate to turn away from the wind. The crisp breeze courses across the port bow and pops the sails full. The ship heels and lunges forward.

Photo by Kevin Smith courtesy of Maple Leaf Adventures

As the engines shut down, the sudden silence sends a shudder through the deck that turns to a tingle at the back of my neck. The creaking of masts and spars as they bend under the weight of the wind, the stretching of lines that hold it all rigid, and the splash of sea water peeling off the bow of the boat seem to have hushed all other sounds. The first mate offers the helm to Kyle. Though he once spent a summer sailing 14-footers, Kyle is rightfully a bit tentative. But he soon picks up the feel for the wheel. He finds a point on a distant island and holds an even port tack.

A pair of bald eagles seems to fall in with us on the same tack. They make long, gliding swoops over the strait 100 yards to our port, plucking fish from the surface. The Maple Leaf has been sailing these waters for 100 years, and the sight of her slipping through the saltwater straits and sounds of the Northwest still makes people pause in wonder. Powerboats circle her at a reverent distance; weekend sailors follow on the same tack, just to sail with her awhile.

In ports around the country there are scenarios much the same, as ships ranging from small clippers to massive square-riggers with sails stacked high up 150-foot masts cruise through harbors from Skagway to San Diego, Boston to Miami. There is something powerful about big sailing ships – the tall ships. Majestic in stature, poised in movement, disciplined in operation, tall ships present a romantic visage of simpler days.

Many of these tall ships are accessible, in various ways. Where the *Maple Leaf* offers extended luxury tours for small groups, tall ships such as the *Lady Washington* cruise the Pacific coast, offering all who are interested a chance to experience sailing for an afternoon or even for a couple of weeks, as a volunteer crew member. From at-risk youth programs to corporate team-building events, from crewing opportunities for the physically disabled to major festivals, there are as many ways to enjoy these magnificent vessels as there are ships themselves.

On the bridge of the U.S.C.G. Barque *Eagle*, Lieutenant Junior Grade Amanda Ausfeld takes a step back, turns to her left rear and shouts, "Helmsman, 10 degrees right rudder." "Ten degrees right rudder. Aye," replies the lead helmsman. He sets the *Eagle's* massive wheel spinning-he along with the five other U.S. Coast Guard Academy cadets who man a set of three highly polished mahogany wheels connected in line. On his command, the wheel crew, three on the port side and three on the starboard, stop the spinning wheel as quickly as they started. "Rudder 10 degrees right," the helmsman barks out.

"Very well," acknowledges Ausfeld, a senior at the academy. She has her eye on a commercial container ship coming down the narrow and winding St. Johns River. Around the next bend is Jacksonville, Florida, and that's where the *Eagle* will join nine other tall ships as part of the TALL SHIPS CHALLENGE® Race Series. For Jacksonville, the tall ships visit is an opportunity for a festival–Sail Jacksonville–celebrating the city's maritime heritage.

It's Friday morning, and the *Eagle* is making a grand entrance. This is "America's Tall Ship"-295 feet of steel hull and spar, three masts, 20 miles of rigging line and nearly 22,000 square feet of sail. Under sail she is a glorious mountain of white on the blue sea, square-rigged on the fore and main masts, and gaff-rigged on the mizzen (that's what makes her a barque). Out front and between the masts, she flies 10 jibs and staysails larger than the sails you'd find on most recreational sloops. It takes more than 200 lines to manage her sails, and each cadet must know every one.

The *Eagle* is a working classroom for the Coast Guard Academy in New London, Connecticut. Every summer she sails with a crew of six officers, 29 enlisted personnel and about 150 academy cadets who put to the test their navigation, engineering and basic seamanship skills. Upper-class trainees, such Ausfeld, exercise leadership skills as they prepare to become officers in our country's smallest military branch.

The *Eagle* has just sailed in from Nassau, and this morning, just inside the mouth of the St. Johns River, has picked up some 50 guests, mostly family of some of the cadets, for

Meka II

the final two-hour leg into the city. Pleasure boats, police boats and fireboats lofting long arcing showers from their water cannons fall in with the *Eagle* as the ship passes beneath two high bridges that seem impossibly low.

Other tall ships sail out to greet her, the first of which is the *Meka II*, a half-scale two-masted brigantine built and skippered by Captain Horatio Sinbad, who fancies himself an 18th century privateer and pirate. As the ships pass port-to-port, Sinbad sends forth a couple of thundering booms, and puffs of blue smoke rise from his cannons.

"He's firing on us," one of the cadets chuckles. The *Eagle* responds: "Fire in the hole!"

Two quick booms from a pair of 12-inch portable cannons acknowledge the *Meka II's* greeting.

"We need a bigger gun," mutters another of the cadets.

As each of the tall ships passes, the salute is repeated, and the reports echo between the walls of the hotels and office buildings of the city.

Ausfeld continues with her commands to the helmsman and the throttlman–nothing hurried, nothing wasted–as she and her crew of

cadets attempt to lay nearly 300 feet of barque delicately up against a seawall in a ripping river current. They have an audience of several hundred spectators, summoned by the cannon fire and the sight of ships under full sail, flying international flags and hundreds of colorful burgees. In the rigging far above deck, dozens of cadets have climbed aloft and stand at crisp attention to greet their host city as the *Eagle* comes to an easy rest.

For the next couple of days the *Eagle* crew will conduct maintenance duties, polish the brass (as they do daily), and host thousands of visitors interested in exploring her decks as will the nine other ships tied up along the seawall for Sail Jacksonville. Coordinating much of this is the American Sail Training Association (ASTA), based in Newport, Rhode Island. ASTA works with communities to sponsor festivals that coincide with the TALL SHIPS CHALLENGE® Race Series. The festivals offer a tremendous opportunity not only to bring communities together to celebrate their histories, but also to view the magnificent ships that still actively sail their waters.

The race series began in Miami the week before, in early June, and has been working its way up the East Coast, toward its final stop in New Brunswick, Canada, on August 12. The ships race from port to port, and then spend each weekend in a different port city as the focal point of a festival. From Jacksonville, the ships will sail to Charleston, South Carolina, then on to Baltimore, Providence and Boston.

In 2005, the TALL SHIPS CHALLENGE® Race Series sails the West Coast, starting in Victoria on June 23. The following weekend and through July 4, the tall ships will gather in Tacoma, Washington. They'll spend July in Anacortes, Washington; Richmond, B.C.; and Port Alberni, B.C., before heading down the coast to San Francisco and Los Angeles.

ASTA is a nonprofit organization that for the last 31 years has overseen and helped coordinate the educational and sail-training efforts of tall ships across the country. Its member-vessel fleet numbers more than 300, with ships hailing from more than 20 countries and sailing all the world's major bodies of water. The organization is primarily focused on youth education and leadership development, says its executive director, Peter Mello. "Most of the ships competing in the TALL SHIPS CHALLENGE® races carry young trainees for educational and character-building experiences," he says. "Tall ships have a unique power to change lives."

That's evident on the ship *Tenacious*, launched in Southampton, England, four years ago. The *Tenacious'* express purpose is to serve people with physical disabilities, not only giving them the opportunity to sail, but also giving able-bodied trainees a better understanding of living and working with the disabled. Everything needed to sail this 213-foot three-masted barque is accessible: The belay pins are situated lower, for

Tenacious

example, and elevators lift wheelchairs from one deck to another. Even the crow's nests high up the masts are oversize to permit wheelchair-bound trainees to man a watch aloft. The typical crew of 40 trainees is split 50/50, half with disabilities and half able-bodied, and there are few jobs on board that a trainee with disabilities wouldn't be assigned.

The CHALLENGE also gives visitors from all kinds of backgrounds a chance to explore maritime history. The *Pride of Baltimore II* is a 157-foot clipper whose fir and mahogany glow a warm amber. Young kids scramble across the deck, climbing on the bowsprit, running their hands along the barrels of her four cannons. On the water, her lines are quite distinctive, her masts raked back in the style of the original Baltimore clippers that during the War of 1812 were the well-armed "privateers" that ran blockades at U.S. ports, and brought supplies and munitions to American troops.

The *Pride II*, launched in 1988, now sails with a crew of 12 as a goodwill ambassador for the businesses and the people of Maryland and the Port of Baltimore. And as with the rest of the ships in the CHALLENGE, her crew is active in promoting and preserving a traditional maritime culture through a range of day-sail, weekend, corporate-retreat and volunteer programs.

And wherever you find tall ships, you'll find pirates-not only aboard the *Meka II*, but prowling the seawalls and streets of the CHALLENGE cities. Somehow, these one-time scurrilous rogues of the high seas have become a likable lot, and here they sing sea chanteys, growl for small children and direct mock cannon fire and musket blasts toward passing vessels.

On the edge of a Jacksonville block devoted to children's activities, a Johnny Depp impersonator vamps for cameras in front of a miniature ship from Pirates of the

Pride of Baltimore II

Caribbean. Its cannons glow red and puff tiny clouds of smoke as mothers snap photos of Captain Jack Sparrow.

She's not a pirate ship, Captain Les Bolton maintains of the *Lady Washington*. Well, she was briefly, but not anymore. Johnny Depp sailed her in Pirates of the Caribbean. The *Lady Washington*, a merchant brig based in Aberdeen, Washington, starred in the film as the HMS *Interceptor*, a pirate chaser and the fastest ship in the Caribbean. Disney contracted with the Grays Harbor Historical Seaport Authority to use the 112-foot *Lady Washington*, and after a few modifications, such as trading her tiller arm for a more dramatic spoked wheel, rebuilding the transom with opening portlights and applying a new paint job, she set sail on a 10,000-mile journey that took her through the Panama Canal to the Caribbean and back. She was boarded by pirates, ghosts and film production crews, all under the watchful eyes of the *Lady Washington's* regular crew.

Lady Washington

In a scene where Depp takes the wheel with the boat under full sail, the real ship's master was lying at Depp's feet, just out of the camera frame.

For the rest of her 15-year career, the *Lady Washington* has served as her namesake state's tall-ship ambassador. Like most of the tall ships, the *Lady Washington* is operated by a nonprofit organization for a specific mission: to provide programs that educate, excite, inspire and empower all who cross her decks. They may be in the form of one-hour elementary-school tours, a three-hour public cruise, or a three-week live-aboard program for at-risk teens. In programs such as the latter, Voyage of Self Discovery, 12 teens sail the ship for three weeks, learning about personal responsibility, trust, open and honest communication, and teamwork.

In other youth programs, such as Science at Sea, participants cruise the Olympic Coast National Marine Sanctuary, working with staff from The Evergreen State College to collect, analyze and forward data for ongoing research.

The *Lady Washington* typically spends her summers touring the Northwest coast as far north as Sitka, Alaska, or even hundreds of miles up the Columbia River to inland ports such as the Tri Cities. The journey gives the people of the state a chance to board the ship and talk with her crew, as well as to sign on for day sails or overnights. In October, the *Lady Washington* works her way south, visiting ports along the way to San Diego.

There she hooks up with the *Hawaiian Chieftain* for 10 days to not only offer tours, but also to engage in weekend mock sea battles.

The *Lady Washington* was built in Aberdeen in 1989 as a replica of the *Lady Washington* that explored the west coast and opened trade between the United States and China. The original was built in the early 1750s and worked as a merchant ship on the eastern seaboard until an investor group purchased her in 1787 and sent her around Cape Horn with the *Columbia Rediviva*. Under the command of Captain Robert Gray, they were to explore the Northwest coast, trade metal and glass goods with Native tribes for sea otter pelts and then journey to the Orient to trade for tea and spices. The ships were the first American vessels to visit the West Coast.

This spring, the new *Lady Washington* finally replaced her Pirates paint, restoring her hull to her historic colors. Weeks before she was to begin her summer sailing season, she rested in Aberdeen with wet paintbrushes of brilliant yellow, blue and red on her deck, rigging dangling slack from her masts, and a blue tarpaulin tented over the bow, where a new bowsprit and anchor windlass-handcrafted by a corps of volunteers-would be installed.

In fact, it is volunteers who make the *Lady Washington*, and many ships such as her, stay afloat. In the shop, Bolton points out a group he calls the Ancient Mariners, a retired Boeing engineer, a retired schoolteacher and a retired millwright, who worked on the original construction of the ship and now are crafting the new windlass. The ship sails with a crew of 12 to 14, most of whom are volunteers who sign on for two weeks to four months, or longer.
"This is one of the few communities where you'll see upper-echelon professional people taking advice comfortably from a 16-year-old," says Captain Mason Marsh, education director for the *Lady Washington*. "They all get an equal chance to get a little dirty and salty."

The *Maple Leaf* offers a different kind of sailing opportunity, an experience that is a bit more intimate and luxurious. At 92 feet in overall length the *Maple Leaf* is smaller than most tall ships, but what she lacks in tonnage she makes up in beauty. When she was built in 1904 in Vancouver for a local timber baron, she was the talk of the yachting community. Crafted from local Douglas fir and cedar, she was one of the first boats to have electric lights, and she carried an innovative lead keel bolted to the bottom. But during World War I, the Canadian government confiscated the keel to use the lead for the war effort, and thus began her transition from yachting sensation to fishing rig. She was not only among the prettiest herring schooners in Alaska, she was also one of the most productive.

The *Maple Leaf* was brought back to Vancouver in 1980, and after a restoration that took nearly seven years, she was rigged for adventure. These days, keeping her shipshape is a business concern as she maintains a busy schedule hosting nine guests on one and two-week luxury sailing adventures.

Jean Rissman, a Sacramento-area elementary schoolteacher, spent 12 nights on the *Maple Leaf*, sailing from Juneau, Alaska, to Prince Rupert, British Columbia. Sailing on a small ship allowed her to do things that would have been impossible on a large cruise ship, such as catching spray from a waterfall in a drinking cup while standing on the bow, or using a hydrophone to listen to humpback whales sing and blow bubbles to school the tiny fish they feed upon.

"At least three times, as we were getting ready for this spectacular evening meal, someone would spot a bear on the shore," she says. "We'd all pile into the Zodiacs with our cameras and just leave dinner sitting on the table."

Brian Falconer

Kevin Smith

Brian Falconer

Photos courtesy of Maple Leaf Adventures

Food is an outstanding part of the cruise, says captain and owner Kevin Smith, but so is having the flexibility to sit and listen to whales until everyone is done. He also includes on his crew a naturalist to interpret it all for guests, including stops at ancient Native sites. "It seems like the crew is sharing this whole experience, their experience, with you," Rissman says. "It seems it never gets old for them." Perhaps that's the way it has always been for sailors, sailing from port to port, just for the adventure.

The *Lady Washington's* Bolton likes to recall a journey he made many years ago, when he was sailing a tall ship between Caribbean ports for another owner. A crewman on watch had spotted something large on the horizon, which they first assumed was a cruise ship. It soon became obvious that it was a sailing ship, then that it was the Soviet sail training ship *Kruzenshtern*, a four-masted barque that is one of the largest operating tall ships in the world. As the ships drew closer, Bolton's crew heard singing–Russian sea chanteys. "As the ships passed, we saw not a dozen sailors, but probably 200 sailors standing in the rigging, singing in the middle of the ocean."

Bolton had a tight schedule to keep, but he and his crew reversed course and fell in with the *Kruzenshtern* for a couple of hours, just for the joy of sailing with such a spectacular tall ship. - Paul Frichtl is editor of Alaska Airlines Magazine.

Skaang Gwaii

Photo courtesy of Maple Leaf Adventures

"Twenty years from now you will be more disappointed by the things that you didn't do than by the ones you did do. So throw off the bowlines. Sail away from the safe harbor. Catch the trade winds in your sails. Explore. Dream. Discover."
-Mark Twain

Only four years ago, the dream that the Michigan Maritime Museum could undertake the daunting task of designing, building, and operating a replica tall ship was just that – a dream. In 1991, the small but respected museum, located near the sandy beaches in one of west Michigan's most picturesque shoreline communities, pursued this dream. Within one year, plans were in place to take the first steps and a $2 million dollar capital campaign was announced. This was the Museum's first capital campaign; and to put this step into perspective, the Museum's annual operating budget was less than $350,000 annually. Indeed, this was a bold and decisive step toward their dream!

Every great dream, like every good story, has layers of promise, adventure, and surprise. The Museum's dream of a tall ship was no different. *Friends Good Will* had a dramatic story to share, full of promise, adventure, and surprise; designing a replica vessel, employing modern construction methods, and meeting USCG requirements for passengers was also laden with promise, adventure, and surprise; and jumping headfirst into a new industry – the tall ship industry – promised even more adventure.

Follow Your Dream:
The Story of a Tall Ship

The First Dreamer

The original *Friends Good Will* began as a dream of Oliver Williams, born in 1774, near Boston. Williams saw opportunity in the vast Northwest Territory and opened a dry goods store in Detroit, Michigan Territory, in 1808. The inventory for his store, like nearly all finished goods, came from the East. He made two trips each year, overland. The trips were slow and the resources he expended were a continuing drain against whatever profits his businesses would permit.

In 1810, Oliver Williams pursued his dream and built a ship. The vessel would use the only "highway" available – Lake Erie; Buffalo to Detroit, non-stop, direct. His inventory would arrive faster, and in greater quantity, and while the vessel was a substantial capital outlay, she would sail for years and could earn money by shipping goods the length of each shipping season. Other vessels plying the Great Lakes were finding cargoes and the steady stream of settlers which seemed to demonstrate that demand for the ship would only grow with each coming season.

Williams built his ship at the River Rouge, on the banks of the Detroit River. A private shipyard was laid out adjacent to the Federal yard, where the army transport *Adams*, the only government vessel on the upper Great Lakes, was built years before. Other ships such as the schooners *Salina* and *Ellen* and the sloop *Contractor* sailed past while this

60

new vessel took shape. The sight of each of them only encouraged Oliver Williams. His dream had merit; pursuing it would make his dream come true. The new ship slid down the ways, in early 1811. He christened her *Friends Good Will*.

At 47 tonnes burthen, the square topsail sloop carried cargo for her owner and others, paying her way in settling the new frontier. Oliver Williams retained an experienced Master, William Lee, formerly Master of *Contractor*, to operate and protect his new dream and avoid the numerous risks endemic to navigating the Great Lakes.

In the summer of 1812, *Friends Good Will* was chartered by the federal government to take military and supplies to Fort Dearborn, at what is now Chicago. She was returning with furs and skins when she was lured into the Harbor of Mackinac Island by the British, who having taken the island just days before, were flying false colors above the fort ramparts. The British confiscated the vessel and cargo, renaming her *Little Belt*.

She was armed, taken into the service, and fought with the Royal Navy until September of 1813 when she was recaptured by United States Commodore Oliver Perry, at the Battle of Lake Erie. Within an hour after the great guns fell silent, Commodore Perry mentioned her in his now famous dispatch, "We have met the enemy and they are ours: Two Ships, two brigs, one schooner and one sloop." That sloop was *Friends Good Will*.

Friends Good Will then served in the United States Navy, transporting General (and later President) William Henry Harrison's troops across Lake Erie in the successful invasion of Southern Ontario. She was driven ashore in a storm south of Buffalo in December 1813. In early January 1814, during efforts to re-launch the ship, the British burned the once-proud vessel during a raid on Buffalo.

Oliver Williams, lost his vessel and his livelihood during the War of 1812 when the British confiscated his ship, took him prisoner, and captured his homeport of Detroit. Williams faced this adversity with courage. He escaped from British imprisonment, pursued his dream afresh, and became a prominent early settler of the Michigan Territory.

A New Dream

The Michigan Maritime Museum now had a dream. A dream of using *Friends Good Will* as an opportunity to make history come alive through educational programs and sailing experiences. But, this dream needed to be designed, built, and operated. The Museum

commissioned Scarano Boat Building of Albany, NY to design and build her. The Scarano staff has experience building in all materials and is considered a leader in building historic replicas using modern wood laminate construction. Among the vessels to Scarano's credit using this type of construction, are the sailing ships *America*, *Madeleine*, *Adirondack*, *Adirondack II*, and *Friendship of Salem*, and the motor vessel *Horicon*.

While only a dream, how could the Museum know exactly how the original *Friends Good Will* looked? Researchers uncovered enough data that the Museum was confident that it commissioned a vessel that might fool even some of the original crew. And yet, she is a modern vessel with all the safety and sailing ability that modern materials and methods afford.

While the ship was being designed and built, others engaged in the dream. From sailors to seamstresses; from historians to housewives; from riggers to retirees; from lawyers to landlubbers; over 100 volunteers joined the *Friends Good Will* Ship's Company. Ship's Company volunteers learned to worm, parcel, and serve the standing rigging. They assembled, finished, and stropped blocks with various knots, splices, whips, and tar. Ship's Company volunteers completed these tasks with rigging knives, fids, and raw mechanical advantage, much like sailors did in the early 19th century.

The Dream Comes True

On Saturday, September 25, 2004, the dream came true. After being launched on August 29, in Albany, NY, traveling through 34 locks in the Erie Canal and 1000 miles on the

Great Lakes, *Friends Good Will* arrived at the Michigan Maritime Museum amidst great fanfare and media attention. Onlookers lined the piers and cheered as she entered her home port for the first time. Uniformed crew greeted guests and demonstrated traditional seamanship.

After years of pursuing the dream, it is time to live it. *Friends Good Will* is making history come alive for youth, families, and visitors to the Michigan Maritime Museum. She is available for guided educational tours, dockside boardings, passenger sails, and charters. She sails the Great Lakes, visiting ports previously never touched by the Michigan Maritime Museum. Visitors to maritime events and tall ship festivals are enthralled with her beauty and craftsmanship.

One Dream Inspires Another

Tall ships touch lives and inspire great dreams. Those ships with a colorful history, presenting numerous and diverse educational possibilities, are the best of the fleet. And while visitors will be impressed with her authentic 6-lb. pivot gun, mounted on the centerline, true to the state-of-the-art 1812 period and with her uniformed crew; the most profound effect will be felt by those whose dreams are inspired to pursue new dreams they had not imagined possible until experiencing *Friends Good Will*.

The opportunities rewarding those who sail on board *Lynx* are adventure, knowledge, personal growth and memories to last a lifetime . . .

Pacific Cruise of Opportunity

By Jeffrey Woods

During the War of 1812, a privateer vessel would seek crew to embark on a "cruise of opportunity". The privateer's crew, if successful, would have the opportunity to advance their career and possibly earn up to a years salary in a few short months at sea, capturing enemy vessels and their cargo. In this century the sail-training vessel *Lynx* still embarks on "cruises of opportunity" with its crew and students. Except that now we are not sailing in search of prize vessels or running blockades. The opportunities rewarding those who sail on board *Lynx* are adventure, knowledge, personal growth and memories to last a lifetime, to name a few, and every summer *Lynx* sails to the Hawaiian Islands with a few selected students eager to sign on.

On 14 July 1812, in Fells Point Maryland the sleek Baltimore Clipper *Lynx* was commissioned as a Letter of Marquee vessel, less than one month after the second declaration of war on England. She was armed with six – 12 pound long guns, rigged as a square topsail schooner, and was crewed by 40 men. *Lynx*, like other Letter of Marquee vessels, was primarily used to carry cargo. These sharp-built Baltimore Clippers were used to carry small highly valuable shipments because of their swiftness and agility. Being commissioned as a Letter of Marquee vessel allowed them to legally attack and capture enemy vessels if the opportunity arose. The additional profits from the

captured vessel would be divided into shares and allotted to the crew, ship owners and government. On the other hand, privateer vessels were outfitted and commissioned for the sole purpose of hunting down and capturing enemy ships. A commissioned privateer would carry twice as many men and would be more heavily armed than a Letter of Marquee vessel.

The Hawaiian Islands, lying about 21N and 158W, are reported to be the most remotely located islands on earth. Rising out of the Pacific Ocean over 2000 nautical miles away from the nearest continent. The youngest and largest of the islands, Hawaii, is still growing. On some days, you can see lava flowing out of the ground and eventually spilling into the streaming sea. Throughout the ages, Hawaii has been a welcome landfall for many mariners, from the original Polynesians who first settled there, to the early explorers like Captain Cook and the whaling ships in the Pacific. Captain Cook made several voyages to the Pacific exploring and charting many new areas. In 1778 on *Resolution*, Captain Cook made his first landfall in the Hawaiian Islands, beginning the influence of European trade and culture.

The student crew of the *Lynx* signs on a day before the scheduled departure. Some who step aboard have sailing experience while others have only seen a sailing ship in a movie or on TV. Family members are given a quick tour, and before saying their final farewells, are sure to remind their child to wear sunscreen, be careful, and to take many pictures! Next, there are the usual crew introductions, assigning the watches and bunk space, and a thorough walk through and ships orientation including all safety equipment and emergency procedures. Everyone on board is very excited, a little apprehensive, and ready to get underway. This is reflected in some of their first journal entries.

Chris Woods from the Sausalito writes:
   "I wasn't about to go sailing on a boat for 2 weeks, I was going to live a whole new life for 2 weeks."

Mike Baker, an Eagle Scout from Orange County writes:
   "This is a once in a lifetime experience and I was one of the lucky few who were chosen to help sail on the *Lynx*."

At 0630, on departure day, all hands are roused and turn to for "soles and bowls". Like many sail training ship's, the crew cleans the below decks area every morning before anything else is done. The soles are swept and washed, the heads are cleaned and sanitized and the rubbish is collected and put in the proper place. Even Captain Cook knew the importance of a clean ship and it is noted that he lost far fewer men (for the time) on his ships partly due to his insistence on cleanliness during long Pacific voyages. After breakfast is cleaned up, the students get their first hands on lesson about line handling and mechanical advantage. All four of the *Lynx's* six-pound carronades, each weighing over 400 pounds, are stowed below the main saloon sole for the offshore passage. This task is achieved by teamwork and the use of block and tackle to hoist, maneuver and lower the carronades into their chocks in the bilge.

Lynx and her crew are ready, but before getting underway and setting sail, the captain calls all hands to muster amidships. *Lynx* is guided by the motto "Be Excellent to Each Other and To Your Ship" and all crewmembers are reminded of this and instructed on the ship's order of importance. First in the order of importance are the needs of the ship; our home for the next 20 days and refuge from a watery grave. Second are the needs of our shipmates, who in return would do the same for you. Last in order are your own individual needs. Like the popular saying goes; there is no "I" in team, and there is no "I" in crew either.

It only takes a few days for everyone to adjust to the ship's 24-hour routine at sea. The students gain confidence and knowledge with every new experience they have both on and off watch.

Alexandra Williams, from Huntington Beach writes:

"There is so much more to the world of sailing that people don't realize. Being here (on board *Lynx*) requires so much knowledge and a complete understanding of your surroundings just to keep things running smoothly. It is unbelievable how much I have learned. We put all we have into the ship, and at the end of the day our hard work pays off. There is so much I can tell you, but you will never completely understand until you experience it for yourself."

Eagle Scout Christian Emseik writes:

"Being at sea for prolonged periods of time allows an individuals thoughts to sail through his mind and captivate his soul. The lessons learned at sea are ones that could never be taught while on land and the ones I learned at sea will stick with me for the rest of my life."

Eric Loss, a Sea Scout Quartermaster writes:

"We saw the moon for the first time last night. It finally broke through the clouds, illuminating the ship like the first rays of dawn through a gray cloud. We rolled down the moon river, Lynx searching earnestly for the source of the silver stream like a cat following a dangling string. No cat ever had such an escort, for what could compare to constellations above, silver dipped flying fish alongside, and the brilliant half circle of the moon leading us onward."

Lessons are taught onboard while on watch and at the all hands muster. The students record their progress on deck using the ASTA Log Books. Everyday the crew gathers on

the quarterdeck for an educational opportunity and ships report for the day. Some of the discussions and activities conducted are about Hawaiian history and culture, Captain Cook's voyages, and Polynesian navigation. This is also a great time for everyone to learn how to set and strike a studdingsail or reef the square fore topsail and mainsail, but it is not all work and lessons. On one day in the middle of the Pacific, when we have reached the halfway mark there is a celebration and festival on board with all hands contributing to the occasion.

Gabrielle DeHeart, a Hawaiian native writes:

"At 1,100 nautical miles on a progressing course to Hawaii, *Lynx* and her crew at the halfway point of our sea odyssey. Ironically, it was June 24th, my birthday! Hearing only wacky bits and pieces of the traditional halfway celebration, I was slightly uneasy yet exulted by the mystery of what was in store for me. Afterwards I felt even more lucky and appreciated that day then on any other birthday I've had."

Lynx sails along easily covering 170 to 200+ nautical miles a day, friendships grow, confidence builds, and students gain more responsibility and knowledge. The individuals that first stepped on board develop and grow into a crew, taking care of each other and

the ship. Each day Hawaii is getting closer and the voyage is getting shorter. Soon the carronades will be hoisted back into their places on deck, the best set of colors will be snapping in the wind from the rigging, and ship and crew alike will be looking their best for the grand arrival. Amidst the excitement of getting shore and the overwhelming sense of accomplishment, there are moments of reflection and a sadness that the voyage is ending. They have completed this adventure and are ready for the next. Hopefully the academic, personal, and physical lessons we have learned will help us stay on course and keep our ship afloat through the squalls, equipment failures, and shoals that lie ahead. Be excellent to each other and to your ship.

What the voyage afforded me cannot be understated. I gained skills, and the confidence to use them.

Around the World Adventure

Excerpts from the Logs of Eric Pickhardt

I discovered the Picton Castle in 1996, when I was only eleven. I happened to meet Captain Moreland, or, at the time "Cappin Dan" at a going away party for the ship held in Kingston, New York, where the ship had been tied up collecting funds for the massive reconstruction it would undergo to become a three-masted Barque. My stepmother, a grandniece of Irving and Exy Johnson, (pioneers of the *Yankee* training ships) introduced me to the captain, who at once looked me over an asked "You look about the right age for a Cabin Boy; do you want to come sail with us for a few weeks?" Naturally I left with the ship two days later, bound for Lunenburg, Nova Scotia, the ships new homeport. The ship, at that time was a rusty old freighter, acquired by the Captain in Norway a few years earlier. She needed a lot of work, inside and out. And she needed masts, masts that could support sails, what she was most desperately lacking. A daunting feat, to be sure. I stayed with the ship in Lunenburg for two weeks, helping out to tear her apart, unload the cargo hold which would eventually be cut in half and transformed into the "Main Salon" living quarters, scrape paint, etc... And I left, on the day the ship went into dry-dock to get the hull work necessary to begin looking like a Barque.

I followed the first two world voyages, and when the third one came around, and it became clear my graduation from high school coincided with the start of it, I decided I wanted to make it a reality. I had a lot of help in this, including an anonymous benefactor who sponsored the second half of my voyage, and two smaller scholarships, one from the Neil Grant Foundation, and one from ASTA. Thus, I was able to leave with the *Picton Castle* on June 15th, 2003, as crew on her 3rd circumnavigation under sail.

What the voyage afforded me cannot be understated. I gained skills, and the confidence to use them. I met people, many people who all had something to teach. We bore witness to those uncharted places people don't even realize exist, where the way of life is unlike anything we in the North-Western hemisphere are accustomed to. We learned seamanship and how to solve problems by looking at them. We became very in tune with our surroundings, noticing all the subtleties in the atmosphere that had slipped our grasp living in doors and in-land. We adapted to living with 40 other people on some 180 feet of wood and steel for weeks and weeks at a time without pause. We saw how fortunate we really are, to be able to see all these things.

And then the voyage was over. It all of a sudden disappeared. Some of us went back to work, some to school, some stayed on the P. C., some went on to sail other ships, and some are somewhere in-between. We all move on, no matter how extraordinary what we shared really was. But we did share that experience, and there are a few handfuls of us who do. But, being that it is a very unique thing, it is also often difficult to relate to those who haven't done it. I remember once, the Captain remarking on the subject, that the way he dealt with the shock of returning home, was "just to keep doing it". When you see all that this experience can bring, that solution makes sense. At present I'm looking into a college education, but a future of life on the waves is my ultimate destination. I wouldn't have it any other way.

June 2003

On June the 15th, the *Picton Castle* and her crew of 37 trainees and 10 professional crew departed from her home port of Lunenburg, Nova Scotia, Canada. We had been working together diligently to ready the ship for several weeks, but much time was spent living in a house owned by the Captain, due to unforeseen delays in dry-dock. Boarding the ship as a crew brought us much relief that we would actually leave port. We spent days rigging, loading cargo, and preparing various odds and ends, while the staff crew worked long hours sometimes far into the night in hopes of leaving on our desired date. However, this didn't happen. We did leave a week later on a Sunday to the cheers of everyone on board and a large number of onlooking friends, family and tourists waving us off at the dock. This was one week ago, and already we've motor sailed from the choppy, cold North Atlantic which plagued nearly everyone with seasickness, too hot southern reaches below Bermuda. Now it's the hot instead of the unpredictable cold weather we saw in Nova Scotia that the crew are complaining of, and we're not even close to the equator yet. Most of us trainees came on knowing basically nothing about Tall Ship Sailing, but within the past week we have learned a tremendous amount of practical knowledge concerning the operation of square rigged ships. Learning the names of lines and such has come much more quickly than I anticipated. Now we're becoming suntanned: in my case sun burned and getting a feel for what life in this small world will be like over the next year. I think we're all looking forward to turning off the engine when we reach the trade winds and setting sail to Panama. For we have not turned the engine off quite yet. It is a beautiful, sunny day and we have made great progress so far. I hope the weather stays fair and we are able to loose all sail soon. I'm looking forward to what our first port of Panama has to offer.

July 2003

Sailing along today with a steady wind, July 31st, 2003, we've been making 5-7 knots for several days now, since we became clear of the Galapagos Islands. We've bent on and set several new sails; the gaff topsail, the mizzen t'gallant staysail (or the mizzen royal staysail) depending on which of the crew you talk to, and the main royal staysail. This has added just enough lines to reinforce us with a slight amount of confusion as to the placement of the halyards and downhauls for reach of the respective new kites. But our voyage from the Galapagos is coming quite nicely and everyone seems in good spirits about the several weeks that lie ahead of us, before we are next greeted by land.

The Galapagos was truly enjoyable. We were able to investigate the spectacle of the Galapagos giant tortoise, snorkel with the innumerable sea lions who seem to own the Island, as well as see large marine Iguanas, Blue Footed Boobies, Pelicans, and a large array of other marine life with which the Galapagos is teeming. We were only allowed port on one island, as tourist travel is limited for obvious reasons, but the island of San Chritobal had much to offer indeed. The town we inhabited while ashore San Barkarito was a small, rather touristy place (in the Ecuadorian sense), but we had a fun visit nevertheless. Although we were originally only going to stay for 3-4 days, we stayed anchored in Wreck Bay for several more and left after nearly a week with a good amount of sightseeing under our belts. Among other things, a first for me here was our visit to the Volcano on the island, but on the day that I went visibility wasn't very good and we ended up seeing lots of fog and what seemed to be the edge of the crater.

Since we've been at sea again, we've seen a number of whales and army of several dozen curious dolphins (to which we were amazed) and today we've already seen 2 sharks off our stern. Perhaps they were checking out the bait hanging form Peter's fishing line, which yesterday, caught us a good 25 lb MahiMahi.

Ships work continues and it seems we've just about painted everything. By the time we finish all the jobs we're required to do as regular maintenance, it'll be about time for another coat. Our Royal yard, which Miles has been working on, is coming along nicely. It's now in the shape of a solid beam and looks about ready to be shaped. That should keep us busy for a good portion of our trip in the following weeks. Personally, it feels great to be at sea again, and I seem to get more and more relaxed and at ease with the sea around me the further form shore that we venture. Celestial navigation classes with Lynsey have just started, and I'm excited to see where that will take us, as it's a subject I have much interest in and no knowledge of. This is promising to be a most interesting and rewarding passage.

August 2003

August 14, 2003 South Pacific- We are now less than 700 miles from our destination of Pitcairn Island. We've been underway now for seventeen days since our departure from San Christobal, and are a bit further than projected. Once we were clear of the Galapagos Islands, we hit the relatively strong tradewinds that carried us at a very good clip for over a week straight. We made between 6.5 and 9 knots throughout, and were all very pleased with our progress. For several days we were in the doldrums, and were forced to take in sail and continue under power, which is our current state. However, we are no longer in the doldrums. A steady force 5 headwind has been limiting us to 4.5 knots, and the seas have grown again so that from time to time we get wet on the windward side, or on the foc's'le head where swells often surge up and over, spraying the lookout thoroughly. The skies are blue and it has warmed up a bit since the last time we set out. The temperature is comfortable and thankfully not so warm as to keep us from sleeping. We hear the Pitcairners are feeling much of the same.

The day before yesterday, when the sea was its calmest, we broke stride for a welcome swim call. The yards were braced around sharp and a rope swing was attached to the end of the fore course yard on the starboard side. We cooled off by swinging off the foc's'le head and jumping into calm, clear water. After we had finished swimming, and the Captain was relaying the story of the Mutiny on the Bounty and the subsequent inhabitation of Pitcairn Island, we were greeted by a whale, which passed underneath the hull of our Barque at midships and surfaced a good 30 yards on the port side. It didn't seem to be in any particular hurry, and slowly receded into the distance, blowing occasional wisps of spray, and we returned our attention to the Captain and stories of Pitcairn. This was just one of a number of whale sightings we have had so far in the Pacific. There is indeed a lot of life in this vast ocean, and we're right in the middle of it.

August 26, 2003-Back to sea in the Barque Picton Castle, after eight days on Pitcairn, we left for the most part reluctantly into a golden orange sunset. Our heading is west-northwest bound for Manga Reva, a mere three days from Pitcairn, from which we departed yesterday evening. I know I for one, was more than a little saddened to see the island descend into the horizon.

The Pitcairners are some of the most kind, hospitable people you could ever hope to meet; their generous and carefree manner will not easily be forgotten. While ashore, crew members stayed with host families. There was a lot to see ashore as the scenery was unlike any I've encountered. The island is very steep, and is around 1,100 ft at its highest point. So hikes are hikes, but certainly worth the climb. I was able to see Christian's cave (an old lookout spot Fletcher Christian used after the Bounty Mutiny). This cave sits halfway up a sheer cliff face that overlooks the small cluster of houses that is Adamstown, and out to sea past Bounty Bay, where the remains of the Bounty lie close to shore. Other worthy sights were "Tedside" where Pitcairn's sole Galapagos tortoise, Mrs. Turpin, resides, as well as any number of the beautiful points on the island where a spectacular view can be taken in.

For income the Pitcairners make crafts which they sell to passing cruise ships and the few yachts that stop to visit the island each year. Popular articles are woodcarvings, which they are so proficient in producing. These include carved fish, turtles, sharks, etc. As well as fids, which we all took advantage of. Many make baskets from the husks of the Pand(?) tree. Some sell t-shirts and goods procured from New Zealand. Pawl Warren, however, in addition to his woodcarvings makes bone carvings, which are fine pieces of Island craftsmanship.

Our last night ashore we were introduced to the game of "rounders" and enjoyed a feast of a potluck dinner to which we'd become only too accustomed to during our stay. We ate plenty and enjoyed ourselves before heaving up the anchor the next day and shoving off to the tune of our beautiful farewell song sung by the islanders as we made our way out of sight.

We unloaded a lot of cargo upon our arrival, and we gained many more times its weight in understanding a perspective too few of us had borne witness to, by the time of our departure. I will be surprised if any place we go can impart the same neighborly friendliness and sense of grace we experienced during our stay in Pitcairn.

October 2003

TONGA-It's the 28th of October and Fiji is behind us. We sailed out of our port in Suva the day before yesterday after spending a week and a half anchored off the main island of Viti Levu, which proved as exciting and beautiful a port as any we've encountered. By my estimations we could have easily spent a month there without getting the least bored or anxious to leave.

But before we arrived in Fiji, we spent a week in Nearby Tonga. We stopped at the sleepy island of Pangai in the Vava'u group of the Tongan islands. The scenery as we made the passage through the surrounding islands into Pangai was breathtaking. Small, mushroom-cap shaped bumps of islands surface here and there out of the deep water. High, flat-topped islands disappeared almost immediately into the blue, leaving sheer cliffs and exposed cavernous holes in the rock to Port and to Starboard.

We were delightfully surprised to see any small sailboats dotting the surrounding waters. Sailboats with sails set, some just day sailing and some we would come to find out were for one reason or another on long ocean cruises, choosing Tonga as one of their many ports of call. Seeing sailboats actually sailing seemed almost shocking to some of us because up until then, most of the ports we'd called at contained mostly the kind of Yachties who used their boats to motor to and from nearby docks. The owners would sit dockside drinking piña coladas, probably never even having taken their sails out of the sail bags that secure them to the boom. But in Tonga we finally found sailboats being used for their intended purpose. Since it's a bit more out of the way, the place seems to attract sailing types of all kinds. And for me, speaking with some of these types was one of the bigger highlights of Tonga. We met people sailing to write guidebooks for the South Pacific. We met retired couples just sailing in no particular direction for the last of their years. And we met some kids, too, who'd basically grown up sailing with their parents. All kinds of people converging in one spot in the middle of the South Pacific, each for their own ends, made for an interesting and unique time here.

While ashore, most of us just relaxed, and did relatively little sightseeing. Many spent much time and money at the local market, buying carvings, tapa-cloth and other native crafts. Some went scuba diving on a sunken wreck; some went on the reef, while some of us kept to snorkeling.

In Tonga we had our first-ever race with the ship's dingy, Carl, which had been salvaged from the beach in Palmerston on the last voyage. She raced against a fleet of worthy opponents, and came in dead last. But we're convinced she would have won had it not been for the lack of the third crew member of the race team who had to constantly bail out the water seeping in through the huge cracks in the Carl's hull. Eh, better luck next time. We saw a few dances, and a few sunsets in Tonga, and were always greeted with an affable smile and a warm conversation wherever we went.

When we left Tonga, we had three temporary crew get on. We took on an older gentleman named Baker, and two young girls, from different boats respectively, for the passage to Fiji. Since they were well adapted to the task of sailing an ocean-going vessel, they took well to their very brief (passage which only took 2-1/2 days under strong winds, which petered out to very light winds, forcing us to fire up and motor for part of the trip.)

The Concordia, a Canadian Barquentine that had also been docked in Tonga for a few days, left a couple of hours after us. We could see them gaining on us throughout the afternoon, until sometime after dusk the fellow training ship overtook us on our starboard side, at a fairly close margin. She illuminated her sails and blew her horn. We responded in turn, with cheering from both sides. The thrill of seeing two tall ships, side-by-side in the middle of a moonlit ocean was phenomenal. Surely a rare sight I don't think any of us will soon forget.

In a couple of days we would anchor outside of the big, city of Suva on Viti Levu. From all the warnings we'd received about Fiji and its high crime rate, our first impressions of Suva when we first arrived couldn't have been all that high. Some in Tonga had told us that it was a potentially dangerous place, with a large number of tourists. Neither felt like particularly handsome references, but with at least a week scheduled as our stay, we felt obliged to find out for ourselves.

During our first stretch of three days in a row off watch, Michael Johnson, Carla, Mike Pritchard, John Gallagher, and I decided to see the island by renting an off-road truck and driving around it. Although the weather when we left looked ominous, we pressed on, rationalizing that it could only get better. We rented a truck from a local dealership, and stole out of Suva pretty much as soon as we got there. We set out for Nadi (pronounced Nandi) on the opposite coast via the coral coast highway, which runs along the southern rim of the island. We stopped at the first straw-thatched "Bhura" village we came to, which turned out to be an asylum for rehabilitating Suvan street kids. We toured the village, met some very friendly people, and continued down our road. We stopped at an old Fijian fort to learn about Fiji's history of war and cannibalism before moving on the Sigatoka, where we saw the awe-inspiring sand dunes. The dunes loom high above the Pacific to the south, and look to the lush greenery of the mountains to the north. This was certainly one of the more impressive sights we'd come across thus far, making us glad we didn't simply "skip it," as we nearly did. We drove into Nadi that night to spend it in one of the few hotels in the city that still had any vacancy.

The next day Mike P, John and I hung around Nadi while Mike and Carla went scuba diving. It was kind of a rainy day, so we lay low and opted not to go snorkeling, even though I'd heard the diving and snorkeling in Fiji is world-renowned. We made the most of our day despite the weather. That night we drove to Lautoka, and although we had planned on spending the night in a nearby village, it was dark and pouring when we got in the city, so we ended up just having dinner and staying at a hotel that night as well. Early the next morning we made the long drive through windy, bumpy back roads through the Nasori Highlands to the small village of Navula, which sits in a valley basically in the middle of nowhere. The views were picturesque, to say the least. Mountains towered over the small Bhuras on all sides, and we were supremely pleased to have made the trek out. We drove back negotiating many a sugar cane train and overstocked sugar cane truck barreling down the narrow road back to the main road that would lead us to the Northern "King's highway."

We took the King's Highway back to Suva, which proved to be a wise choice, as we would realize that hardly any tourists traveled this road. It was a longer passage between the two major cities, and it contained a 60 km unfinished section that was muddy, rutted, and slow. This was a great way for us to see all the little villages that never get visitors, and they were thus very excited to see us. Everyone, literally everyone that you drive by shouts an enthusiastic greeting, "Bula!" and waves at you, obviously delighted to see a new face. It seemed pretty obvious as well, that the locals don't get much attention from foreigners in those villages, as the children would swarm around the truck, and we spent much of the long drive through the King's highway reaching out of the windows to give kids just getting out of school a High Five, or wave at people gathered in their lawns to watch as the spectacle rolled slowly by. The scenery along the entire route was rainforest and river, flower and tree. Absolutely the most glorious drive I've ever had. We got back to Suva barely in time for the seven o'clock skiff. We were thoroughly satisfied with our three-day trek across the island, which proved to be much larger than any other we'd been on so far.

Except for those of us who went to a nearby waterfall in the rainforest for a daytrip, we spent our remaining Fiji time in Suva. Suva wasn't as bad as we'd been led to imagine. People were friendly, some of the friendliest we'd met, and most were genuinely interested in speaking with us, and didn't just want our money. My time in Fiji was altogether eventful, and one of the best times I've ever had. We sailed off the refueling dock in Fiji, sailing up until this morning, when our wind died, and we were forced against our will to stow sail and turn on the main engine. We're motor-sailing through calm waters to Vanuatu, and the first of three ports there. We're on the other side of the map now and still going west. Happy to be back at sea, happy to be here. Looks like it'll be a fine day.

December 2003

NEARING BALI,-It's the seventh of December; we're now nearing Bali and the passage from Vanuatu seemed to fly by. It seems we've hardly been at sea even though we've been out for almost three weeks. I could have sworn the passage to Panama was farther. But we kept busy this passage, seemingly everyone adopting a craft or a project to keep himself occupied. A number tackled fids, a few made canvas duffle bags, and some who hadn't previously gotten around to making their ditty bags took care of that in short order. We've had quite a few workshop classes this passage, nearly every day. Workshops on seamanship, navigation, and the like are held most afternoons for the distinct benefit of all who partake. Basically we've just been keeping with the routine of things here, which still remains variably constant. That is, of course, except for the ever-changing scenery and inclining temperature.

We went through the very narrow, very shallow Torres Straits. It was all hands on deck for the narrowest part of the channel, which requires precision steering and an attentive lookout, for there was much traffic in the area, as well as many neighboring islands. Not to mention that the channel itself, at its most narrow, was too small for the passage of two large ships at the same time. The swells were sizable and the chop kept the helmsmen on their toes. The channel was at times 15 meters deep or less in its center, and in one narrow section the markers divided a shallow bottom of 3 meters of open water on one side, and 9 meters on the other. To deviate from the channel could have meant for us what it meant for a lone derelict we passed at one point in the day on the 29th. An old freighter that had at one time run aground a little ways distant could be seen standing almost entirely out of the water, lying to rest on a reef which it had hit at high tide. It was a stunning sight; one you'd love to get a closer look at if it weren't for the obvious consequences. Though we had been making great speed with a strong wind up to the straits, the captain decided to play the passage through safe and motor, making it a bit easier on the helmsman and the crew to maneuver, (as well as assuring that we got through by the light of day and before the tide started going out again.) While in the channel, we used the 3-6 knot current in our favor to good advantage, and at times we could boast upwards of 11-12 knots-quite a good pull for our little Barque. Once through the straits, we resumed sailing until our wind dissipated a few days ago, and we began motoring again. The 27th of November was Thanksgiving at sea. We were sailing along beautifully, under a perfectly sunny sky. There was a lot to be thankful for. Preparations had been going on for several days, baking pies and such, so by the time Thanksgiving rolled around we were allotted quite the feast. With a brisk clip and a blue sky we couldn't have asked for anything more in the eye of the Coral Sea. Now we're through the Arafura Sea and into the Sea of Timor. The water is still rather light in hue, but presently it's dead calm, save for the amount of sea life we've been encountering. Lots of dolphins, sea turtles, and sea snakes are about the ship. The sea snakes are apparently very poisonous and are in such numbers that we have temporarily suspended our mid-ocean swim calls. This is unfortunate because it doesn't seem to be getting any cooler. We've been catching a lot of fish lately. Tuna and barracuda have been biting most readily over the past few days. The sea is full of sea life, as well as a growing number of ocean-going vessels. Lots of tankers now that we're near Australia, and today we saw several sailboats off on the horizon that appeared to be part of a race. The Australian Coast Guard planes, as well curious dolphins, have been keeping their eye on us lately. Seems we're a bit of a phenomenon. We're only a few days from Bali. We're all excited to see Indonesia, I'm sure. But I think for the most part the crew could be content with a slow pace just as much as a fast one, as the cohesiveness of a crew is greatly strengthened at sea. That's something I think few of us would be anxious to dispense with just yet. But then again when we get close to a port some people usually get antsy to set foot on land, and I'm sure this is no exception. So I'll just bite my tongue. In any case, Bali is my, and I'm sure others', most anticipated port.

We pulled out of our overcrowded harbor in Benoa on the 21st of December. After filling the cargo hold with as many sea chests as it would carry, taking as many cab rides as we could stand, and meeting up with the Concordia for the third time, we set out for the four-thousand mile trek to Mauritius, a port at least a month distant.

Christmas at sea was a time for nostalgia. We all enjoyed the company of our family here as we though of our families back "there." We sailed on the starboard tack with topsails set in a Force 6 wind, drinking eggnog as Miles read aloud "The Night Before Christmas" on the evening of the 24th. We sang "Silent Night" around our little Christmas tree, which stood lashed to the hatch, before we gradually descended to bed. The next day we enjoyed a day of rest and an exchange of goodies among ourselves. We were finally able to open those packages from home marked, "Do not open until December 25th!" It was a good holiday, a unique one for most of us. I'm sure we'll never forget our first Christmas at sea, sailing in the strong grip of the Indian Ocean trades. At the moment, things are as usual on the P.C. We've been cut down to 34 crew members in total, so galley duty comes around a little more often. Our frigid night watches make sleeping below decks something to look forward to. The tuna keep jumping. The wind is still following us. Onward to Mauritius we go...

January 2004

January 1, 2004-I was on forward lookout at midnight, when the dropping anchor ball amidships sounded the start of the New Year. It was the latest of several cold nights we've had in the Indian Ocean. The low-pressure trough that we're currently in had brought out our long sleeves, pants and winter hats. Some donned several layers and still shivered. New Year's was a celebration kept in check by the cold. No one wanted particularly to be above decks last night, but most did appear for the dropping of the ball, only to disappear into their bunks as soon as it was officially 2004. Night watch is sometimes like that. You're still shaking away the sleep and drinking your midnight coffee when it hits you that it's inordinately cold, or rainy, or windy. Last night it was the first and the last of these three.

We spent eleven days in Bali. I think we can all agree it wasn't even enough time to scratch the surface of Bali, but we were all easily pleased to have our eleven days consumed by such a place, and truly grateful to be able to see

what we did. The cities, namely Kuta and Denpassar, were chaotic. Kuta was filled with the chaos of hustlers, duped tourists, Australian surfers, and a thousand people a minute asking us if we needed "transport." Kuta was the place to go for tattoos, upscale hotels and nightclubs. Denpassar, on the other hand, was very much a genuine Asian city. There could be found the chaos of any other functioning city, minus the tourists (save for the endeavoring few).

We visited the Monkey Forest Temple in Ubud, where the thieving and surprisingly intelligent primates that inhabit the grounds viciously (and I mean that) went after the bananas that we were tricked into buying at the gate. These furry little buggers stop at nothing, and it is folly to try to hide bananas or to dole them out equally. If you have them, you are prey. (And watch out for cameras and necklaces and anything else easily accessible to their greedy little fingers.) The most impressive of the dances I witnessed in Bali was at the palace in Ubud. The Legong Dance is purely stunning, for lack of a better word. The precision and skill with which the dancers exercise their artistry is mesmerizing. The dances alone, in my estimation, would be worth the trip. There are the dances, and then there are the temples at which you can find most of the dances. Temples are everywhere, ranging from the small and personal temples that every Hindu person in Bali erects, to the enormous structures that are used as mass gathering places for the overwhelming Hindu population in Bali to worship. I was able to see a few of these larger temples. The temple at Tanah Lot is carved out of a small island of rock that sits in the churning sea about fifty yards off the shoreline. You have to wade out through the breaking surf to get there. In Ulu Watu, you can find a temple perched on the precipice of a sheer cliff that rises five hundred feet out of the water, overlooking the Indian Ocean to the South of Bali. The Mother Temple at Besakih is immense. A complex of eighteen smaller temples plus the temple of Besakih itself lie on the hillside leading up to the base of Mount Agung, the largest volcano in Bali. Mount Agung towers up ten thousand feet into the clouds. This was a magnificent sight, and one that was supremely worth the drive to the northeast corner of the island.

The last night we were ashore, most of the crew convened for dinner with the prince at his palace, a long bus ride from Benoa harbor. We had good food and were able to see several more dances. The Barong Dance made the long bus ride well worth it. Any description would be inadequate, so let me just reiterate that the dances alone would be well worth the trip.

January 24th, 2004-We are now thirty-three days out of port, and nearly to our destination. We had a great sail this passage, only motoring in brief stints, a bit right out of Bali, and now these last few days because we're trying to beat a cyclone to landfall on Mauritius, if that's what it's going to do. Wisely, the Captain's decided that it's safer to be tied up at a wharf during a cyclone than out at sea, especially near-to-land in one. So although the tradewinds have kept us steadily westward this passage, and they continue to bear on our stern, we're chugging away these last few hundred miles to be on the safe side. Not bad, considering we sailed the overwhelming majority of four thousand sea miles. We have long since gotten accustomed to the routine of being at sea, so this passage of five weeks seemed hardly like two. It's odd to think that Christmas, which now seems so long ago, was celebrated on this passage, when the passage itself seems to have flown by. That may have been due highly to the nature of the work we busied ourselves with this passage. There was much to be done in the way of re-leading blocks and fairleads, and figuring out the best ways to lead our running rigging to minimize chafe aloft. As well as much general maintenance new seizings, new lines, and everything else that needed to be done to ensure that things run smoothly. It was, and is good work, and there still is much of it to do while we're in port in Mauritius. We finally got our Stun'sls up during some light airs a couple of weeks ago. Our three brand-new stun'sls went up to windward on the foremast much more smoothly than we might have predicted, and proved to be quite useful, too. In a Force 2-3 they gave us upwards of a knot more speed than we would have had otherwise. That's quite considerable, and could mean a lot in a long, light-air passage. Before the wind picked up and we had to take them in, we launched the skiff so that we all could get a chance to take some photos of our new crowning achievement. I must say, they do make us look pretty slick. Just about daily we have workshops on this or that. Lynsey might teach one on piloting and navigation, while the next day the Captain will hold another on wire splicing. Wire splicing is something we've just delved into. For being the total amateurs that we are, I think our splices are coming along quite nicely. Today we're supposed to be finishing our splices and serving them so that they can be put to use as strops. We should be in Mauritius tomorrow. It'll be nice to stretch our legs and relax on the beach for a few days, however great the sailing's been. And it surely has been great.

June 2004

June 14-We are North of Bermuda and bound for home. The air is now undeniably colder, and the water lacks that tropical warmth and bright, shiny blue we've all come to rely on. There's no mistaking it, we're in the North Atlantic and our islands are far from view.

It was an interesting few days in Bermuda. We performed the usual sightseeing exercises, saw our dear Sailmaker Paulina off at her home on the island and had one last warm weather barbeque to celebrate, gained a new chief mate fresh from blustery Nova Scotia and his place on the Bluenose Crew, and got to experience some of the nasty North Atlantic weather we'd forgotten all about.

The weather, came a day before we were going to leave on the 12th. I, and everyone else were woken by shouts and the Clank-Clank of the anchor chain in the Hawse-Pipe. I came outside into half-a-gale of wind and rain. We had apparently dragged anchor very suddenly and were now dangerously close to a nearby island. The engine was fired up immediately and we were powering into the wind. The general crowd of us stuck to the Windlass, and hoisted a sluggish anchor in sheets of rain, our eyes plastered half-shut. When the anchor was off the bottom we motored back to a convenient location and dropped our Starboard anchor again. We let some chain out, then dropped our much heavier Port anchor before backing down on both, letting out 3 and 3 shots of chain respectively, restoring our security in the turbulent harbor. Orvel, our new Mate, who was on watch at the time, was put to the test. He of course handled the situation as any master of a ship should, and had a very exciting, if wet first day.

When we heaved up yesterday, our anchors that had proved so helpful the day before gave us more than a fair amount of grief. When we brought them in, both anchors were wrapped around each other a solid five times. We learned that dealing with huge steel chain under tremendous amounts of strain signifies a royal hassle. I mean Royal. We spent the afternoon hauling tackles to free the mess, and were relieved to in the end be leaving Bermuda after all.

We left sometime around 4:30 yesterday afternoon, and by dinnertime turned an East Northeasterly breeze into a driving force of 5-6 knots. The wind was, and is off our Starboard beam, but has since eased off in its intensity. We were lucky to get to sail out of Bermuda, but it looks like soon, tonight we'll have to take in canvas and fire up. This wind looks like a trend until we cross the Gulf Stream. Then who knows what weather we'll get. Right now the only sounds are the gentle bubbling and churning of the sea against the hull, and the creaking of rigging and the occasional sound of a luffing Fores'l.

We have to make Lunenburg by the 19th, so chances are we'll be motor-sailing with our topsails set through the light airs that seem to be in our near future. I imagine it's going to get a lot colder very quickly here, and I think we're all a little unprepared. Everyone's already in there warm clothes, and we aren't even on the other side of the Gulf Stream.

The usual every-day stuff continues. We spent the day finishing to re-caulk the Quarterdeck, a much needed job and a satisfying one to have completed. The sailmakers are still at work on new sails, and daymen take care of things here and there. But most of us are on a regular watch again. The next few days will likely be stormy, so we need all the help on watch that we can get. Its amazing how fast the weather changes 180 degrees here. Let's just hope Neptune gives us a break in his most unpredictable of watery deeps.

June 18-This is it. We're anchored snug outside of Lunenburg, off nearby Cross Island. The last morning before we dropped the hook was cold. But the few days before that defied the hype and expectations by being unseasonably warm for the Northeast States, although by no means tropical, the climate didn't take our breath away. What a surprise! This morning was the only one that was really biting.

And now we're here. We made it through the fog, and are now looking at our last night aboard (for most of us), before we again have hot showers and clean beds to sleep in. This is sort of a novelty that hasn't really set in yet. It's only beginning to creep in on us that yes, soon we'll be off "The Ship". Our very intimate home for the last year that seems in retrospect like a decade.

Tomorrow, when we all depart, we go off to different things. Some go back to school, some straight back to work at their respective careers, some will continue with tall ships, some with boats, and some have no agenda at all. We will all go our separate ways, but we all share a common bond. Over the last year we have learned the points of seamanship, navigation, social prowess and ingenuity. We can splice manilla running rigging, hemp ratlines and wire strops. We know the points of the compass and how to plot our way across a chart. We have learned to figure out logical problems logically, and how to meet strangers and not feel so strange at all. We can do these things and they are second nature. And it would be easy for us to give no more thought to it than that. Whatever we each chose to do, we will all retain this. This experience will stay with us throughout our lives, and we can all be eternally grateful, for that.

Before I came on this voyage a crew member from the last trip told me that the hardest part about it, was coming home. I see what he meant now, and the question of how I'll ever be able to describe this voyage and what it really meant to me occurs. I'm at a loss for words. The fact is, you can tell someone a story, and attempt to describe what it was like seeing a native custom dance in Vanuatu, or the heartbreaking poverty of Capetown, or the most gorgeous tropical sunset multiplied over and over, but the fact is, it's just a story, a description. This voyage has meant many things to me. It's hard enough to describe them to myself, and as for everyone else we'll see... If you really want to know what this voyage is all about, forget any description you've ever heard, and just do it. The End.

Cuauhtemoc

Puerto de Acapulco, Mexico

Alma

San Francisco, California

Dar Mlodziezy

Gdynia, Poland

Fryderyk Chopin

Szczecin, Poland

Benson Lee

Stad Amsterdam

Amsterdam, The Netherlands

Benson Lee

Talofa

Lady Washington

Grays Harbor, Aberdeen, Washington

Bill of Rights

Los Angeles, California

Exy and Irving Johnson

Los Angeles, California

Benson Lee

Pilgrim

Dana Point, California

Benson Lee

Lord Nelson

Southampton, Hampshire, United Kingdom

Benson Lee

Tenacious

Southampton, Hampshire, United Kingdom

Benson Lee

Stad Amsterdam

Amsterdam, The Netherlands

Dar Mlodziezy

Gdynia, Poland

Benson Lee

Dar Mlodziezy

Gdynia, Poland

Benson Lee

Tenacious

Southampton, Hampshire, United Kingdom

Benson Lee

Lynx

Newport Beach, California

Benson Lee

Pallada

Vladivostok, Russia

About Sail Training

Tole Mour

Take Responsibility for Your Adventure!

By Michael J. Rauworth

> In short, you must satisfy yourself that the trip you are looking into is the right thing for you to do, considering safety, risk, suitability, challenge, comfort, convenience, educational value, cost, and any other factors you consider important.

One of the most important products of sail training is the development of a sense of judgment about what and whom you can rely on, and to what degree. This applies to: the compass, the weather forecast, your shipmates, the depths on the chart, the strength of the anchor cable, the vigilance of the lookout on the other ship, and many other things. Sail training also builds a reasoned sense of self-reliance. All of this starts from the moment you begin to think about a voyage. Use the information in this Directory to begin to evaluate and decide what might be the best sail training experience for you.

Recognize who you are dealing with and what is included. When you book a sail training trip, you are dealing with the vessel owner or its representatives—ASTA is not involved. You must evaluate whether the financial and business arrangements make sense for you. If there is connecting travel involved, for example, find out if you must make the arrangements, or if it is somehow tied into those you make with the vessel. What happens if you miss your ship because your plane is delayed, or vice versa? Do you need trip insurance? Have you confirmed with the vessel owner any possible customs or immigration issues? Will you need a passport or a pre-purchased air ticket? You must seek out the answers to these questions.

Make informed, responsible decisions about risk and safety, level of challenge, physical suitability and other important issues. One of the important reasons to embark on a sail training trip is to engage the world in a different, stimulating, and challenging way—if you want to stay warm and dry, you should stay at home by the fireplace. Much of the point is to come face-to-face with the elements. At the very least, this probably means that you will find yourself wet, chilled, or tired at some point in a challenging voyage. But everyone's threshold for this is different, and you need to find out what you are likely to be experiencing in order to find out if it is well matched for you.

Since the beginning of time, going to sea has been recognized as carrying an element of risk. These days, we more commonly think about risk in connection with highway travel or aviation, but the idea is the same: you get a pre-flight safety brief on an airliner, you get a lifeboat drill on a cruise ship. Part of the value of sail training is addressing these issues head on. You need to decide whether you are comfortable with the combination of risks and safety measures connected with your proposed sail training trip.

For example, will you be able to go aloft? Will trips in smaller craft be involved? Will you be expected to stand watch at night? Do the demands of the ship match your physical and health capabilities? Are you on medication that will (or may) become necessary during the voyage, or do you have a condition (for example, hemophilia or epilepsy) that may require special access to medical attention; if so, is the vessel operator aware of this? Will you be able to get up and down the ladders, in and out of your berth, and along a heeled-over deck? If there is an emergency, will you be needed to handle safety equipment or to help operate the vessel?

Remember that sail training is often not intended to be like a vacation. Some vessels, on the other hand, may offer leisurely voyages, where very little will be asked of you. You should arrive at a clear understanding of these issues prior to setting sail.

In short, you must satisfy yourself that the trip you are looking into is the right thing for you to do, considering safety, risk, suitability, challenge, comfort, convenience, educational value, cost, and any other factors you consider important.

Does the American Sail Training Association have a hand in any of this? In a word—no! ASTA is your "bulletin board" to introduce you to opportunities. However, the American Sail Training Association does not operate any vessels, and has no ability or authority to inspect, approve, or even recommend vessels or programs because programs are constantly evolving and changing.

The American Sail Training Association is a nonprofit organization with a limited staff. It serves as a forum for the sail training community, but it has no authority over what programs are offered, or how vessels are operated. The information in this Directory is supplied by the vessel operators, and ASTA can not possibly verify all the information, nor visit all the ships in order to evaluate programs. For these reasons, you must take the information in this Directory as a starting point only, subject to change and correction, and proceed directly with the vessel operator. The American Sail Training Association is not an agent or business partner for the vessel operators, and is not a travel agent.

ASTA believes in the value of sail training as a concept, but remember, from the moment you step beyond looking at this book, the decision and the resulting experiences rest with you.

> The four essential components of any sail training program are a seaworthy vessel, a competent captain and crew, qualified instructors, and a sound educational program appropriate and suited to the needs of the trainees onboard.

Choosing a Sail Training Program

There are as many sail training programs as there are ships, and choosing the right one depends a great deal on your personal needs and desires. Sail training differs from going on a cruise ship, in that you are expected to take part in the running of the ship by handling sail and line and standing watch, as well as working in the galley (the ship's kitchen) or performing routine cleaning or maintenance duties. To what degree depends on the sail training program you select.

Do you want a program that specializes in marine biology or adventure travel? Would you like to ship out for a day, a week, a school semester—or, for as long as it takes to circumnavigate the world? Are you interested in maritime history? In celestial navigation? Whales? Do you want the unique challenge of climbing aloft in a square-rigger? A race across the Atlantic? Maine lobster dinners aboard classic windjammers? Exotic ports of call? Will you be bringing your wheelchair? Would you like to receive academic credit?

The answers to the above questions provide a profile for just some of the options available to you. As to what sail training programs require of you—beyond an eager willingness to get the most out of your voyage—the requirements are few:

Safety First!

Take a close look at the vessel's credentials. In the US, check to see if the vessel operates under United States Coast Guard regulations. Does the vessel currently hold a USCG-issued Certificate of Inspection (see pg. 60 "Regulations for US Vessels") or comparable certification from the authorities of the country in which it is registered? If it is a non-US vessel you should ensure that the vessel operates in accordance with the maritime safety rules of that country. In most cases this is supervised by a government agency similar to the US Coast Guard. The resources section of the ASTA Web site lists the latest known web sites of some of these agencies.

Talk to the program provider! Ask questions! Read the organization or company's literature; check out their website. Most important: visit the ship if you can. Get a sense of the professionalism of the operation and the quality of its program. Find out about the experience level of the captain and officers. How long have they served the ship you are looking into? If you will be joining the vessel in a distant port, or if it does not hold a current USCG Certificate of Inspection, be especially diligent in your research. Ask the program operator for the names of past trainees or clients and give them a call and ask about their experience. The amazingly diverse range of opportunities featured in this book provides each of us with a variety of options.

Experience

With very few exceptions, no prior sailing experience is required of trainees. Some programs do accept non-paying volunteers as crewmembers, but typically require experience in similar vessels or a long-term commitment—or both. Paying positions typically require a license—"Able-bodied Seaman" papers document a minimum of 180 days spent underway and successfully passing an exam administered by the US Coast Guard. Licenses are awarded to crew based on additional time underway, the tonnage of vessels served in, waters sailed, technical training, and additional testing.

Trainees are encouraged to have the ability to feel comfortable in and around the water; however, many programs have no formal swimming requirements.

Age

Most voyages are planned with a specific age group in mind. This varies from program to program, but many sail training programs start accepting unaccompanied trainees from the age of 14 (ninth grade). Ask what the composition of the ship's complement will be and, if you plan to send a young person on an extended voyage, what the in-port supervisory arrangements will be. Day sails and dockside education programs are readily available for elementary school students and overnight trips can be arranged for older school groups as well. There are a tremendous variety of adventure programs for adults of all ages, including "Elderhostel" voyages for seniors.

Academic credit

Some vessels are tied directly to academic institutions that grant academic credit to trainees who successfully complete sail training programs as part of a course of study or project in a wide range of subjects. Some educational institutions will also grant credit for on-board independent study.

Co-education

Just about every sail training vessel in the US sails with both male and female professional crew and programs are typically co-ed. Others are designed specifically for groups such as the Girl Scouts or in conjunction with a single-gender school or affiliated program.

Cost

Prices vary considerably depending on the nature and the duration of the program and the type of vessel. Some vessels have limited financial assistance available, and some trainees, Scouting, and school groups have successfully sought private, business, and/or community support . Check with the sail training program you are interested in to see what opportunities may be available. The American Sail Training Association offers sail training scholarships and criteria and applications can be found on the ASTA Website, or by calling the ASTA office.

Regulation of Vessels

Virtually all vessels are subject to some form of regulation by the national maritime authority of their "flag state"- the country in which they are registered. In the United States, these regulations are written and enforced by the US Coast Guard, pursuant to laws enacted by Congress.

Virtually all vessels are subject to some form of regulation by the national maritime authority of their "flag state"—the country in which they are registered. In the United States, these regulations are written and enforced by the US Coast Guard, pursuant to laws enacted by Congress. Under the Safety of Life at Sea (SOLAS) Convention, administered by the International Maritime Organization (IMO), vessels of any nation signatory to the convention and over a certain size or carrying more than 12 passengers and operating internationally must comply with the requirements of the Convention with regard to construction, safety equipment, manning, crew training, etc. Compliance is documented in a "SOLAS Certificate" issued by the ship's national maritime authority.

US-registered vessels listed in this directory will generally fall into one of the following categories: Small Passenger Vessel, Sailing School Vessel, Oceanographic Research Vessel, and Uninspected Vessel. For each category there is a comprehensive set of regulatory requirements governing construction and arrangement, watertight integrity and stability, lifesaving and firefighting equipment, machinery and electrical systems, vessel control and equipment, and operations.

With the exception of Uninspected Vessels, all categories of US-registered vessel are subject to Coast Guard inspection on an annual basis. Upon satisfactory completion of the inspection, a Certificate of Inspection (COI) is issued, and must be permanently displayed on board the vessel. The COI spells out what waters the vessel may operate in (its authorized route), how many passengers or sailing school students may be carried, how many crew must be carried and what qualifications the master and crew must have, the requirement for and location of lifesaving and firefighting equipment, and so forth. Although not inspected annually, Uninspected Vessels (which are generally vessels less than 65 feet in length and carrying 6 or fewer passengers for hire) must still comply with requirements for safety equipment and a licensed skipper. The type of COI to be issued to inspected vessels is determined by both the size and construction of the vessel and the operating intentions of the owner. Some vessels carry dual certification.

The Coast Guard also prescribes the qualifications for the officers and crew of inspected vessels, and requires both that they have certain minimum levels of experience and training and that they be examined and issued licenses or documents before they can lawfully serve on board. Following is a brief description of the various types of certifications governing the operation of US-flagged vessels:

Sailing School Vessels (SSV) are inspected under Title 46, Subchapter R of the Code of Federal Regulations (CFR). An SSV is a vessel of less than 500 gross tons carrying six or more sailing school students or instructors, principally propelled by sail, and operated by a nonprofit educational organization exclusively for the purpose of sailing education. Sailing School Vessels are required to pass regular inspection by the USCG in order to maintain their certification.

Passenger Vessels are certified according to size and number of passengers (not engaged in educational activities or in the operation of the vessel) carried under Title 46 of the CFR:

Subchapter C – Uninspected vessels which operate with no more than six passengers.

Subchapter T – Small passenger vessels of under 100 gross tons that carry more than six passengers and are required to pass regular USCG inspection of the ship and all onboard equipment.

Subchapter K – Small passenger vessels of under 100 gross tons that carry more than 150 passengers and are required to pass regular USCG inspection of the ship and all onboard equipment.

Subchapter H – Passenger vessels more than 100 gross tons that carry passengers for hire and are required to pass regular USCG inspection of the ship and all onboard equipment.

Attraction Vessel certification is required whenever a vessel is open to public boarding or conducts dockside programs. The vessel may be permanently moored to a pier, or it may also be certified under one or more of the above subchapters, but the Attraction Vessel COI (ATCOI) certifies its safety for dockside programs and visitation only.

Oceanographic Research Vessels (ORV) are certified under Subchapter U of Title 46 of the CFR. An ORV is a vessel employed exclusively in either oceanographic (saltwater) or limnologic (freshwater) instruction and/or research, and is not necessarily equipped for passengers or other non-professionals.

For more information, access the United States Coast Guard through the link on ASTA's website or contact the Government Printing Office for the above listed sections of the Code of Federal Regulations.

Schooner
VIRGINIA
Circa 1917

The Virginia Maritime Heritage Foundation is a nonprofit organization established to promote the maritime heritage of the Commonwealth through the successful operation of the recreated Pilot Schooner Virginia - and the engagement of this vessel in the education of its youth, tourism expansion, and the state's future economic development.

Sailing on board Virginia

Virginia's mission is to serve as the Commonwealth of Virginia's Goodwill Ambassador. As such she often hosts sailing or dockside receptions for individual, corporate, or government groups

Virginia is the world's only example of the last pilot schooner that sailed on the Chesapeake Bay over 79 years ago. Sailing aboard a traditional vessel such as the *Virginia* is a unique experience. Passage aboard is available to qualified individuals from port to port.

As a working crew member you will be working alongside the crew during the passage. You are encouraged to take part in the day to day operations of the vessel by handling sail, standing watch, maintaining the vessel and fulfilling the other duties of a deckhand. Participating in the watch system is the most rewarding part of the passenger experience.

Fresh water is limited. Hot showers are restricted while underway and a Navy shower is generally available every other day.

Three meals are provided daily and served according to watch routine.

Linens, blanket, and pillow case are provided.

There are a number of items you will need to bring with you during your passage aboard *Virginia*. It is colder on the water. Dress wisely with layers of clothing.

In order to better prepare you for the journey, here is a list we feel is a must:

Duffle bag or other soft luggage

Foul weather gear and sea boots

Heavyweight sweater or sweatshirt

Nit turtle/pullover

Waterproof shoes with nonskid soles

Sturdy jeans or khakis

Shorts, tee shirts, underwear

Several pairs of socks

Hat/gloves/scarf

Books, cards, or other recreational items

Toiletries, including sunscreen

Valid US passport (International including Canada)

Personal medications

Sleeping bag (cold weather only)

Full-Rigged Ship

A tall ship is not a strictly defined type of sailing vessel. Most of us use the term to mean a large traditionally rigged sailing vessel, whether or not it is technically a "ship". The United States Coast Guard's training ship *Eagle*, for example, is technically a "barque". A tall ship can also be a schooner, brigantine, barquentine, brig, ketch, sloop, or a full-rigged ship depending on the number of masts and the cut of the sails.

For the purposes of classification and race rating, the American Sail Training Association adheres to the descriptions found in the Racing and Sailing Rules and Special Regulations established by Sail Training International.

CLASS A
All square-rigged vessels and all other vessels over 40m (131 feet) length overall (LOA)

CLASS B
Traditional-rigged vessels with a LOA of less than 40m (131 feet) and with a waterline length (LWL) of at least 9.14m (30 feet).

CLASS C
Modern-rigged vessels with a LOA of less than 40m (131 feet) and with a LWL of at least 9.14m (30 feet), not carrying spinnaker-like sails.

CLASS D
Modern-rigged vessels with a LOA of less than 40m (131 feet) and with a LWL of at least 9.14m (30 feet), carrying spinnaker-like sails.

- Square-rigged vessels (Class A) are defined as those vessels whose sail plan is ship, barque, barquentine, brig or brigantine.
- Traditional-rigged vessels (Class B) are defined as those vessels whose sail-plan has predominance of gaff sails.
- Modern-rigged vessels (Class C and D) are defined as those vessels whose sail-plan has a predominance of Bermudan sails.
- Length Overall (LOA) is the length between the forward end of the stem post and the after end of the stern post. It does not include the bowsprit, pulpit or any other extension at the bow or stern.

Sail training vessels are as varied as the programs operated on board them. Below are examples of the different rig configurations used by ASTA's Member Vessels. On the following page you will find a diagram of the different sails carried by a full-rigged ship as well as a glossary of terms commonly used in this book.

Two-Masted Schooner   Topsail Schooner   Three-Masted Schooner

Brigantine   Brig

Barquentine   Barque

91

Ship Rigging Identification

SAIL NAMES

1. Fore mast
2. Main mast
3. Mizzen mast
4. Flying jib
5. Outer jib
6. Inner jib
7. Fore topmast staysail
8. Fore sail, fore course
9. Fore lower topsail
10. Fore upper topsail
11. Fore lower topgallant sail
12. Fore upper topgallant sail
13. Fore royal
14. Main royal staysail
15. Main topgallant staysail
16. Main topmast staysail
17. Main sail, main course
18. Main lower topsail
19. Main upper topsail
20. Main lower topgallant sail
21. Main upper topgallant sail
22. Main royal
23. Mizzen royal staysail
24. Mizzen topgallant staysail
25. Mizzen topmast staysail
26. Main spencer
27. Crossjack, mizzen course
28. Mizzen lower topsail
29. Mizzen upper topsail
30. Mizzen lower topgallant sail
31. Mizzen upper topgallant sail
32. Mizzen royal
33. Spanker

Key Terms

Sparred length - The length between the extremities of any spars that overhang the bow or the stern of a vessel, such as a bowsprit or a boomkin.

LOA - Length overall. The length between the forwardmost and the aftermost points on the hull of a vessel.

LOD - Length on deck. The length between the forwardmost and the aftermost points on a specified deck measured along the deck, excluding sheer.

Sheer - The fore-and-aft curvature of a vessel's main deck from bow to stern.

LWL - Length on the waterline. The length between the forwardmost and the after most points on a vessel's waterline.

Draft - The depth of water required to float a vessel.

Beam - Width of a vessel at its widest part.

Rig height - Maximum height of rig above waterline.

Freeboard - The vertical distance from the waterline to the freeboard deck, usually measured amidships.

Freeboard deck - The uppermost deck that is designed to be watertight.

GRT - Gross registered tonnage. The volume, expressed in units of 100 cubic feet to the ton, of a vessel's total enclosed spaces below the weather deck and enclosed spaces above the deck including the bridge and accommodations.

ASTA Member Vessels

ADASTRA

SPECIFICATIONS

Flag: USA
Homeport: Key West, Florida
Normal cruising waters:
Key West, FL; East Coast, USA
Sparred length: 78'
LOA: 65'
Draft: 6'
Beam: 17'
Rig height: 83'

Built in 1986 by Irwin Yachts, *Adastra* was originally named the *Tasa Grande*. She operated in the charter trade throughout the Caribbean and East Coast. Today she makes her home in Key West, Florida and is available for day sails, sunset cruises, and private charters.

Who sails: Groups and individuals of all ages
Program type: Day sails and overnight passages for paying passengers
Designer: Irwin
Built: 1986: St. Petersburg, FL, Irwin
Crew: 2 **Trainees-passengers:** 6 day sails, 6 overnight
Contact: Mr. Corey Hanson or Angela Persinger, National Boat Owner's Association (NBOA), 4404 N. Tamiam Trail, Sarasota, FL 34234 USA
Tel: 800-248-3572
E-mail: crhanson@nboat.com or apersinger@nboat.com
Website: www.nboat.com

SPECIFICATIONS

Flag: USA
Rig: Gaff schooner
Homeport: New York, New York
Normal cruising waters:
New York Harbor
Sparred length: 80'
LOA: 65'
LOD: 64' 6"
LWL: 58'
Draft: 8'
Beam: 16'
Rig height: 62'
Freeboard: 3' 4"
Sail area: 1,850 square feet
Tons: 41 GRT
Power: twin 50 HP diesels
Hull: Wood

ADIRONDACK

The schooner *Adirondack* is the third of five schooners to come out of the Scarano Boat Building yard, beginning with the 59-foot schooner *Madeline* and the 61-foot *Woodwind* in 1991, and followed by the 105-foot schooner *America* in 1995 and a sister ship, *Adirondack II*, launched in 1999. *Adirondack* combines the virtues of turn-of-the-century schooner yachts with the latest in laminated wood technology. Offering an enviable combination of stability and speed, the *Adirondack* fulfills the builder and owner's ambition of providing a quality sail for people of all ages and experience.

Who sails: School groups from elementary through college, private and corporate charters, families, and individuals of all ages
Program type: Sail training with paying trainees, passenger day sails
Built: 1996: Albany, NY, Scarano Boat
Coast Guard certification: Passenger vessel (Subchapter T)
Crew: 3 **Trainees-passengers:** 49 day sails
Contact: Rick Scarano, Manager, Sailing Excursions, Inc., c/o Scarano Boat, Port of Albany, Albany, NY 12202 USA
Tel: 800-701-SAIL; 518-463-3401
Fax: 518-463-3403
E-mail: mail@scaranoboat.com
Website: www.scaranoboat.com

SPECIFICATIONS

Flag: USA
Rig: Gaff schooner
Homeport:
Newport, Rhode Island
Normal cruising waters:
Narragansett Bay
Sparred length: 80'
LOA: 65'
LOD: 64' 6"
LWL: 58'
Draft: 8'
Beam: 16'
Rig height: 62'
Freeboard: 3' 4"
Sail area: 1,850 square feet
Tons: 41 GRT
Power: twin 50 HP diesels
Hull: Wood

ADIRONDACK II

The schooner *Adirondack II* is the latest sailing vessel to be launched from the Scarano Boat Building yard in Albany, New York. Launched in August of 1999, the near sister ship of the *Adirondack* joins the fleet of schooners known for their performance-oriented design/construction combined with classic traditional aesthetics. With its wide-open cockpit, *Adirondack II* can comfortably accommodate groups of up to 65 trainees/passengers. While dockside, spacious cockpit doghouses double as serving space for food and beverages or classroom navigation paperwork. *Adirondack II* affirms that modern wood composite construction and 19th century elegance blend seamlessly to the benefit of all.

Who sails: Private charters, families, and individuals of all ages
Program type: Sail training with paying trainees, passenger day sails
Built: 1999: Albany, NY, Scarano Boat
Coast Guard certification: Passenger vessel (Subchapter T)
Crew: 3 **Trainees-passengers:** 65 day sails
Contact: Rick Scarano, Manager, Sailing Excursions, Inc., c/o Scarano Boat, Port of Albany, Albany, NY 12202 USA
Tel: 800-701-SAIL; 518-463-3401
Fax: 518-463-3403
E-mail: mail@scaranoboat.com
Website: www.scaranoboat.com

SPECIFICATIONS

Flag: USA
Rig: Gaff topsail schooner
Homeport:
Gloucester, Massachusetts
LOA: 122'
LOD: 122'
LWL: 109'
Draft: 13' 6"
Beam: 24' 6"
Rig height: 110'
Sail area: 6,500 square feet
Tons: 130 GRT
Hull: Wood

ADVENTURE

The schooner *Adventure* is one of the last of the Gloucester fishing schooners, an icon of our nation's fishing industry and Gloucester's heritage. Gloucester's fishing schooners, known as "Gloucestermen", were famous throughout the world. Built in 1926, the 122-foot *Adventure* represents the pinnacle of schooner design, embodying grace, speed, and functionality. Fast and able under sail and carrying 14 dories, *Adventure* was the "highliner" of the North Atlantic fleet, earning more money than any other fishing vessel of her era. After retiring from fishing in 1953, *Adventure* was refitted as a windjammer and carried passengers along the coast of Maine until 1987. In 1988 she was given to the people of Gloucester to be preserved as Gloucester's historic tall ship. Today *Adventure* is being restored as a 1926 Gloucester fishing schooner and will resume sailing once work is completed. She will serve as a community resource for educational programming, focusing on maritime, cultural, and environmental issues, and will sail as a living symbol of Gloucester's maritime heritage.

Program type: Dockside interpretation; educational programs for schools
Designer: Tom McManus
Built: 1926: Essex, MA, John F. James & Son Yard
Coast Guard certification: Moored Attraction Vessel (dockside)
Contact: Sally Curry, Gloucester Adventure, Inc,
PO Box 1306, Gloucester, MA 01931-1306 USA
Tel: 978-281-8079
Fax: 978-281-2393
E-mail: scurry@schooner-adventure.org
Website: www.schooner-adventure.org

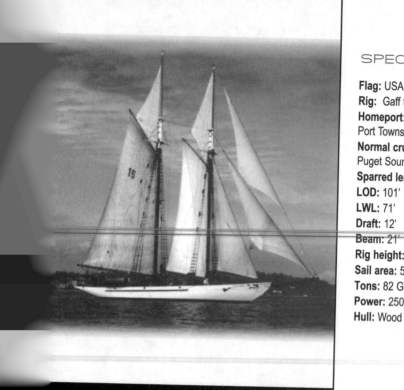

Flag: USA
Rig: Gaff topsail schooner
Homeport:
Port Townsend, Washington
Normal cruising waters:
Puget Sound and Salish Sea
Sparred length: 135'
LOD: 101'
LWL: 71'
Draft: 12'
Beam: 21'
Rig height: 110'
Sail area: 5,478 square feet
Tons: 82 GRT
Power: 250 HP diesel
Hull: Wood

ADVENTURESS

The 1913 schooner *Adventuress* sails to increase awareness of the majesty and vulnerability of Puget Sound. Since 1989, the non-profit environmental education organization, Sound Experience, has provided hands-on education aboard *Adventuress* in response to the area's urgent environmental issues. Volunteer and paid crew receive environmental and sail training. The ship's apprentice program for youth 14 – 18, and month-long internships for adult sailor/educators also feature extensive sail training. The non-competitive environment fosters cooperation, teamwork, and leadership skills. A National Historic Landmark and a Puget Sound treasure, the *Adventuress* is truly a boat for the people, providing empowering, life-changing experiences to more than 3,500 youth and adults each year.

Who sails: Schools and other groups from elementary through college, individuals and families
Program type: Sea education in marine science, maritime history, and ecology; passenger day and overnight sails; dockside interpretation during port visits
Season: March - October
Designer: B. B. Crowninshield
Built: 1913: East Boothbay, ME, Rice Brothers
Coast Guard certification: Passenger vessel (Subchapter T)
Crew: 4-5, with an additional 8-10 instructors **Trainees-passengers:** 45 day sails, 25 overnight
Contact: Geoff Ball, Sound Experience, 2310 Washington Street, Port Townsend, WA 98368 USA
Tel: 360-379-0438
Fax: 360-379-0439
E-mail: email@soundexp.org
Website: www.soundexp.org

Flag: USA
Rig: Schooner
Homeport: Bivalve, NJ
Normal Cruising waters:
Delaware Bay, Deleware River, NJ
Coastal Waters
Sparred length: 115'
LOA: 85'
LOD: 81' 7"
LWL: 78' 3"
Draft: 6'
Beam: 22' 1"
Rig height: 67' 8"
Sail area: 3,560 square feet
Freeboard: 3' 6"
Tons: 57 GRT
Power: 225 HP diesel
Hull: Wood

AJ MEERWALD

The Bayshore Discovery Project operates the schooner *A. J. Meerwald*, New Jersey's official tall ship as an experiential classroom. This authentically restored 1928 Delaware Bay oyster schooner sails from her homeport of Bivalve, New Jersey as well as annual visits to cities and coastal towns throughout New Jersey, Pennsylvania and Delaware and occasional special trips into the Chesapeake and the Northeast Atlantic Seaboard. Students range from fourth graders to senior citizens; subject matter ranges from the history of Delaware Bay oystering to present water quality issues. Motivating people to take care of the environment, the history and the culture of New Jersey's Bayshore region are the primary goals of all activities on the *A. J. Meerwald*, regardless of their target audience, length of program, and/or port of origin. The Bayshore Discovery Project also conducts shore-based programs, lecture series, hosts Delaware Bay Day (the first Saturday in June), and provides leadership on watershed issues throughout the Delaware Estuary. Members and volunteers are the lifeblood of the organization and are always welcome.

Who sails: School groups 4th grade through college, private and corporate charters, and individuals of all ages
Program type: Sail training for professional crew, volunteers, and paying trainees; three hour educational sails, summer camp, family sails, teacher workshops, overnight programs, team building, and theme sails; sea education in marine science, maritime history, ecology, and watershed awareness in cooperation with accredited institutions and other groups and as informal, in-house programming
Season: April 1 - November 1
Designer: Charles H. Stowman & Sons Shipyard
Built: 1928: Dorchester, NJ, Charles H. Stowman & Sons
Coast Guard certification: Passenger vessel (Subchapter T)
Crew: 11, augmented by volunteers **Trainees-passengers:** 45 day sails, 6 overnight
Contact: Meghan E. Wren, Executive Director, Bayshore Discovery Project, 2800 High Street-Bivalve, Port Norris, NJ 08349 USA
Tel: 856-785-2060 **Fax:** 856-785-2893 **Email:** info@bayshorediscoveryproject.org
Website: www.bayshorediscoveryproject.org

SPECIFICATIONS

Flag: USA
Rig: Gaff schooner
Homeport:
Vineyard Haven, Massachusetts
Normal cruising waters:
Southern New England
Sparred length: 126'
LOA: 90'
LOD: 85'
LWL: 78'
Draft: 12' 6"
Beam: 21'
Rig height: 94'
Freeboard: 5'
Sail area: 5,000 square feet
Tons: 85 GRT
Power: twin diesels
Hull: Wood

ALABAMA

The ex-pilot schooner *Alabama* is an authentic example of a typical Gloucester fishing schooner of the early 1900s. She was built for the Mobile Bar Pilot Association in Pensacola, Florida in 1926 and designed by the greatest New England designer of Gloucester schooners, Thomas F. McManus. After a major three-year reconstruction, the summer of 1998 marked her first year sailing the waters of southern New England joining the *Shenandoah* in The Black Dog Tall Ships fleet of Martha's Vineyard. The *Alabama* runs 6-day sailing trips for youth ages 9 to14 from late June through late August and is available for day and sunset sails and private charter each year from June 1 through late June and late August through mid-October.

Who sails: School groups elementary through college, private and corporate charters, and individuals of all ages
Program type: Sail training for paying trainees ages 9 - 15; private charters and public days sails
Designer: Thomas F. McManus
Built: 1926: Pensacola, FL, Pensacola Shipbuilding Company
Coast Guard certification: Passenger vessel (Subchapter T)
Crew: 6 **Trainees-passengers:** 49 day sails, 27 overnight
Contact: Captain Robert Douglas, Coastwise Packet Co., dba The Black Dog Tall Ships, PO Box 429, Vineyard Haven, MA 02568 USA
Tel: 508-693-1699
Fax: 508-693-1881
Website: www.theblackdogtallships.com

SPECIFICATIONS

Flag: USA
Rig: Schooner, two-masted
Homeport:
San Francisco, California
Normal cruising waters:
San Francisco Bay
Sparred length: 88'
LOA: 62'
LOD: 61' 4"
LWL: 59' 5"
Draft: 3' 6"'
Beam: 23' 6"
Rig height: 76'
Freeboard: 4'
Sail area: 2,684 square feet
Tons: 47GRT
Power: twin diesels
Hull: Wood

ALMA

The last of approximately 400 scow schooners that carried cargo in the San Francisco Bay area at the turn of the century, *Alma* was built at Hunter's Point in San Francisco Bay in 1891. Today she is owned and operated by the San Francisco Maritime National Historical Park, and docked at Hyde Street Pier near Fisherman's Wharf. From March to November, the *Alma* sails with a crew of volunteers, representing and interpreting a time when commerce moved by boat around the Bay. The volunteer program enables trainees to learn about traditional sailing and wooden boat maintenance. No fees are required as all crew volunteer to sail and maintain the *Alma* and other park vessels.

Who sails: Adult education groups, families, students, and individuals of all ages
Program type: Sail training for professional crew and apprentices; sea education based on informal in-house programming focused of maritime history; dockside interpretation; affiliated groups include the National Maritime Museum Association, San Francisco National Maritime Historical Park, and National Park Service
Designer: Fred Siemers
Built: 1891: San Francisco, CA, Fred Siemers
Crew: 6 **Trainees-passengers:** 40 day sails, 28 overnight
Contact: Elizabeth Kibbey, Executive Director, San Francisco Maritime National Historical Park, Building E, Fort Mason Center, San Francisco, CA 94123 USA
Tel: 415-561-7000
Fax: 415-556-1624
E-mail: lynn_cullivan@nps.gov
Website: www.nps.gov/safr/local/alma.html

SPECIFICATIONS

Flag: Republic of Vanuatu
Rig: Main topsail schooner
Homeport:
Port Vila, Republic of Vanuatu
Normal cruising waters:
Tropical waters worldwide
Sparred length: 126'
LOA: 92'
LOD: 92'
LWL: 87'
Draft: 10'
Beam: 19'
Rig height: 85'
Freeboard: 2' 6"
Sail area: 5,700 square feet
Tons: 87 GRT
Power: Wichmann 2-cycle diesel 160 HP
Hull: Riveted steel

ALVEI

After an extensive 8-year refit *Alvei's* rigging, deck and accommodations have been completely renewed. Underway since 1995, *Alvei* uses the old sailing ship routes and now spends the Southern Hemisphere winter visiting the islands of the South Pacific and the summer cyclone season in either Australia or New Zealand. *Alvei's* rig, the main topsail schooner, was popular among privateering vessels of the early 1800s. There are 124 lines of running rigging totaling over 3 miles in length. She carries 16 sails providing experience in both fore and aft and square sail handling - learning the ropes the old way. Raising the anchor, rowing the shore boat, and laundry are all done by hand. *Alvei* has a full participation crew. This provides practical experience in all aspects of maintaining traditional a vessel. At sea the crew stands watch 4 hours on and 8 hours off. Duties include steering, lookout, sail handling, docking, and anchoring. While in port it is 1 day on and 2 days off. One of the three watches has the 24-hour duty from 08:00. It is their responsibility to prepare the meals, keep the galley clean, row the shore boat, do ongoing maintenance, and stand anchor watch. The other 2 watches are free to explore the area.

Who sails: Adults 18 and over
Program type: Sail training for volunteers and paying trainees; sea education based on informal in-house participation; coastal and offshore passages
Season: Year-round
Designer: Hull unknown, accommodations and rigging, Evan Logan
Built: 1920: Montrose, Scotland
Certification: Vanuatu Maritime Authority, Charter Vessel (pending final topsides inspection)
Crew: 6, volunteer crew and 12 paying trainees **Trainees-passengers:** 36 day sails, 18 overnight
Contact: Evan Logan, Owner/Operator, Alvei Sail Training Cooperative, PO Box 415, Nelson, New Zealand
Tel: 6421-111-8501
Fax: 643-546-8505
E-mail: alvei@yahoo.com
Website: www.alvei.com or www.alvei.de

SPECIFICATIONS

Flag: USA
Rig: Gaff schooner
Homeport: Key West, Florida
Normal cruising waters:
Key West, FL (winter)
Newport, RI (summer)
Sparred length: 139'
LOD: 105'
LWL: 97'
Draft: 10' 6"
Beam: 25'
Rig height: 108'
Freeboard: 6'
Sail area: 6,400 square feet
Tons: 129 GRT
Power:
twin 220hp John Deere diesels
Hull: Wood

AMERICA

America is a waterline-up recreation of the famous "Low Black Schooner", originally designed by 31-year old Naval Architect George Steers. In 1851 she successfully represented the New York Yacht Club in the 1851 challenge race with the Royal Yacht Squadron. History and racing buffs know the famous reply to Queen Victoria's inquiry about the second-place boat, "Madam, there is no second..." The race itself was later renamed the America's Cup, in honor of the original winner, and now represents the world's most coveted yachting trophy. The schooner *America* was built in 1995 to continue the tradition of the original vessel and to be a sailing ambassador for the United States. In 1998, she was purchased by Historic Tours of America and now makes her home in Key West, Florida. The *America* offers exciting day sails as well as romantic sunset cruises, to visitors in Key West. While onboard, passengers are invited to help raise her sails and steer the ship under the guidance of her experienced and professional crew.

Who sails: Young and old
Program type: Novice sailor training vessel
Season: Year-round
Designer: George Steers (with modifications by Scarano Boat)
Built: 1995: Port Albany, NY, Scarano Boat
Coast Guard certification: Passenger vessel (Subchapter T)
Crew: 1 captain, 6 crew members **Trainees:** 2 trainees per rotation **Passengers:** 64 day sails, 6 overnight
Contact: Sunny Andracchio, General Manager, Historic Tours of America,
201 Front St., Key West, FL 33040 USA
Tel: 800-868-7482
Fax: 305-292-7701
E-mail: schooneramerica@historictours.com
Website: www.historictours.com

AMERICAN PRIDE

SPECIFICATIONS

Flag: USA
Rig: Schooner, three-masted
Homeport: Long Beach, California
Normal cruising waters:
Southern California
Sparred length: 129'
LOA: 105'
LOD: 101'
LWL: 92'
Draft: 10'
Beam: 22'
Rig height: 98'
Freeboard: 6'
Sail area: 4,900 square feet
Tons: 203 GRT
Power: diesel
Hull: Wood

Built in 1941 as a two-masted "schooner-dragger", the *American Pride* spent over 40 years commercially fishing the Grand Banks and George's Banks. In 1986, completely restored and with a third mast added, she operated as a charter boat out of Bar Harbor, Maine. She was purchased by the American Heritage Marine Institute (AHMI) in 1996, and sailed to her new home in Long Beach, California. Aboard the *American Pride*, the AHMI offers hands-on educational programs stressing science, marine biology, history, and sail training. Programs encourage teamwork, good communication, problem solving and leadership. Actively engaged in sharing the thrill of sailing with people of all ages, the AHMI frequently donates sails to child welfare groups, fundraising guilds, and others. A professional crew and strong volunteer group generously give time, talents, and resources in support of the programs.

Who sails: School groups elementary through college, private and corporate charters, and individuals of all ages
Program type: Scientific or living history educational programs, sail training, team building, sailing adventures
Season: Year-round
Built: 1941: Brooklyn, NY, Muller Boatworks
Coast Guard certification: Passenger vessel (Subchapter T)
Crew: 6 (paid and volunteer) **Trainees-passengers:** 100 day sails, 48 overnight
Contact: Helen H. Clinton, Director, American Heritage Marine Institute,
21520 "G" Yorba Linda Blvd. #444, Yorba Linda, CA 92887 USA
Tel: 714-970-8800
Fax: 714-970-8474
E-mail: americprd@aol.com
Website: www.americanpride.org

SPECIFICATIONS

Flag: USA
Rig: Schooner
Homeport: Washington DC
Normal cruising waters:
East Coast of the United States
Sparred length: 58'
LOD: 46' 6"
LWL: 41'
Draft: 3'
Beam: 17'
Rig height: 60'
Power: diesel
Hull: Steel

AMERICAN SPIRIT

In the summer of 2004, she was donated to the National Maritime Heritage Foundation, located in Washington, DC, where she is used as an educational platform for middle school students and a charter boat. She provides guests with a unique view of our nation's capitol with an engaging historical point of reference. Built at the fall line of the Potomac river at the original site of the port of Georgetown, Washington DC enjoyed a rich maritime past throughout the pre-colonial, colonial and post-colonial periods. *American Spirit* is a custom-built, steel schooner, gaff rigged on the foremast, with a club-footed jib and a Marconi main. She was originally launched as a day passenger boat and used for whale watching in New England and day cruises in the winter months on the west coast of Florida. The *American Spirit* program is an educational outreach effort of the National Maritime Heritage Foundation dedicated to expanding the cultural horizons of our guests by giving students and adults a sense of their place in the maritime history of our nation's capitol.

Who sails: All ages
Program type: Educational outreach
Season: April through October
Designer: Frank Meigs
Coast Guard certification: Passenger vessel (Subchapter T)
Crew: 4 **Trainees-passengers:** 35 day sails, 8 overnight
Contact: Kevin Traver, Executive Director, National Maritime Heritage Foundation, 236 Massachusetts Ave NE, Suite 410, Washington, DC 20002 USA
Tel: 202-547-1250
Fax: 202-547-0250
E-mail: info@nmhf.org
Website: www.nmhf.org

Photo and text by Thad Koza

SPECIFICATIONS

Flag: Italy
Rig: Full-rigged ship
Homeport: La Spezia, Italy
Normal cruising waters: Worldwide
Sparred length: 330'
Draft: 23' 6"
Beam: 50' 9"
Hull: Steel

AMERIGO VESPUCCI

The pride of the Italian navy, *Amerigo Vespucci* conjures up memories of men-of-war from two centuries ago. Riding high in the water, with triple decks indicated by painted stripes, *Amerigo Vespucci* is a gracious twentieth-century goodwill ambassador, as well as a symbol of Italy's global maritime heritage and tradition. Named for the great explorer and cartographer of the seventeenth century, this elegant, full-rigged ship is a grand visitor to many ceremonial parades of sail. Since her launch, *Amerigo Vespucci* has been used to train junior officers of the Italian navy.

Who sails: Junior officers of the Italian navy
Program type: Sail training
Season: Year round
Built: 1931
Contact: Embassy of Italy, 3000 Whitehaven Street, NW, Washington, DC 20008 USA
Tel: 202-612-4400
Fax: 202-518-2151

SPECIFICATIONS

Flag: USA
Rig: Topsail schooner
Homeport:
New Haven, Connecticut
Normal cruising waters:
East Coast of the United States
Sparred length: 129'
LOA: 85'
LOD: 81'
LWL: 79'
Draft: 10' 6"
Beam: 23'
Rig height: 100'
Sail area: 5,200 square feet
Power: cat 3304 x 2, 135
Hull: Wood

AMISTAD

AMISTAD America, Inc. is a national, non-profit educational organization. We promote improved relationships between races and cultures by acknowledging our common experiences and encouraging dialogue that is based on respect. The inherent lessons and legacies of freedom, justice, perseverance, cooperation and leadership arising from the historic Amistad Incident of 1839 are symbolized by the re-created *Amistad*, Connecticut's Flagship and Tall Ship Ambassador. The Freedom Schooner visits ports nationally and internationally as an ambassador for friendship and goodwill. It serves as a floating classroom, icon and as a monument to the millions of souls that were broken or lost as a result of the insidious Transatlantic slave trade. The vessel offers an important message for all Americans about our collective history and future. The home port for Freedom Schooner *Amistad* is Long Wharf Pier in New Haven, Connecticut.

Who sails: School groups elementary through college
Program type: Sail training for crew and apprentices and paying trainees; maritime history and a full range of programming are expected; sea education in cooperation with accredited institutions and other groups; passenger day sails and dockside interpretation during home and port visits
Designer: Tri-Coastal Marine
Built: 1998 – 2000: Mystic Seaport, Mystic, CT
Coast Guard certification: Passenger vessel (Subchapter T), Sailing School Vessel (Subchapter R)
Crew: 8, combination paid and volunteer **Trainees-passengers:** 49 day sails
Contact: AMISTAD America, Inc., 746 Chapel Street, Suite 300, New Haven, CT 06510-3102 USA
Tel: 203-495-1839 or 866-AMISTAD
Fax: 203-495-9647
E-mail: operations@amistadamerica.org
Website: www.amistadamerica.org

SPECIFICATIONS

Flag: USA
Rig: Gaff topsail schooner
Homeport: Camden, Maine
Normal cruising waters:
Maine to the Florida Keys
Sparred length: 86'
LOA: 82'
LOD: 65'
LWL: 53'
Draft: 10' 6"
Beam: 18' 9"
Rig height: 75'
Freeboard: 8'
Sail area: 2,815 square feet
Tons: 63 GRT
Power: 210 HP diesel
Hull: Wood

APPLEDORE II

The *Appledore II* is a traditional gaff-rigged schooner designed for ocean sailing. Launched in 1978 she circumnavigated the world on her maiden voyage. From her homeport of Camden, Maine, the *Appledore II* makes day sails from late June through mid-October. During the winter months, she operates out of Key West, Florida, offering day sails, snorkeling trips on North America's only living coral reef, and sunset cruises. Committed to sail training, the crew of the *Appledore II* are trained in sailing and marlinspike seamanship through operation of the vessel on day sails as well as two 2,000-mile offshore voyages yearly. Those interested should contact the *Appledore II* for possible payroll and/or volunteer positions.

Who sails: School groups elementary through college, families, and individuals of all ages
Program type: Sail training for crew and apprentices; sea education based on informal in-house programming; passenger day sails
Season: June – October (Maine) December – May (Florida)
Designer: Bud McIntosh
Built: 1978: South Bristol, ME, Gamage Shipyard, Herb Smith
Coast Guard certification: Passenger vessel (Subchapter T)
Crew: 7 **Trainees-passengers:** 49 day sails, 26 overnight
Contact: John P. McKean. President, Schooner Exploration Associates, Ltd. (summer) "O" Lily Pond Drive, Camden, ME 04843 USA (winter) PO Box 4114, Key West, FL 33041-4414 USA
Tel: 207-236-8353 (summer) 305-292-9898 (winter)
Email: sail@appledore2.com

SPECIFICATIONS

Flag: USA
Rig: Topsail schooner
Homeport: Bay City, Michigan
Normal cruising waters:
Saginaw Bay and Lake Huron
Sparred length: 85'
LOA: 65'
LOD: 65'
LWL: 53'
Draft: 8' 6"
Beam: 18' 5"
Rig height: 76'
Freeboard: 6'
Sail area: 3,560 square feet
Tons: 48 GRT
Power: 135 HP diesel
Hull: Steel

APPLEDORE IV

The schooner *Appledore IV* is owned and operated by BaySail, a 501(C) 3 non-profit corporation. Tall ship adventures aboard the *Appledore IV* further BaySail's mission: "To foster environmental stewardship of the Saginaw Bay watershed and the Great Lakes ecosystem and to provide personal development opportunities for learners of all ages through shipboard and land based educational experiences." BaySail's environmental education program, Science Under Sail, begins and ends in the classroom with materials designed to prepare students for their sailing experience and reinforce the lessons learned while on board the *Appledore IV*. During the three-and-a-half-hour excursion, trained volunteer teachers lead small groups of students through hands-on activities including collecting and analyzing water, sediment, and plankton samples. Land use, maritime history, navigation, and weather observation are also discussed. To date over 16,000 K-12 students have taken part in BaySail's award winning education programs. *Appledore IV* is also available for private charter to companies, organizations, and other groups of up to 48 people, and for weekend public sails from May through September.

Who sails: School groups elementary through college and individuals of all ages.
Program type: Half-day K-12 marine science and ecology education; public sails and private charters.
Affiliated institutions include: Saginaw Valley State University, Delta College, and the Boy's and Girl's Clubs of Michigan.
Season: April – October
Designer: Bud McIntosh
Built: 1989: Palm Coast, FL, Treworgy Yachts
Coast Guard certification: Passenger vessel (Subchapter T)
Crew: 4 **Trainees-passengers:** 48 day sails, 7 overnight
Contact: Roger Nugent, Executive Director, BaySail, 901 Saginaw Street, Bay City, MI 48708 USA
Tel: 989-895-5193
Fax: 989-893-7016
E-mail: info@baysailbaycity.org
Website: www.baysailbaycity.org

APPLEDORE V

SPECIFICATIONS

Flag: USA
Rig: Gaff topsail schooner, 2-masted
Homeport: Bay City, Michigan
Normal cruising waters:
Saginaw Bay and Lake Huron
Sparred length: 65'
LOD: 58'
LWL: 49'
Draft: 7' 6"
Beam: 14'
Rig height: 63' 6"
Tons: 34 GRT
Power: 90 HP diesel
Freeboard: 4'
Hull: Steel

Through the summer months the *Appledore V* delivers BaySail's youth sail training program "Windward Bound". During the 5 – 10 day Windward Bound voyages *Appledore V* is sailed by a professional captain and mate, three youth officers, and six youth trainees. On their regular watches trainees are involved in every aspect of running the ship, from navigating and steering, to galley duty, to manning the oars in *Appledore's* tender on trips ashore. Trainees who successfully complete a summer training voyage become eligible to join the year-round program and train to qualify as youth officers. In 2004 the *Appledore V* took part in "Salute to L'Acadie" joining other tall ships for port visits on Canada's Atlantic Coast. In 2005, 10 voyages are scheduled which include passages in Lake Huron's North Channel, visits to Mackinac Island, and participation in a gathering of tall ships in Sault Ste. Marie, Michigan. The *Appledore V* is owned and operated by BaySail, a 501(C) 3 non-profit corporation.

Who sails: Youth ages 14 – 18.
Program type: Youth Sail Training. Affiliated with Boy's and Girl's Clubs of Michigan.
Season: April to October
Designer: Bud McIntosh
Built: 1992: Palm Coast, FL, Treworgy Yachts
Coast Guard certification: Passenger Vessel (Subchapter T)
Crew: 2 **Youth Officers:** 3 **Trainees-passengers:** 29 (day sails), 6 overnight.
Contact: Roger C. Nugent, Executive Director, BaySail, 901 Saginaw Street, Bay City, MI 48708
Tel: 989-895-5193
Fax: 989-893-7016
E-mail: info@baysailbaycity.org
Website: www.baysailbaycity.org

SPECIFICATIONS

Flag: USA
Rig: Gaff topsail schooner
Homeport: Mystic, Connecticut
Normal cruising waters:
Fishers Island, Block Island and
Long Island Sounds
Sparred length: 81'
LOD: 56'
LWL: 48'
Draft: 7' 6"
Beam: 20'
Rig height: 75'
Freeboard: 5'
Sail area: 1,800 square feet
Tons: 20 GRT
Power: 100 HP diesel
Hull: Honduran Mahogany
White Oak frames

ARGIA

Voyager Cruises operates the *Argia* out of Mystic, Connecticut during the months of May through October. She is a replica of a 19th Century schooner and was designed and built by Captain Frank Fulchiero for the day passenger trade. She carries 49 passengers on the waters of Block Island and Long Island Sounds for 2 to 3 hour day sails, charters, and marine science/coastal ecology programs. The Coastal Ecology Program utilizes various sampling and testing techniques to provide students with a better understanding of marine and coastal ecosystems. Volunteer and intern positions are available for this program which runs in Spring and Fall. Paid crew positions include: deckhand, 1st and 2nd mate, and licensed captain.

Who sails: All ages
Program type: Sail training for paying trainees and passengers; sea education in marine science, maritime history, and ecology in cooperation with accredited institutions and other groups; passenger day sails
Season: May – October
Designer: Frank Fulchiero
Built: 1986: Reedville, VA and Mystic, CT, Frank Fulchiero and Jennings Boat Yard
Coast Guard certification: Passenger vessel (Subchapter T) Inland
Crew: 5 **Trainees-passengers:** 49 day sails
Contact: Captain Amy Blumberg, Voyager Cruises, 15 Holmes Street, Schooner Wharf, Mystic, CT 06355 USA
Tel: 860-536-0416
Fax: 860-536-0416
Email: alblumberg@voyagermystic.com
Website: www.voyagermystic.com

Photo by Stephen Peregrin

ARGUS

SPECIFICATIONS

Flag: USA
Rig: Topsail ketch
Homeport:
Newport Beach, California
Normal cruising waters:
Catalina Island, Long Beach
Harbor, Dana Point, CA
Sparred length: 92'
LOA: 68'
LOD: 65'
Draft: 8'
Beam: 18'
Rig height: 60'
Freeboard: 4' 6"
Sail area: 2,510 square feet
Tons: 53 GRT
Power: Detroit 671 diesel
Hull: Wood

Built in Marstal, Denmark, in 1905, *Argus* celebrates her 100th birthday in 2005. During her early years she hauled cement and lumber around the Baltic Sea and although records are vague, it is believed she was also used to haul grain and other goods to Greenland, salt and fish to Spain, and spices back up north from Spain. The pride of the Newport Sea Base, *Argus* has served scouting since 1972, allowing scouts to step back in history as part of a one-day, weekend, or five-day program at sea. Participants crew the ship, learn teamwork and leadership, stand watch, and keep a lookout for dolphins, whales, and sometimes people. The ship drew national media attention when on April 25th, 2004 during a return voyage from Catalina Island the *Argus* crew did their "daily good turn" by rescuing a diver who had been drifting at sea for hours after he lost his dive boat.

Who sails: Groups registered with Boy Scouts of America with participants ages 12 and up under the direction of the *Argus* captain and staff
Program type: Sail training and sea education. Affiliated with the Boy Scouts of America
Built: 1905: Marstal, Denmark
Coast Guard certification: Passenger vessel (Subchapter T)
Crew: 6 **Trainees-passengers:** 34 day sails, 20 overnight
Contact: Boy Scouts of America Newport Sea Base, 1931 W. Coast Highway, Newport Beach, CA 92663 USA
Tel: 949-642-5031
Fax: 949-650-5407
E-mail: seabase@ocbsa.org
Website: www.seabase.org

Flag: Indonesia
Rig: Schooner
Homeport: Jakarta, Indonesia
Normal cruising waters:
Worldwide
Sparred length: 129'
Draft: 9'
Beam: 22'
Hull: Steel

Photo and text by Thad Koza

ARUNG SAMUDERA

In 1995 the Indonesian government celebrated their golden anniversary of independence by hosting a conference, heralded the Arung Samudera '95, to draw attention to the archipelago nation. At the conclusion of the conference, a 129-foot staysail schooner purchased in New Zealand was commissioned as Indonesia's first sail training ship. Know originally as *Adventurer*, the schooner was built in 1991 to serve as a sail training vessel based in Auckland, New Zealand She was renamed Kri *Arung Samudera* to reflect her new home and service. The honorific "kri" is used just as "HMS" is used in Britain to designate a ship in service of the Royal Navy. Together the words "arung" and "samudera" in this context mean "cruise the ocean" a fitting goal for this adventurous schooner. *Arung Samudera* embarked on a circumnavigation of the globe as her first assignment.

Program type: Sail training vessel of the Indonesian Navy
Built: 1991
Contact: Embassy of the Republic of Indonesia, 2020 Massachusetts Avenue, NW, Washington DC 20036 USA
Tel: 202-775-5200
Fax: 202-775-5365

AURORA

SPECIFICATIONS

Flag: USA
Rig: Gaff topsail schooner
Homeport: Newport, Rhode Island
Normal cruising waters: Narragansett Bay
Sparred length: 101'
LOD: 80'
Draft: 8'
Beam: 17' 6"
Rig height: 82'
Sail area: 2,800 square feet
Tons: 53 GRT
Hull: Wood

Formerly known as the *Francis Todd*, the *Aurora* is a two-masted schooner built in 1947 for work in the fishing industry. She retired from fishery work in 1991 and has since been rebuilt to offer ample seating, a spacious deck plan, and amenability to charter arrangements. Perfect for entertaining and special occasions, the *Aurora* is inspected and certified by the US Coast Guard as a Passenger Vessel. She is stable, seaworthy, and professionally maintained for comfort and safety. Based in Newport, Rhode Island, the *Aurora* sails New England waters and Narragansett Bay and is available for day sails and private charter.

Who sails: School groups elementary through college, individuals, families, corporate and social groups
Program type: Passenger day sails and informal sail training
Designer: Newbert & Wallace
Built: 1947: Thomaston, ME, Newbert & Wallace
Crew: 3 **Trainees-passengers:** 75 day sails
Contact: IDC Charters, Inc. Goat Island Marina, Newport, RI 02840 USA
Tel: 401-849-6683
Website: www.newportexperience.com

SPECIFICATIONS

Flag: USA
Rig: Staysail schooner
Homeport: Portland, Maine
Normal Cruising Waters:
Casco Bay
Sparred length: 72'
LOA: 55' 6"
LOD: 54'
LWL: 44'
Draft: 7' 6"
Beam: 14' 6"
Rig height: 65'
Freeboard: 4'
Tons: 21 GRT
Power: 72 HP diesel
Hull: Wood

BAGHEERA

The schooner *Bagheera* was designed by John G. Alden and built in 1924 in East Boothbay, Maine. Shortly after launching she sailed in the Bermuda Race, and then spent the next 50 years sailing in the Great Lakes. *Bagheera* was entered in the Chicago Mackinac Race numerous times, winning in 1930. The vessel was sailed to the Caribbean in the 1970s, eventually finding her way to the Galapagos Islands. She was converted to the passenger trade in the 1980s. She then sailed out of Los Angeles, San Diego and San Francisco before being shipped to Maine in 2002 to serve Portland Schooner Co., her current stewards. Today *Bagheera* sails Memorial Day through Columbus Day from the Old Port in Portland, Maine, offering a variety of educational courses, public sails, and private charters.

Who sails: Schools, camps, organizations, families and individuals of all ages
Program type: Sea education based on in-house programming
Season: Memorial Day through Columbus Day
Designer: John G. Alden
Built: 1924: East Boothbay, ME, Rice Brothers
Coast Guard certification: Passenger vessel (Subchapter T)
Crew: 2 **Trainees-passengers:** 48 day sails
Contact: Scott Reischmann, Portland Schooner Company, Box 111, Pears Island, Portland, ME 04108 USA
Tel: 207-766-2500 or (toll free) 1-87-SCHOONER
Fax: 207-766-2240
E-mail: scott@portlandschooner.com
Website: www.portlandschooner.com

Photo by Steve Danford

BALCLUTHA

SPECIFICATIONS

Flag: USA
Rig: Full-rigged ship
Homeport:
San Francisco, California
Sparred length: 301'
LOD: 256'
Draft: 22' 7"
Beam: 38' 6"
Rig height: 145'
Tons: 1,689 GRT
Hull: Steel

The three-masted, riveted steel ship *Balclutha* was built in Glasgow, Scotland, in 1886 "to the highest class in Lloyd's Registry." As a deepwaterman, *Balclutha* and a 26-man crew rounded Cape Horn with grain for Great Britain, and later ran Pacific Coast lumber to Australia. Each year as a salmon packet, the vessel carried hundreds of men (with boats and supplies) to the salmon fishing grounds of Alaska. She was rescued from decay by the San Francisco Bay Area community in 1954, and has been restored as a memorial to the men and times of the grand days of sail. Today, the *Balclutha* (a National Historic Landmark) is open to the public daily as a part of the San Francisco Maritime National Historical Park.

Program type: Dockside sea education in maritime history
Designer: Charles Connell
Built: 1886: Scotland, Charles
Contact: Elizabeth Kibbey, Executive Director, San Francisco Maritime National Historical Park, Building E, Fort Mason Center, San Francisco, CA 94123 USA
Tel: 415-561-7000
Fax: 415-556-1624
E-mail: lynn_cullivan@nps.gov
Website: www.nps.gov/safr/local/balc.html

SPECIFICATIONS

Flag: Bermuda
Rig: Bermudian
Homeport: Dockyard, Bermuda
Normal cruising waters: Bermuda
waters and Western Atlantic
Sparred length: 112'
LOA: 112'
LOD: 88'
LWL: 75'
Draft: 9' 6"
Beam: 23"
Rig height: 93'
Freeboard: 5'
Sail area: 4,437 square feet
Tons: 88 GRT
Power: Cat 3126 Mechanical
385 HP diesel
Hull: Cold-moulded epoxy

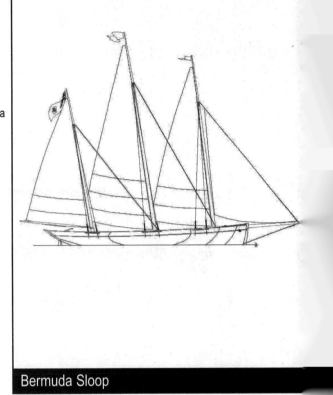

Bermuda Sloop

The purpose-built sail training vessel is based on civilian Bermudian-type schooners built 1810-1840. Bermudians, enslaved and free, built the schooners in the period spanning the Emancipation of Slavery in the British Empire (Aug 1st, 1834). The original hull shape were adapted from the Bermuda-built RN "Shamrock" class, fast dispatch / patrol vessels that ran from the RN Dockyard, Bermuda, northwest to Halifax and Southwest to Jamaica to contain the rebel colonies. Noteworthy is the Bermuda rig that was innovated on the coastal Bermuda sloops that abounded in the 17th, 18th and early part of the 19th century; faced with impassable pathways by land, locals had evolved the lateen rig to short-tack up(wind) the island and up to the fishing banks to windward of Bermuda.

Who sails: 14+ years
Program type: Extra-curricular team (high school) and curricular learning expeditions (middle school 3)
Season: February through December
Designer: Bill Nash / Langan Design Associates, Newport, RI **Built:** 2006: Rockport, ME, Rockport Marine
Coast Guard certification: Passenger vessel (Subchapter T)
Crew: 3 professional, 8 volunteer **Trainees-passengers:** 40 inside the reef, 26 coastal
Contact: Mr. Malcolm Kirkland, Executive Director, Bermuda Sloop Foundation, Suite 1151, 48 Par-la-Ville Road, Hamilton HM11 Bermuda
Tel: 441-236-0383
Fax: 441-292-3744
Website: www.bermudasloop.org/

BILL OF RIGHTS

SPECIFICATIONS

Flag: USA
Rig: Gaff rigged topsail schooner, two-masted
Homeport: Los Angeles, California
Sparred length: 136'
LOA: 129'
LOD: 94'
LWL: 85'
Draft: 10'
Beam: 23'
Rig height: 100'
Sail area: 6,300 square feet
Freeboard: 5' 8"
Tons: 95 GRT
Power: 210 HP diesel
Hull: Wood

Photo from the Port of LA Collection

As this is written, *Bill of Rights* is on long-term bareboat charter sailing with *Lady Washington* to the Pacific Northwest. After considerable restoration work at Grays Harbor Historical Seaport, *Bill of Rights* will join the TALL SHIPS CHALLENGE in Victoria, BC. Continuing with the fleet until a grand reentry into her homeport of San Pedro with the Grand Parade of Sail with Tall Ships® Los Angeles! *Bill of Rights* is being offered for sale at this time. Inquiries about subsequent use may be directed to Los Angeles Maritime Institute. Los Angeles Maritime Institute, the owners, operates the TopSail Youth Program, character-building sail training adventures for youth aboard the twin brigantines *Irving Johnson* and *Exy Johnson*, and the schooner *Swift of Ipswich*. TopSail can be adjusted to fit the age, interests, and abilities of any participants. *Bill of Rights* is a beautiful learning environment for 'youth-of-all-ages,' creating real-world challenges in the sea-world setting.

Who sails: Referred youth-at-risk and other groups catering to students and adults
Program type: Educational
Season: Year-round
Designer: McCurdy, Rhodes & Bates
Built: 1971: South Bristol, ME, Harvey F. Gamage
Coast Guard certification: Passenger vessel (Subchapter T)
Crew: 5 (day), 8 (overnight), 5 instructors **Trainees-passengers:** 52 day sails, 39 overnight
Contact: Captain Jim Gladson, Los Angeles Maritime Institute, Berth 84, Foot of Sixth Street, San Pedro, CA 90731 USA
Tel: 310-833-6055
Fax: 310-548-2055
Website: www.lamitopsail.org

SPECIFICATIONS

Flag: Canada
Rig: Brigantine
Homeport: Ottawa, Ontario, Canada
Normal Cruising Waters: Upper Ottawa River
Sparred length: 90'
LOA: 87'
LOD: 68'
LWL: 57'
Draft: 6'
Beam: 15'
Rig height: 60'
Sail area: 2,300 square feet
Freeboard: 3'
Tons: 42 GRT
Power: 235 HP diesel
Hull: Steel

Photo by Cal Vandergeest

BLACK JACK

On May 2, 1904 G. B. Pattee II, a steam tugboat, was launched in Quyon, Quebec, Canada. She worked the logging industry for 50 years on the Upper Ottawa River. In 1952 the hull was purchased by the late Captain Thomas G. Fuller and converted into a tall ship brigantine, *Black Jack*, for a family yacht. On May 2, 2004, after a major refit, *Black Jack* was re-christened and launched at Britannia Yacht Club by Her Excellency, the Right Honorable Adrienne Clarkson, Canada's Governor General. At the same time the vessel was designated Ottawa's Signature Vessel by the City of Ottawa. Bytown Brigantine was founded by the Thomas G. Fuller Family as a charitable foundation to provide opportunities for youth to experience adventure in the time honored traditions inherent in square rigged sailing. *Black Jack* is now the centerpiece of the Black Jack Island Adventure Camp, a 10 day program where youth 12-15 sail this tall ship or one of our 27' navy whalers as well as participating in other various camp activities.

Who sails: Middle school 12 – 15 year olds
Program type: Sail training for paying trainees, overnight voyages, Island Adventure Camp
Season: Summer and fall
Built: 1904: Scotland
Coast Guard certification: Sailing School Vessel, Inland/Minor Waters
Crew: 6 high school and university officers **Trainees-passengers:** 30 day sails,18 overnight
Contact: Bytown Brigantine, 2700 Queensview Drive, Ottawa, Ontario K2B 8H6 Canada
Tel: 613-596-6258
Fax: 613-596-5947
E-mail: tallshipinfo@tallshipsadventure.org
Website: www.tallshipsadventure.org

Photo by Captain Wendell Corey

BLACK PEARL

SPECIFICATIONS

Flag: USA
Rig: Brigantine
Homeport:
Bridgeport, Connecticut
Sparred length: 79'
LOD: 52'
LWL: 43'
Draft: 9"
Beam: 14'
Rig height: 63'
Sail area: 2,000 square feet
Freeboard: 6'
Tons: 28 GRT
Power: Diesel
Hull: Wood

Built in 1938 by Lincoln Vaughan for his own use, *Black Pearl* was purchased by Barclay H. Warburton III in 1958. Long a believer in the sea as a teacher, Warburton selected the rig as a good one for sail training. In 1972, Warburton sailed the *Black Pearl* to England to participate in the Tall Ship Race in European waters becoming, along with the USCG Barque *Eagle*, the first Americans to do so. On his return to Newport, Warburton founded the American Sail Training Association. *Black Pearl* is currently operated by the Aquaculture Foundation, a non-profit corporation formed to promote quality education in marine studies.

Who sails: Individuals and groups
Program type: Sail training for crew; passenger day sails; dockside interpretation
Season: April – November
Designer: Edson Schock
Built: 1938: Wickford, RI, C. Lincoln Vaughan
Crew: 6 **Trainees-Passengers:** 6
Contact: The Tall Ship Black Pearl, PO Box 678, Block Island, RI 02807

SPECIFICATIONS

Flag: Canada
Rig: Gaff topsail schooner
Homeport: Lunenburg,
Nova Scotia, Canada
Normal cruising waters:
East Coast of Canada and the
United States
Sparred length: 181'
LOD: 143'
LWL: 112'
Draft: 16'
Beam: 27'
Rig height: 132'
Sail area: 11,139 square feet
Tons: 285 GRT
Power: 250 HP twin diesels
Hull: Wood

BLUENOSE II

The original *Bluenose*, launched on March 26, 1921, was a typical Nova Scotia Grand Banks fishing schooner. Built at Lunenburg both for fishing and for the International Fishermen's Trophy series of races between Canada and the United States, *Bluenose* was undefeated under her legendary master, Captain Angus J. Walters of Lunenburg. Her likeness became a national emblem and it is depicted on stamps and the ten-cent coin of Canada. Launched on July 24, 1963, *Bluenose II* was built from the same plans at the same yard and by some of the same men. The only difference lies in the accommodations for the co-ed crew of 18 and the modern navigation and communication instruments. She serves as a goodwill ambassador for the Province of Nova Scotia, participating in tall ship events throughout the Western Hemisphere. *Bluenose II*'s 12 deckhands receive instructions from her officers in all matters of seamanship. Today she sails in the best *Bluenose* tradition, and all officers and deckhands are encouraged to enhance their skills and certifications. *(BLUENOSE II© Bluenose II Preservation Trust. Used with permission. All rights reserved.)*

Who sails: Individuals and groups
Program type: Sail training for crew; passenger day sails; dockside interpretation
Season: April – November
Designer: William J. Roué, Halifax, Nova Scotia, Canada
Built: 1963: Lunenburg, Nova Scotia, Canada, Smith & Rhuland Shipyards
Coast Guard certification: Canadian Coast Guard certified
Crew: 18
Contact: Lunenburg Marine Museum Society, C/O Fisheries Museum of the Atlantic, PO Box 1363 Lunenburg Nova Scotia, B0J 2C0, Canada
Tel: 866-579-4909 or 902-634-4794
Fax: 902-634-8990
E-mail: bluenoseII@gov.ns.ca
Website: www.museum.gov.ns.ca/fma/

Flag: USA
Rig: Schooner
Homeport: Islesboro, Maine
Normal cruising waters:
New England (summer),
Caribbean (winter)
Sparred length: 72'
LOA: 57'
LOD: 57'
LWL: 49'
Draft: 7'
Beam: 15' 3"
Rig height: 63'
Sail area: 2,500 square feet
Tons: 32 GRT
Power: 220 HP diesel
Hull: Steel

BONNIE LYNN

Bonnie Lynn is one of the most unique of the Maine Windjammer Fleet. She is a modified version of designer Merrit Walter's *Trade Rover*, the hull being built by Treworgy Yachts and then the interior and rigging completed in Maine. Being a serious offshore cruising vessel, she is built to very high standards. The steel hull is 57-feet on deck, with an overall length of 72-feet. She was completed in July of 1998 and has been actively chartering since then. *Bonnie Lynn* charters from the Virgin Islands through the Grenadines in the winters, and returns to her homeport of Islesboro, Maine in the summers, where she charters from New England to Nova Scotia. She is Coast Guard certified for 38 passengers for day sails and 10 for ocean. Although she has a very traditional look, passengers rest in the serenity and luxury of modern day technology and amenities. Extraordinary means have been taken to make the *Bonnie Lynn* a most comfortable and seaworthy vessel.

Who sails: Families and groups
Program type: Sail training for volunteer crew and for volunteer and paying trainees; dockside interpretation during port visits
Designer: Merrit Walter
Built: 1997: Palm Coast, FL, Islesboro, ME, Treworgy
Coast Guard certification: Passenger vessel (Subchapter T)
Crew: 3 **Trainees-passengers:** 38 day sails, 10 overnight
Contact: Captains Bonnie and Earl MacKenzie, PO Box 41, Islesboro, ME 04848 USA
Tel: 401-862-1115 (summer)
E-mail: mack@kona.midcoast.com
Website: www.bonnielynn.com

SPECIFICATIONS

Flag: USA
Rig: Full rigged ship
Homeport: Greenport,
Long Island, New York
Normal cruising waters:
East Coast US and
Canada (summer),
St. Petersburg, Florida (winter)
Sparred length: 180'
LOD: 120'
Draft: 13'
Beam: 30'
Rig height: 115'
Sail area: 10,000 square feet
Tons: 412 GRT
Power: (2) twin 370
John Deere Diesel
Hull: Wood

BOUNTY

Bounty was Built for the 1962 movie *Mutiny on the Bounty* by MGM Studios, and later operated as a sail training vessel. The *Bounty* and her crew helped prepare the officers and crew to sail USS *Constitution* for her bicentennial sail in 1997. Now owned and operated by the HMS Bounty Organization LLC, she makes her homeport in Greenport, Long Island, New York. The famous ship recently underwent an extensive renovation from the waterline down 2001-2002 in Maine and is sailing again. The ship carries 18 full time paid crewmembers that work side by side with our sail trainees and passengers. When docked in port the *Bounty* is open for dockside tours, private functions and educational programs. She offers day sails for individuals and groups, sail passages, and corporate sail training. She is available for private functions (at your location or our homeport), film production, commercials and documentaries. The *Bounty* works closely with Tall Ship Bounty Educational Program Inc. a not- for- profit organization, which offers youth education, and sail training programs with funding from Corporate Sponsorships and participant fees. *The Mission of the Bounty is to uphold the skills of square rig sailing through the preservation of the ship in conjunction with youth education and sail training.*

Who sails: Students, individuals, and groups of all ages
Program type: Sail passages, dockside interpretations, school groups
Season: Year-round
Designer: British Admiralty
Built: 1960: Lunenburg, Nova Scotia, Smith & Rhuland
Coast Guard certification: Moored Attraction Vessel
Crew: 18 **Trainees-passengers:** 12 (Day sails & Overnight Sails)
Contact: Margaret Ramsey, Executive Director, HMS Bounty Organization, LLC, PO Box 141, Oakdale, NY 11769 USA
Tel: 631-588-7900
Fax: 631-737-1771
E-mail: mramsey@tallshipbounty.org
Website: www.tallshipbounty.org

BOUNTY OF KRISTER

SPECIFICATIONS

Flag: USA
Rig: Sprits'l schooner (Hessian Rig)
Homeport: Vashon Island, Washington
Normal Cruising Waters: Puget Sound, Straits of Juan de Fuca, Straits of Georgia
Sparred length: 33'
LOA: 23'
LWL: 22'
Draft: 14"
Beam: 7' 2"
Rig height: 22'
Sail area: 460 square feet
Freeboard: 18"
Power: oars/sail (can be fitted with OB aux. as necessary for delivery)
Hull: Canadian Yellow Cedar on Oak

Vashon-Maury Island Maritime Heritage Society was formed to provide the youth of Vashon and Maury Islands an opportunity to connect with the history and flavor of the age of European discovery. Following in the footsteps of Captains Cook and Vancouver, and Lt. Peter Puget, local youth ages 12-18 learn traditional maritime skills and Pacific NW history aboard a faithful reproduction of the vessel Lt. Wm. Bligh, RN, was cast adrift in after the mutiny on HMS *Bounty*. The boat was constructed true to lines provided by the Royal Navy Museum in Portsmouth, England, and is extremely seaworthy. The vessel has worked successfully in the somewhat open waters of the Straits of Juan de Fuca, and has crossed the Straits of Georgia under oars. Built in memory of youth leader Krister Osterlund, the vessel was graciously donated to VMIMHS by the Delta Maritime Heritage Society.

Who sails: Members of Society and guests
Program type: Teen maritime training
Designer: British Royal Navy
Built: 1996: Peter London, Delta Maritime Heritage Society, Delta, BC, Canada
Sailing Season: February through October
Crew: 10-12 **Trainees-passengers:** In a rowing boat all participants are crew!
Contact: Captain John J. Burke, Executive Director, Port Captain, Vashon-Maury Island Maritime Heritage Society, PO Box 13039, Burton, WA 98013 USA
Tel: 206-463-3262
E-mail: vashonmaritime@comcast.net

SPECIFICATIONS

Flag: USA
Rig: Schooner
Homeport: Castine, Maine
Sparred length: 100'
LOA: 88'
LOD: 83'
LWL: 72'
Draft: 10'
Beam: 20'
Rig height: 70'
Sail area: 200 square feet
Freeboard: 4'
Tons: 66 GRT
Power: 190 HP Diesel
Hull: Wood

BOWDOIN

The schooner *Bowdoin* is the flaghip of Maine Maritime Academy (MMA) sail training fleet, and the official sailing vessel of the state of Maine. Built in 1921 for exploring the Arctic waters, she is one of the strongest wooden vessels ever constructed. Between 1921 and 1954 she made 26 voyages above the Arctic Circle under the command of explorer Donald B. MacMillian. Today, *Bowdoin* serves the students of MMA, the state of Maine, and New England. She is the flagship of MMA's Sail Training Curriculum (http://bell.mma.edu/~bowdoin/sailtraining/) in which students learn to sail and manage traditional and modern sailing vessels. *Bowdoin's* sailing grounds include New England, Nova Scotia, Newfoundland, Labrador, and Greenland. Training afloat is performed on the Academy's fleet of over 100 vessels, including a 500 foot training ship, a 35 foot schooner, a Tugboat, 5 Colgate 26's, and numerous other sailing and power vessels from 15 to 50 feet.

Who Sails: Students of the Maine Maritime Academy
Program type: Sail Training
Season: June to October
Designer: William Hand
Built: 1921, East Boothbay, ME, Hodgdon Brothers Shipyard
Coast Guard certification: Sailing School Vessel (Subchapter R), Passenger Vessel (Subchapter T), Ocean
Crew: 6 **Trainees-passengers:** 40 day sails, 11 overnight
Contact: Tim Leach, Marine Operations Manager, Castine, ME, 04421, USA
Tel: 207-326-2364
Fax: 207-326-2377
E-mail: tleach@mma.edu
Website: http://bell.mma.edu/~bowdoin/

SPECIFICATIONS

Flag: USA
Rig: Cutter/sloop
Homeport:
Wickford, Rhode Island
Normal cruising waters:
Narragansett Bay, Rhode Island
Sparred length: 63'
LOA: 58'
LOD: 55'
LWL: 53'
Draft: 2' 6"
Beam: 18'
Rig height: 59'
Sail area: 1,317 square feet
Freeboard: 4' 6"
Tons: 60 GRT
Power: 135 HP Ford
Hull: Riveted iron

BRANDARIS

Brandaris, the 63-foot Dutch-design sailing vessel, was launched in 1938 as the private yacht of William De Vries Lentsch, Jr., shipyard owner and famous Dutch designer. After a colorful escape from German occupation in WWII, *Brandaris* participated in the evacuation of Dunkirk. Now berthed in Wickford, Rhode Island, she is available for excursions, sailing charters, and special occasion functions from weddings to funerals. *Brandaris* also offers a Classroom Afloat program featuring educational field trips and curriculum based experiential learning programs. Many of these programs have received sponsorship from corporate and grant-based underwriters at no charge to schools.

Who sails: School groups from elementary through college; individuals and families; charter groups
Program type: Sail training for volunteer and paying trainees; sea education in marine science, maritime history, and ecology, in cooperation with organized groups; passenger day sails and overnight voyages
Designer: William De Vries Lentsch, Jr.
Built: 1938: Amsterdam, The Netherlands, Amsterdam Shipyard
Coast Guard certification: Passenger vessel (Subchapter T) Inland, Near Coastal
Crew: 2 **Trainees-passengers:** 32 day sails
Contact: Captain Douglas Somers, Owner, Brandaris Sailing Charters/Friends of Brandaris, 7 Main Street, Wickford, RI 02852 US
Tel: 401-294-1481
Fax: 401-294-1938
E-mail: brandaris@earthlink.net

SPECIFICATIONS

Flag: USA
Rig: Gaff schooner, two-masted
Homeport: Mystic, Connecticut
Normal cruising waters:
New England, Nova Scotia,
Chesapeake Bay
Sparred length: 74'
LOA: 61' 6"
LOD: 61' 6
LWL: 49'
Draft: 9'
Beam: 14' 8"
Rig height: 81'
Tons: 30 GRT
Power: 97 HP diesel
Hull: Wood

BRILLIANT

Winner of the Tall Ships 2000® transatlantic race from Halifax to Amsterdam and captained by ASTA's 2000 "Sail Trainer of the Year," George Moffett, *Brilliant* is the traveling ambassador of Mystic Seaport, our nation's leading maritime museum. In service for more than 45 years – the oldest sail-education program in the nation – *Brilliant* has introduced more than 8,000 people to the lessons a sailing ship naturally teaches. Board this classic schooner and become the crew; steer, handle sails, cook and clean as you learn the venerable maritime tradition of "for the good of the ship." *Brilliant* has two other ASTA awards to her credit: "First in Class" in the 2000 Boston to Halifax race and "Sail Training Vessel of the Year" in 1996. She also won the 1997 Nantucket Lighthouse Opera Cup.

Who sails: Teens ages 15–19 and adults 20+; participants must be physically fit, agile, and competent swimmers; affiliated institution is Mystic Seaport
Program type: Sail training with paying trainees; sea education in cooperation with organized groups such as Scouts, based on informal, in-house programming
Season: May through October
Designer: Sparkman & Stephens
Built: 1932: City Island, New York, Henry B. Nevins
Coast Guard certification: Sailing School Vessel (Subchapter R), Passenger Vessel (Subchapter T)
Crew: 3 day sails, 4 overnight **Trainees-passengers:** 10 day sails, 6 overnight
Contact: Brilliant Program, Museum Education Division, Mystic Seaport, PO Box 6000, Mystic, CT 06355-0990 USA
Tel: 860-572-5323
Fax: 860-572-5355
Website: www.mysticseaport.org/brilliant

CALEDONIA

SPECIFICATIONS

Flag: Canada
Rig: Barquentine
Homeport:
Halifax, Nova Scotia, Canada
Normal cruising waters:
North American waters and
the Caribbean
Sparred length: 245'
Draft: 15'
Beam: 30'
Rig height: 132'
Sail area: 17,000 square feet
Power: 1500 HP Deutz diesel
Hull: Steel

Canadian Sailing Expeditions (CSE) has developed the concept of a traditional tall ship cruise product for Atlantic Canada and the Caribbean. The square-rigged *Caledonia* hosts corporate clients and leisure travelers in old world charm onboard a traditional tall ship, with new world amenities including local gourmet cuisine prepared by our onboard chefs and finely appointed cabins with queen size berths, ensuite toilet and shower, a/c and heat. While onboard guests enjoy a Reading Room, Saloon, and Dining Salon, as well as large open spaces on deck. Three large Zodiacs, mountain bikes, and sea kayaks are available for the guests use. CSE is currently developing academic programming which will be carried out in the early spring and late fall onboard *Caledonia*. Become part of the crew of a traditional sailing ship and participate in the highly challenging and rewarding life on board a tall ship at sea. *Caledonia* is designed to enable guests to have a unique and personal experience with the ship, the crew, and the cruising destination. CSE's product, offers a high level of education, accommodation, adventure, and scenery.

Who sails: Groups and individuals of all ages
Program type: Sail training for paying trainees, day sails, overnight passages, adventure travel cruises
Season: Year-round
Built: 1947: Beverley, United Kingdom
Trainees-passengers: 40
Contact: Captain Doug Prothero, Canadian Sailing Expeditions, PO box 2613, Halifax, NS B3J 3N5 Canada
Tel: 902-429-1474
Fax: 902-429-1475
E-mail: doug@canadiansailingexpeditions.com
Website: www.canadiansailingexpeditions.com

SPECIFICATIONS

Flag: USA
Rig: Topsail schooner
Homeport: San Diego, California
Normal cruising waters: Southern California and the California Coast
Sparred length: 145'
LOA: 93' 4"
LWL: 84'
Draft: 9' 5"
Beam: 24'
Rig height: 95'
Freeboard: 6'
Sail area: 7,000 square feet
Tons: 130 GRT
Power: 140 HP diesel
Hull: Wood

CALIFORNIAN

Californian was launched in celebration of the 1984 Summer Olympics in Los Angeles. In 2003, *Californian* was designated the official tall ship of the State of California. She is the only ship to carry this prestigious title. A 145-foot topsail schooner, *Californian* is a replica of a mid-19th century revenue cutter. She has played host to thousands of adventure travelers, sailing enthusiasts, students and history buffs during her career. In 2003, she underwent an extensive refit including a haul out, re-stepping the masts, replacing the standing rigging, new sails and mechanical systems and a re-design and re-furbishing of the areas below deck. The Maritime Museum of San Diego uses her for a variety of educational programs and public adventure sails. Her annual coastal tour offers residents and visitors throughout California an opportunity to enjoy the State of California's official tall ship.

Who sails: Groups and individuals of all ages
Program type: At sea and dockside education programs in maritime history and programs for at-risk youth in cooperation with area schools and social services agencies, passenger day sails and overnight passages
Season: Year-round
Designer: Melbourne Smith
Built: 1984: San Diego, CA, Nautical Heritage Society
Trainees-passengers: 60 day sails
Contact: Jeff Loman, Director of Ships Operations, Maritime Museum of San Diego, 1492 North Harbor Drive, San Diego, CA 92101 USA
Tel: 619-234-9153 ext. 105
Fax: 619-234-8345
E-mail: shipsoperations@sdmaritime.org
Website: www.sdmaritime.org

SPECIFICATIONS

Flag: USA
Rig: Gaff topsail schooner
Homeport: Key Largo, Florida
Normal cruising waters:
Florida Keys
Sparred length: 105'
LOD: 65'
LWL: 60'
Draft: 7' 6"
Beam: 21'
Rig height: 75'
Freeboard: 6'
Sail area: 3,000 square feet
Tons: 73 GRT
Power: 136 HP diesel
Hull: ferro-steel

CALYPSO EXPLORER

Captain Lance Holmquist is the owner/operator of Calypso Watersports and Charters. He grew up in California, owned a dive business in Australia before he moved to the Florida Keys, and has sailed the Caribbean Sea for over a decade. Let him introduce you to the magic of sailing and tropical reefs. His great personality together with his knowledge and passion for boats, the sea and life in the tropics will guarantee your cruise to become a great experience! S/V *Calypso Explorer* is a 105-foot gaff rigged schooner. Built in Bath, Maine, she is designed following the lines and layout of a traditional 18th century coastal trader. With accommodations for a total of 28 people in 8 staterooms your group will step back in time as you hoist the sails for another adventure. Like aboard all our vessels you will become part of the crew as you pilot this classic through the tropical waters of the Florida Keys. Her experienced crew will introduce you the secrets of sailing and navigating as well as to life on the islands and under the ocean surface. Members and volunteers are the lifeblood of the organization and are always welcome.

Who sails: Groups and individuals of all ages
Program type: Sail training for paying trainees; sea education in cooperation with organized groups; passenger day sails and overnight passages
Designer: M. D. Lee
Built: 1975: Bath, ME, Long Beach Shipyard
Coast Guard certification: Passenger vessel (Subchapter T)
Crew: 3 **Trainees-passengers:** 49 day sails, 28 overnight
Contact: Lance Holmquist, Calypso Watersports and Charters, PO Box 2037, Key Largo, FL 33037 USA
Tel: 305-451-1988
E-mail: Lance@calypsosailing.com
Website: www.calypsosailing.com

SPECIFICATIONS

Flag: Uruguay
Rig: Staysail schooner
Homeport: Montevideo, Uruguay
Normal cruising waters:
Worldwide
Sparred length: 205'
LOA: 198'
LOD: 172'
LWL: 147' 5"
Draft: 12'
Beam: 27'
Hull: Steel

Photo and text by Thad Koza

CAPITAN MIRANDA

Built in 1930 in the Matagorda Shipyard and factory located in Cadiz, Spain, the *Capitan Miranda* originally served as a hydrographic vessel. As such, she carried out an outstanding and extensive career, performing countless cartographical surveys which were, and still are, highly useful to seamen. The ship honors the memory of Captain Francisco P. Miranda (1869 – 1925), who was not only a bright professional but also an exceptional teacher, particularly remembered for his research in sea subjects. In 1977 the vessel underwent a major refit and in 1978 was rededicated as a sail training vessel for the Uruguayan navy teaching newly graduated midshipmen to apply the knowledge acquired at the Naval Academy.

Who sails: Midshipmen, civilian students, foreign guests
Program type: Sail training vessel of the Uruguayan navy.
Built: 1930: Cadiz, Spain, Astiueros Matagorda
Crew: 12 officers, 39 enlisted **Trainees-passengers:** 35
Contact: Captain Nelson Olivera, Naval Attache, Embassy of Uruguay, 1913 I Street, NW, Suite 419, Washington, DC 20006 USA
Tel: 202-331-1313
Fax: 202-331-8142
E-mail: navyofuruguay@yahoo.com
Website: www.armada.mil.uy

Photo by Steve Danford

C. A. THAYER

SPECIFICATIONS

Flag: USA
Rig: Schooner, three-masted
Homeport: San Francisco, California
Sparred length: 219'
LOD: 156'
Draft: 11' 3"
Beam: 36'
Rig height: 105'
Tons: 453 GRT
Hull: Wood

Built in 1895, the *C. A. Thayer* was part of a mighty Pacific Coast fleet of sailing schooners that carried lumber to San Francisco from Washington, Oregon, and the California Redwood Coast. Later, the vessel supplied the Alaskan salt-salmon canneries, anchoring out during the summer, and returning in September with the season's catch packed in her hold. From 1925 to 1950, *C. A. Thayer* carried men north to the Bering Sea cod-fishing grounds. She was purchased by the State of California in 1957, and transferred to the National Park Service in 1977. Now a National Historic Landmark, the *C. A. Thayer* is a rare survivor from the days when strong canvas sails billowed over tall deckloads of freshly milled fir and redwood. Today the vessel hosts a slate of unique school education programs presented by the San Francisco National Maritime National Park Association and is open to the public as part of the San Francisco Maritime National Historical Park.

Program type: Dockside sea education programs in maritime history
Designer: Hans Bendixsen
Built: 1895: Fairhaven, CA, Hans Bendixsen
Contact: Elizabeth Kibbey, Executive Director, San Francisco Maritime National Historical Park, Building E, Fort Mason Center, San Francisco, CA 94123 USA
Tel: 415-561-7006
Fax: 415-556-1624
E-mail: lynn_cullivan@nps.gov
Website: www.nps.gov/safr/local/thayer.html

Flag: USA
Rig: Gaff rig sloop
Homeport: Oyster Bay, New York
Normal cruising waters:
Long Island Sound
Sparred length: 60'
LOA: 52'
LOD: 40'
LWL: 35' 6"
Draft: 3'
Beam: 15' 2"
Rig height: 50'
Freeboard: 18"
Sail area: 960 square feet
Tons: 11 GRT
Power: 63 HP diesel
Hull: Wood

CHRISTEEN

The *Christeen* is the oldest remaining oyster sloop in North America and a National Historic Landmark. She was originally built in 1883 for Captain William Smith in Glenwood Landing, New York to harvest oysters in nearby Oyster Bay and Cold Spring Harbors. Over her 121 years, *Christeen* served not only as an oyster dredge but also as a cargo carrier and live aboard between Connecticut, New York and New Jersey. After surviving 16 major hurricanes, numerous nor'easters, two sinkings and severe neglect, *Christeen* was returned home to Oyster Bay in 1992 and completely restored in 1999. *Christeen's* new mission is to serve as a floating classroom. Her Coast Guard Certified Captains and experienced crew will instruct passengers about maritime history, marine science, coastal ecology and aquaculture. The *Christeen* is available for education, member and public sails, special events, and corporate charters.

Who sails: Students of all ages, individuals, families, and groups
Program type: Marine science, maritime history, marine trades (ie. commercial fishing, oystering)
Season: April through October
Designer: Traditional
Built: 1883: Glenwood Landing, NY
Coast Guard certification: Passenger vessel (Subchapter T)
Crew: 3 **Trainees-passengers:** 20 day sails
Contact: Rob Crafa, The Waterfront Center, PO Box 187, West End Avenue, Oyster Bay, NY 11771 USA
Tel: 516-922-7245
Fax: 516-922-3970
E-mail: info@thewaterfrontcenter.org
Website: www.thewaterfrontcenter.org

Photo by Thad Koca

CISNE BRANCO

SPECIFICATIONS

Flag: Brazil
Rig: Full-rigged ship
Homeport: Rio de Janeiro, Brazil
Normal Cruising Waters: Worldwide
Sparred Length: 254'
LOA: 249'
LOD: 205'
LWL: 183'
Draft: 15' 9"
Beam: 34' 6"
Rig Height: 152'
Sail Area: 23,627 square feet
Freeboard: 5' 3"
Tons: 703 GRT
Power: 1001 HP Diesel
Hull: Steel

The *Cisne Branco* (White Swan) is a Brazilian navy tall ship which was built in Amsterdam, Netherlands, by Damen Shipyard. Its keel was laid on November 9th, 1998, launched and christened on August 4th, 1999, delivered to Brazilian navy on February 4th, 2000 and commissioned as a Brazilian naval vessel on March 9th, 2000. *Cisne Branco* made its maiden voyage across the Atlantic Ocean to Brazil, celebrating the 500th anniversary of the discovery of Brazil by the Portuguese Admiral Pedro Alvares Cabral. The ship's project is inspired in the design of the 19th century clippers. The *Cisne Branco* is normally used in national and international representation activities, to divulge Brazilian navy and Brazilian culture. As well, it is used as an instructional sailing ship to the cadets of Brazilian Naval Academy, Academy of Merchant Marine and other naval schools.

Who Sails: Sail Training for Officers and Cadets from Brazilian Navy, Academy of Merchant Marine and other Naval schools.
Program type: Sail training, goodwill ship and representation for Brazilian Navy
Season: Year-round
Designer: Gerard Djikstra
Built: 2000: Amsterdam, Holland, Damen shipyards
Certification: Brazilian Naval Vessel
Crew: 52 **Trainees-passengers:** 31
Contact: Oficial de Relações Públicas, Marinha do Brazil, Centro Postal da Marinha - Praça Barão de Ladário, s/nº - Centro, Rio de Janeiro 20091-000 Brazil
Tel: 0021871762149980
Fax: 0021871762149982
E-mail: msgcisnebr@uol.com.br or msgcisnebr@yahoo.com.br
Website: www.cisnebranco.mar.mil.br

SPECIFICATIONS

Flag: USA
Rig: Gaff topsail sloop
Homeport: Poughkeepsie, New York
Normal cruising waters: Hudson River, New York Harbor, Long Island Sound
Sparred length: 106'
LOA: 76' 6"
LOD: 76' 6"
LWL: 67'
Draft: 6' 6"
Beam: 24'
Rig height: 108'
Sail area: 4,350 square feet
Tons: 69 GRT
Power: 190 HP diesel
Hull: Wood

Photo by Mitch Carrucci

CLEARWATER

The *Clearwater* is the only full-sized replica of the 18th and 19th century merchant vessels known as Hudson River sloops. Owned and operated by the Hudson River Sloop Clearwater, Inc., a non-profit membership organization dedicated to defending and restoring the Hudson River and related waterways, the *Clearwater* has served as both a platform for hands-on environmental education and as a symbol for grassroots action, since 1969. She sails seven days a week, carrying as many as 50 passengers for three to five-hour educational programs. Adults and children take part in a range of activities involving water life, water chemistry, sail raising, steering, piloting, and more. A USCG licensed captain is in charge, and an education specialist directs the program. The permanent crew is composed of apprentices, ages 16 and older, an education assistant and volunteers.

Who sails: Students of all ages, individuals, families, and groups
Program type: Sail training for crew and apprentices; sea education in marine science, maritime history, and ecology; passenger day sails; dockside interpretation during port visits
Season: April through November
Designer: Cy Hamlin
Built: 1969: South Bristol, ME, Harvey Gamage Shipyard
Coast Guard certification: Passenger vessel (Subchapter T)
Crew: 6 **Trainees-passengers:** 50
Contact: Captain, Hudson River Sloop Clearwater, Inc., 112 Little Market Street, Poughkeepsie, NY 12601 USA
Tel: 845-454-7673
Fax: 845-454-7953
E-mail: captain@mail.clearwater.org
Website: www.clearwater.org

CLIPPER CITY

SPECIFICATIONS

Flag: USA
Rig: Gaff topsail schooner
Homeport:
Baltimore, Maryland
Normal cruising waters:
Chesapeake Bay (summer),
Caribbean (winter)
Sparred length: 158'
LOD: 120'
Draft: 14'
Beam: 27' 6"
Rig height: 135'
Sail area: 10,200 square feet
Tons: 210 GRT
Power: CAT 3200 SS
Hull: Steel

A replica of a Great Lakes lumber schooner of the same name which sailed from 1854 until 1892, the plans for the *Clipper City* of today were obtained from the Smithsonian Institute and adapted for modern use. *Clipper City* sails Baltimore's Inner Harbor and the waters of the Chesapeake Bay from April through October each year. She sails up to 21 times a week and has carried as many as 30,000 passengers in a single season, providing two and three-hour public excursions, and private charters for corporate groups and families. *Clipper City* is also available for winter charter.

Who sails: Individuals and groups
Program type: Public day sails and private charters
Season: Year-round
Built: 1985: Jacksonville, FL USA
Contact: Clipper City, Inc. 5022 Campbell Blvd., Suite F, Baltimore, MD 21236 USA
Tel: 410-931-6777
Fax: 410-931-6705
E-mail: info@sailingship.com
Website: www.sailingship.com

SPECIFICATIONS

Flag: Barbados
Rig: Barquentine, three-masted
Homeport: Bridgetown, Barbados
Normal cruising waters:
Worldwide
Sparred length: 188'
LOA: 154'
LOD: 152' 6"
Draft: 13' 6"
Beam: 31'
Rig height: 115'
Freeboard: 8'
Sail area: 10,000 square feet
Tons: 495 GRT
Power: 570 HP diesel
Hull: Steel

Photo by Voytec Wacowski

CONCORDIA

Class Afloat is a nonprofit educational program affiliated with high schools across the United States and Canada. Its mission is to broaden students understanding of international issues while preparing them for responsible global citizenship in the 21st century. The concept of "taking the classroom to the world" is intended to encourage self-sufficiency, cooperation, and a clear awareness of other cultures. Each semester, 48 qualifying students work as crew and study aboard the *Concordia*, a modern tall ship. A fully certified faculty instructs students in a full curriculum including social studies and global issues, anthropology, marine biology, and physical education. Optional non-credit enrichment courses are also offered in seamanship, celestial navigation, and the history and traditions of the sea. Over 700 international students have joined Class Afloat and sailed the world for an entire academic year. Applications from 11th and 12th grade coeds are encouraged.

Who sails: 11th and 12th grade students
Program type: Full-curriculum academics and marine biology for high school students
Season: Year-round
Built: 1992: Poland
Certification: Sailing School Vessel (Subchapter R), Lloyds 100A1 and LMC
Crew: 8 **Instructors:** 8 **Trainees-passengers:** 48
Contact: Kathleen Knight, Director of Development, Class Afloat, West Island College International, 851 Tecumseh, Montreal, Quebec, H9B 2L2 Canada
Tel: 514-683-9052
Fax: 514-683-1702
E-mail: kknight@classafloat.com
Website: www.classafloat.com

SPECIFICATIONS

Flag: USA
Rig: Full-rigged ship
Homeport:
Baltimore, Maryland
Sparred length: 282'
LOA: 200'
LOD: 176'
LWL: 179'
Draft: 21'
Beam: 42'
Rig height: 165'
Freeboard: 16'
Sail area: 20,000 square feet
Hull: Wood

USS CONSTELLATION

The last all-sail warship built by the US Navy, the *USS Constellation* was launched in 1854 at the Gosport Naval Shipyard in Portsmouth, Virginia. *Constellation* served the country for over 90 years in both military and non-military roles. Before the Civil War, she was the flagship of an international squadron charged with the mission of intercepting vessels engaged in the illegal trade of slaves along the coast of West Africa. During the Civil War, *Constellation* saw duty in the Mediterranean Sea protecting American interests there, and as part of the Gulf Coast blockading squadron. During her later years, she sailed as a training ship for the US Naval Academy and then as a stationary training ship at the Naval War College in Newport, Rhode Island. She was last under sail in 1893. Her final role as a commissioned vessel came during World War II when *Constellation* served as flagship of the Atlantic Fleet. In 1955, *Constellation* was brought to Baltimore to be preserved as a national shrine. The ship has recently undergone a nine million dollar reconstruction that has restored her to her original 1854 configuration. She is now open for public tours, offering a wide array of living history and educational programs under the management of the Living Classroom Foundation.

Program type: Dockside interpretation and educational programming
Designer: John Lenthall
Built: 1854: Portsmouth, VA, US Navy
Contact: USS Constellation Museum, Pier 1, 301 East Pratt Street, Baltimore, MD 21202 USA
Tel: 410-539-1797
Fax: 410-539-6238
E-mail: rowsom@constellation.org
Website: www.constellation.org

SPECIFICATIONS

Flag: USA
Rig: Full-rigged ship
Normal cruising waters: Boston Harbor
Homeport: Charlestown, Massachusetts
Sparred length: 306'
LOA: 204'
LOD: 174' 10" (gun deck)
LWL: 175'
Draft: 22'
Beam: 43' 6"
Rig height: 189' 2"
Freeboard: 15'
Sail area: 42,710 square feet
Tons: 2,200 GRT
Hull: Wood

USS CONSTITUTION

"Old Ironsides" is the oldest commissioned warship afloat in the world. One of six ships ordered by President George Washington to protect America's growing maritime interests in the 1790s, *Constitution* earned widespread renown for her ability to punish French privateers in the Caribbean and thwart Barbary pirates of the Mediterranean. The ship's greatest glory came during the war of 1812 when she defeated four British frigates. During her first engagement against HMS Guerriére in 1812, seamen nicknamed her "Old Ironsides" when they saw British cannonballs glance off her 21-inch thick oak hull. In the 1830s, the ship was going to be to be disassembled, but the public outcry sparked by the publication of an Oliver Wendell Holmes poem saved her. Over the following century, the ship undertook many military assignments and served as a barracks and as a training ship. She was restored in 1927, and after a coast-to-coast tour, *Constitution* was moored in the Charlestown Navy yard in 1934 where she is now open year-round to the public for free tours.

Program type: Dockside interpretation; US Naval history
Built: 1797: Boston, MA, US Navy, Edmond Hartt Shipyard
Certification: Commissioned Naval Vessel
Crew: 75
Contact: Commanding Officer, USS Constitution, Charlestown Navy Yard, Charlestown, MA 02129-1797 USA
Tel: 617-242-5670
Fax: 617-242-2308
Website: www.ussconstitution.navy.mil

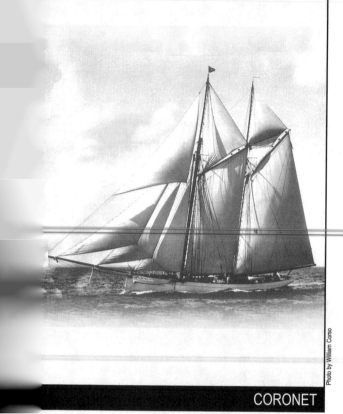

Photo by William Corso

SPECIFICATIONS

Flag: USA
Rig: Gaff topsail schooner
Homeport:
Newport, Rhode Island
Sparred length: 190'
LOA: 133'
LOD: 133'
LWL: 125'
Draft: 12'
Beam: 27'
Freeboard: 6'
Sail area: 8,300 square feet
Tons: 174 GRT
Hull: Wood

CORONET

Built in 1885, *Coronet* is America's most historic yacht, and the last remaining grand yacht from the gilded age. She has voyaged far and wide during her career, twice circumnavigating the globe. In 1995 *Coronet* was acquired by the International Yacht Restoration School (IYRS), in Newport, Rhode Island. Founded in 1993, IYRS teaches the skills, history, and related sciences needed to restore classic yachts. IYRS will carry out a comprehensive and well-documented restoration to return *Coronet* to her late 19th century condition. She will have no engines, electricity, or modern equipment. When completed, she will sail as the school's flagship and a living museum of yachting history. *Coronet* is open to visitors, dockside from May to October each year.

Program type: Walk-on visitation and dockside interpretation for groups and individuals of all ages
Season: May to October
Designer: Smith & Terry, Christopher Crosby, William Townsend
Built: 1885: Brooklyn, NY, C & R Poillon
Contact: Susan Daly, Development/Coronet, International Yacht Restoration School, 449 Thames Street, Newport, RI 02840 USA
Tel: 401-849-1995
Fax: 401-842-0669
E-mail: sdaly@iyrs.org
Website: www.iyrs.org

Flag: USA
Rig: Ketch
Homeport:
San Francisco, California
Normal cruising waters:
San Francisco Bay and tributaries
LOA: 30'
LOD: 30'
LWL: 28'
Draft: 4' 6"
Beam: 8'
Rig height: 35'
Freeboard: 2'
Sail area: 600 square feet
Hull: Wood

CORSAIR

Corsair is a sailing whaleboat, and an open boat designed to be launched by a larger ship while at sea. She was built at Puget Sound Naval Shipyard in 1939 for use in the Navy's fleet sailing program. As the US prepared for war, the Navy stripped its ships and whaleboats were sent ashore. The sailing program was never reinstated, and surplus Navy whaleboats found their way to Sea Scout units around the country, offering thousands of youth the opportunity to learn sailing, seamanship, and teamwork on the water. Of these boats, only a handful of them remain. The Sea Scout ship *Corsair* has been serving the youth of the Bay Area for over 60 years, offering programs that teach sailing, seamanship, and leadership to young men ages 14 to 21. Her sister ship, *Viking*, offers similar programs for young women. The two ships sponsor many joint activities and new members are always welcome.

Who sails: Young men ages 14 – 21
Program type: Sail training; sea education in marine science and maritime history in cooperation with organized groups
Designer: US Navy
Built: 1939: US Navy, Puget Sound Naval Shipyard
Crew: Up to 18
Contact: Nick Tarlson, Sea Scout Ship Viking, 220 Sansome Street, Suite 900, San Francisco, CA 94104 USA
Tel: 415-956-5700
Fax: 415-982-2528
E-mail: seascouts@dictyon.com
Website: http://wregion.seascout.org/corsair/

CORWITH CRAMER

SPECIFICATIONS

Flag: USA
Rig: Brigantine
Homeport: Woods Hole, Massachusetts
Normal cruising waters: Worldwide
Sparred length: 134'
LWL: 87' 6"
Draft: 13'
Beam: 26'
Sail area: 7,380 square feet
Tons: 158 GRT
Power: 500 HP diesel
Hull: Steel

The *Corwith Cramer* was the first ship built to the USCG's regulations for Sailing School Vessels. The Sea Education Association (SEA), working through ASTA, was instrumental in helping the Coast Guard shape these regulations. The *Corwith Cramer* was built in Bilbao, Spain, and it took the largest floating crane in northern Spain to launch her. She is a safe, stable vessel and a platform for SEA's educational and oceanographic research missions. Along with the *Robert C. Seamans*, the *Corwith Cramer* is owned and operated by the Sea Education Association of Woods Hole, Massachusetts.

Who sails: Educators and students who are admitted by competitive selection; over 150 colleges and universities award credit for SEA programs
Program type: Marine and maritime studies including oceanography, nautical science, history, literature, and contemporary maritime affairs
Season: Year-round
Designer: Woodin & Marean
Built: 1987: Bilbao, Spain, ASTACE
Coast Guard certification: Sailing School Vessel (Subchapter R)
Crew: 6 professional mariners and 4 scientists **Trainees-passengers:** 25
Contact: Sea Education Association (SEA), PO Box 6, Woods Hole, MA 02543 USA
Tel: 508-540-3954 OR 800-552-3633 **Fax:** 508-546-0558
E-mail: admission@sea.edu
Website: www.sea.edu

Flag: Mexico
Rig: Barque
Homeport: Puerto de Acapulco, Mexico
Normal cruising waters: Worldwide
Sparred length: 270'
LWL: 220' 4"
Draft: 17' 1"
Beam: 39' 4"
Sail area: 25,489 square feet
Power: 1,125 HP engine
Hull: Steel

Photo by Thad Koza

CUAUHTEMOC

The sail training ship *Cuauhtemoc*, tireless navigator, has covered 378,725 miles of nautical days and trained officers of the Mexican navy for nearly 20 years. Through almost two decades, its accomplishments have been acknowledged and praised by other navies in the world. The ship has participated in important regattas like the Colón Regatta, the Cutty Sark tall ship races, and the Centenary of Osaka Port Modernization Regatta, among others. The sail training ship *Cuauhtemoc* is undoubtedly, a living symbol of the sailor spirit that characterizes the personnel of the Mexican navy, who are always ready to serve their country.

Who sails: Captains, officers, cadets, and sailors of the Mexican navy
Program type: Sail training vessel
Season: Year-round
Built: 1982: Bilbao, Spain, Celaya Shipyards
Crew: 123 (officers and sailors)
Contact: Rear Admiral Conrado Aparicio Blanco, Naval Attache of Mexico, Embassy of Mexico, 1911 Pennsylvania Avenue, NW, Washington, DC 20006 USA
Tel: 202-728-1760
E-mail: navalmx@msn.com or buquetemoc@hotmail.com

DANIEL WEBSTER CLEMENTS

SPECIFICATIONS

Flag: USA
Rig: Gaff topsail schooner
Homeport: Destin, Florida
Normal cruising waters: Northern Florida's Emerald Coast
Sparred length: 75'
LOA: 53'
LOD: 53'
LWL: 48'
Draft: 3' 2"
Beam: 18'
Rig height: 61'
Freeboard: 4' 2"
Sail area: 2,000 square feet
Tons: 32 GRT
Power: 150 HP diesel
Hull: Yellow pine

The gaff rigged topsail schooner *Daniel Webster Clements* was constructed as a replica of a "Biloxi" design Gulf Coast fishing and trading schooner that evolved in the late 1800s and remained active through the l930s. Launched in l996, her shallow draft and plentiful sail area make her ideal for the shallow coastal waters and light airs that prevail much of the time on the Gulf Coast. The *Daniel Webster Clements* is operated by Sailing South Charters of Destin, Florida, in the heart of Florida's Emerald Coast. She offers an onboard nautical classroom for school groups of up to 47 participants and two overnight sail training programs for up to 20 participants. A structured youth adventure program emphasizes character education and an adult teamwork program provides leadership training for organizations and businesses. Both overnight programs feature an effective combination of team instruction on the schooner and in traditionally rigged skiffs. Practical sailing skills best learned on these smaller vessels are applied with ease to the operation of the larger vessel. The *Clements* specializes in service to youth scouting groups and meets all requirements for sailing merit badges.

Who sails: Students grades elementary through college, groups and individuals of all ages
Program type: Sail training for paying trainees; sea education in maritime history, ecology, and marine science in cooperation with accredited institutions and other organized groups
Season: Year-round
Designer: Gene Zirlott
Built: 1996: Coden, AL, Nathanial Zirlott Yard
Coast Guard certification: Passenger vessel (Subchapter T)
Crew: 4 **Trainees-passengers:** 47 day sails, 20 overnight
Contact: William Campbell, Manager, Sailing South Charters, 600 Highway 98 East, Destin, FL 32541 USA
Tel: 850-837-7245
E-mail: schoonerdwc@cox.net
Website: www.sailingsouth.com

SPECIFICATIONS

Flag: Poland
Rig: Full-rigged ship
Homeport: Gdynia, Poland
Normal cruising waters:
World wide
Sparred length: 360'
LOD: 311'
Draft: 20' 7"
Beam: 45' 9"
Rig height: 162'
Sail area: 32,453 square feet
Tons: 2,385 GRT
Power: Cegielski - Sulzer type 8
AL 20/24, 2 * 750 PS (552 kW)
Hull: Steel

Photo and text by Thad Koza

DAR MLODZIEZY

Dar Mlodziezy "gift of the children" is a full-rigged, 360-foot ship designed by the distinguished Polish naval architect Zygmunt Choren and is the flagship of the Merchant Marine Academy in Gdynia, Poland. *Dar Mlodziezy* was funded in part by contributions of elementary school children during the 1960s and 1970s. Commissioned in 1982, she replaced the venerable *Dar Pomorza* "gift of Pomoraze" (a reference to the coastal region of Poland), which served Poland for more than six decades before her retirement. *Dar Mlodziezy's* distinctive design served as the prototype for a class of vessels (five in all) built in Gdansk for the Russian confederation of the 1980's. Four of the five vessels – *Mir, Druzhba, Pallada, and Nasheba* – now fly the Russian flag, while *Khersones* flies the flag of Ukraine. These are true sister ships and vary only slightly in dimensions and configuration.

Who sails: Students of the Gdynia Maritime University
Season: Year-round
Designer: Zygmunt Choren
Built: 1982: Gdansk, Poland
Crew: 40 **Trainees-passengers:** 150
Contact: Gdynia Maritime University, Morska 81-8, 81-225 Gdynia, Poland
Tel: 48 58 621-70-41
Fax: 48 58 620-67-01
Website: www.wsm.gdynia.pl/

DENIS SULLIVAN

SPECIFICATIONS

Flag: USA
Rig: Schooner, three-masted
Homeport:
Milwaukee, Wisconsin
Normal cruising waters:
Great Lakes, Florida,
Bahamas
Sparred length: 137'
LOA: 99'
LOD: 98'
LWL: 88' 4"
Draft: 8' 9"
Beam: 24"
Rig height: 95'
Sail area: 5,916 square feet
Tons: 99 GRT
Power: Twin 180 HP diesels
Hull: Wood

The S/V *Denis Sullivan*, owned and operated by Pier Wisconsin Ltd., was completed by over 900 volunteers in 2000. This replica of a Great Lakes schooner and Flagship of Wisconsin operates as a floating classroom and goodwill ambassador for the State of Wisconsin. From her homeport in Milwaukee on Lake Michigan, the schooner offers educational day sails and private charters for people of all ages from May through September and is committed to re-establishing the historical, cultural and environmental bonds between the community and one of its most valuable resources, the Great Lakes. She winters in Florida, the Bahamas and Caribbean. Three hour LakeWatch Expeditions and Dockside Discovery educational programs are offered for 5th through 12th graders. High school and college students can partake in 5 to 14 day Science Under Sail programs in the Great Lakes, Bahamas and Caribbean.

Who sails: Students and the general public
Program type: Sail training for crew, volunteers, and paying trainees; sea education in maritime history, ecology, and marine science; professional development for educators; "themed" sails and passenger day sails; dockside interpretation while in port
Season: Year-round
Designer: Timothy Graul
Built: 2000: Milwaukee, WI, Rob Stevens
Coast Guard certification: Passenger vessel (Subchapter T), Sailing School Vessel (Subchapter R)
Crew: 10 **Trainees-passengers:** 50 daysails, 16 overnight
Contact: John Lorenz, Senior Captain, Pier Wisconsin, 500 North Harbor Drive, Milwaukee, WI 53202 USA
Tel: 414-276-7700
Fax: 414-276-8838
E-mail: jlorenz@pierwisonsin.org
Website: www.pierwisconsin.org

SPECIFICATIONS

Flag: Indonesia
Rig: Barquentine
Homeport: Surabaya, Indonesia
Normal cruising waters:
Indonesian waters, Indian Ocean,
Pacific Ocean
Sparred length: 191'
LOA: 165'
LOD: 163' 1"
LWL: 138' 4"
Draft: 13'
Beam: 31'
Rig height: 119' 7"
Freeboard: 15' 1"
Sail area: 11,738 square feet
Tons: 847 GRT
Power: 986 HP diesel
Hull: Steel

Photo by Benson Lee

DEWARUCI

KRI *Dewaruci*, the beautiful barquentine flying the red and white Indonesian flag, is the largest tall ship in the Indonesian navy. She was built in 1952 by H. C. Stulchen and Son of Hamburg, Germany and launched in 1953. Since then the ship has served the Indonesian Navy as a sail training vessel and a successful ambassador of goodwill for the people of Indonesia. *Dewaruci's* name and figurehead represent the mythological Indonesian god of truth and courage.

Who sails: Cadets of the Indonesian Naval Academy
Program type: Sail training and sea education for Indonesian Naval cadets
Season: Year-round
Built: 1952: Hamburg, Germany, H.C. Stulchen & Sohn
Crew: 70 **Trainees-passengers:** 80
Contact: Indonesian Naval Attaché, Defense Attaché Office, 2020 Massachusetts Avenue NW, Washington, DC 20036 USA

DREAM CATCHER

SPECIFICATIONS

Flag: USA
Rig: Schooner
Homeport: Key West, Florida
Normal cruising waters:
Florida Keys, Bahamas
Sparred length: 74'
LOA: 69'
LOD: 65'
LWL: 62'
Draft: 5'
Beam: 20'
Rig height: 73'
Freeboard: 5'
Sail area: 1,700 square feet
Tons: 49 GRT
Power: 130 John Deere
Hull: Steel

Designed by marine architects Woodin and Marean from Maine, and built by Treworgy Yachts in Palm Coast, Florida in 1996, *Dream Catcher's* conception, design factors, and interior design came from Captain John Duke. John grew up on the waters of Biscayne Bay in Miami, Florida, has been USCG licensed since 1979, and has been sailing the waters of the lower Florida Keys, South Florida, and the Bahamas for 30 years. During this time he has worked with scientific research groups, environmental groups, and has introduced hundreds of marine enthusiasts to the many wonders of the sea. The *Dream Catcher* provides sailing adventures designed to be informative for both environmental professionals and individuals interested in marine habitat. Ideal for large families and groups interested in participating in and learning all aspects of sailing and navigation, *Dream Catcher* is looking for groups that want to be part of an adventure!

Who sails: Students, families, groups and individuals of all ages
Program type: Sail training for volunteer crew and paying trainees; sea education in cooperation with accredited institutions and other organized groups; longboat rowing aboard *Aida*, a 32' longboat that is used on *Dream Catcher's* extended voyages
Designer: Woodin and Marean
Built: 1996: Hammocks, FL, Treworgy Yachts
Coast Guard certification: Passenger vessel (Subchapter T)
Trainees-passengers: 49 day sails, 19 overnight
Contact: Captain John Duke, Coastal Sailing Adventures, Inc., 28555 Jolly Roger Drive, Little Torch Key, FL 33042 USA
Tel: 305-304-5100
E-mail: saildreamcatcher@mindspring.com
Website: www.keywest.com/dreamcatcher/

SPECIFICATIONS

Flag: USA
Rig: Barque, three-masted
Homeport: New London, Connecticut
Normal cruising waters: Atlantic Ocean, Pacific Ocean, Caribbean
Sparred length: 295'
LOA: 266' 8"
LWL: 231'
Draft: 17'
Beam: 40'
Rig height: 147' 4"
Sail area: 22,245 square feet
Tons: 2,186 GRT
Power: 1,000 HP diesel
Hull: Steel

Photo by Thad Koza

EAGLE (WIX 327)

One of five sister ships built for sail training in Germany in the 1930s, *Eagle* was included in reparations paid to the United States following World War II and the Coast Guard took her over as a training ship. Aboard the *Eagle*, cadets have a chance to put into practice the navigation, engineering, and other skills they are taught at the Coast Guard Academy. As underclassmen, they fill positions normally taken by the enlisted crew of a ship, including watches. They handle the more than 20,000 square feet of sail and more than 20 miles of rigging. Over 200 lines must be coordinated during a major ship maneuver, and the cadets must learn the name and function of each. As upperclassmen, they perform officer-level functions. For many, their tour of duty aboard the *Eagle* is their first experience of life at sea; but it is here that they learn to serve as the leaders they will one day become in the Coast Guard.

Who sails: US Coast Guard Academy cadets, US Coast Guard officer Candidates, and other USCG personnel
Program type: Seamanship training
Season: Year-round
Built: 1936: Hamburg, Germany, Blohm & Voss
Contact: Commanding Officer, USCGC EAGLE (WIX-327), 45 Mohegan Ave., New London, CT 06320 USA
Tel: 860-444-8595
Fax: 860-444-8445
Website: www.cga.edu/eagle

ELISSA

SPECIFICATIONS

Flag: USA
Rig: Barque, three-masted
Homeport: Galveston, Texas
Normal cruising waters: Coastal waters near Galveston
Sparred length: 205'
LOA: 155'
LOD: 150'
Draft: 10'
Beam: 28'
Rig height: 110'
Freeboard: 10'
Sail area: 12,000 square feet
Tons: 411 GRT
Power: 450 HP diesel
Hull: Iron

In 1975, a rusted iron hulk lay in the waters of Piraeus, Greece. Nearly 100 years earlier, she had sailed the world's oceans as a proud square-rigged sailing ship. Cut down, leaking, and decrepit, she waited a cable's length from the scrap yard. Today, *Elissa* remains one of the hallmarks of maritime preservation. Lovingly restored and maintained, she sails again, continuing a far longer life than most ships are ever granted. She tests her readiness annually in a series of sea trials amid the oilrigs and shrimpers off Galveston Island. Working under professional officers, her volunteer crew completes an extensive dockside-training program. As funds allow, she makes longer voyages.

Who sails: School groups from middle school through college; individuals of all ages
Program type: Sail training for crew and apprentices; sea education in maritime history based on informal, in-house training; dockside interpretation
Season: April to November
Built: 1877: Aberdeen, Scotland, Alexander Hall and Sons Yard
Coast Guard certification: Cargo and Miscellaneous Goods (Subchapter I)
Crew: 40 **Trainees-passengers:** 85 day sails
Contact: Kurt Voss, Director, Texas Seaport Museum/Galveston Historical Foundation, Pier 21, No. 8, Galveston, TX USA
Tel: 409-763-1877
Fax: 409-763-3037
E-mail: elissa@galvestonhistory.org
Website: www.tsm-elissa.org

Flag: USA
Rig: Barque, three-masted
(lateen mizzen)
Homeport: Manteo,
North Carolina
Normal cruising waters:
Inland sounds of North Carolina
Sparred length: 78'
LOA: 68' 6"
LOD: 55'
LWL: 59'
Draft: 8'
Beam: 16' 6"
Rig height: 65'
Sail area: 1,920 square feet
Tons: 97 GRT
Hull: Wood

ELIZABETH II

Built with private funds to commemorate the 400th Anniversary of the English colonization of the America's, *Elizabeth II* is named for a vessel that sailed from Plymouth, England on the second of the three Roanoke voyages sponsored by Sir Walter Raleigh between 1584 and 1587. She probably carried marines, colonists, and supplies to establish a military garrison to support England's claim to the New World. *Elizabeth II's* sail training program teaches volunteer crew about America's 16th century maritime heritage. In addition to classroom instruction and dockside training, crewmembers participate in the care and maintenance of the vessel. Voyages are scheduled during the spring and fall seasons. Sponsorship for the volunteer crew program is provided by the nonprofit Friends of *Elizabeth II*, Inc.

Who sails: Volunteer crew
Program type: Sail training for volunteer crew and apprentices; dockside interpretation
Season: Spring and fall
Designer: W. A. Baker and Stanley Potter
Built: 1983: Manteo, North Carolina, O. Lie-Nielsen, Creef-Davis Shipyard
Contact: Scott Stroh, Executive Director, Roanoke Island Festival Park, One Festival Park, Manteo, NC 27954 USA
Tel: 252-475-1500
Fax: 252-475-1507
E-mail: scott.stroh@ncmail.net
Website: www.roanokeisland.com

SPECIFICATIONS

Flag: USA
Rig: Marconi Main Schooner
Homeport: Rockland, Maine
Normal cruising waters:
Midcoast Maine
Sparred length: 80'
LOA: 65'
LOD: 62'
LWL: 49'
Draft: 8' 6"
Beam: 16'
Rig height: 70'
Freeboard: 3' 6"
Sail area: 2,000 square feet
Tons: 30 GRT
Power: diesel

ELLIDA

The *Ellida* was designed by John Alden and built in 1922 at the Morse Boat Yard in Thomaston, Maine for the renowned psychiatrist, Dr. Austin Fox Riggs. For a great part of her life she remained in the Marble Head / Gloucester area. During the Second World War, *Ellida* served as a coastal patrol vessel. Kristina and Paul Williamson purchased Ellida in 1999 and added her to their established Maine windjammer business, Maine Classic Schooners. She now operates as a windjammer cruise vessel entertaining 11 guests on 3 to 6 day cruises and private charters. On board, *Ellida* offers three cabins which feature double beds and private heads, two cabins which feature two twin berths and share a head. There is a fresh hot water shower on board. One of *Ellida's* nicest features is a fully enclosed, heated deck side awning with roll down sides for dining and entertaining in all weather. The comfort is enhanced by the plentiful elegant fare freshly prepared on board. *Ellida* carries a licensed Captain, deck hand, and chef. Passengers are always welcome to participate. *Ellida* is fast and graceful and her beautiful lines turn heads everywhere she travels.

Who sails: Groups and individuals of all ages
Program type: Sail training for paying trainees
Season: Late May to mid-October
Designer: John Alden
Built: 1922: Thomaston, ME, Morse
Coast Guard certification: Passenger Vessel (Subchapter T)
Crew: 3 **Trainees-passengers:** 30 day sails, 11 overnight
Contact: Captain Paul & Kristina Williamson, Maine Classic Schooners, Inc., 178 East Pond Road, Jefferson, ME 04348 USA
Tel: 888-807-6921, 207-549-3908
Fax: 207-549-4519 (call first)
E-mail: schoonerff@aol.com
Website: www.maineclassicschooners.com

SPECIFICATIONS

Flag: USA
Rig: Gaff topsail schooner, two-masted
Homeport: New Bedford, Massachusetts
Normal cruising waters: East Coast US and Canada
Sparred length: 156'
LOD: 106'
LWL: 94'
Draft: 13'
Beam: 24' 5"
Rig height: 115'
Sail area: 8,323 square feet
Tons: 98 GRT
Power: 259 HP diesel
Hull: Wood

ERNESTINA

On February 5, 1894, a single line in a corner of the Gloucester Daily Times recorded an addition to the Massachusetts fishing fleet: "The new schooner for J. F. Wonson and Co. has been named *Effie M. Morrissey.*" This marked the birth of a schooner that would become famous as a Grand Banks fisher, an arctic expeditionary vessel under the command of Captain Robert Abrams Bartlett, and as a World War II survey vessel under Commander Alexander Forbes. After a fire in 1947, the *Morrissey* was raised and renamed *Ernestina* to serve in the transatlantic Cape Verdean packet trade. In 1982 she was gifted by the Republic of Cape Verde to the people of the United States as a symbol of the close ties between lands. The essence of *Ernestina's* educational mission today extends from the vessel's phenomenal track through history. Aboard *Ernestina*, learners of all ages use the ship as a platform to study the marine environment and human impacts during structured underway and dockside programs. They gain confidence and self-esteem by learning how to orient themselves in the natural world while solving real-world problems.

Who sails: School groups from elementary through college and individuals of all ages
Program type: Sail training for volunteer and paying trainees; sea education in marine science, maritime history, and ecology in cooperation with accredited schools and colleges, Scouts, and other groups; passenger day sails; dockside interpretation
Season: Year-round
Designer: George M. McClain
Built: 1894: Essex, MA, Tarr and James Shipyard
Coast Guard certification: Sailing School Vessel (Subchapter R), Passenger vessel (Subchapter T)
Crew: 11 **Trainees-passengers:** 80 day sails, 24 overnight
Contact: Gregg Swanzey, Executive Director, Schooner Ernestina Commission, PO Box 2010, New Bedford, MA 02741 USA
Tel: 508-992-4900
Fax: 508-984-7719
E-mail: gswanzey@ernestina.org
Website: www.ernestina.org

Photo and text by Thad Koza

SPECIFICATIONS

Flag: Chile
Rig: Barquentine, 4-masted
Homeport: Valparaiso, Chile
Normal cruising waters:
Worldwide
Sparred length: 371'
Draft: 19' 8"
Beam: 42' 8"
Hull: Steel

ESMERALDA

The pride of the Chilean navy, *Esmeralda* was built in Cadiz Spain, from plans used to build Spain's *Juan Sebastian de Elcano*. Both vessels were constructed from Camper & Nicholson design at the same yard, though some twenty-seven years apart. The only difference between these two elegant four-masters are the additional fore-and-aft sail on the *Sebastian's* foremast, designating her as a topsail schooner, and the slightly flatter angle of *Esmeralda's* bowsprit. Esmeralda was completed in 1954. Her distinctive figurehead represents a giant Andes condor, the national bird of Chile.

Program type: Sail training vessel of the Chilean navy
Design: Camper & Nicholson
Built: 1952 – 1954, Cadiz, Spain
Contact: Embassy of the Republic of Chile, 1732 Massachusetts Avenu, NW, Washington, DC 20036 USA
Tel: 202-785-1746
Fax: 202-887-5579

SPECIFICATIONS

Flag: France
Rig: Topsail schooner
Homeport: Brest, France
Sparred length: 124'
Draft: 12'
Beam: 24'
Hull: Wood

Photo and text by Thad Koza

ETOILE AND LA BELLE POULE

Along with her sister ship *La Belle Poule*, the schooner *Etoile* serves the French navy in the training of future officers. Designed with the hull shape and the rigging of fishing vessels from Breton, *La Belle Poule* and *Etoile* were built in 1932 in the fishing port of Fecamp in northern Normandy, France. During World War II, both vessels relocated to Portsmouth, England, where they served the Free France Forces. They are permitted to fly the French ensign with the imposed Cross of Lorraine in recognition of their service during the war.

Program type: Sail training vessel of the French navy
Built: 1932: Fecamp, Normandy, France
Contact: Embassy of France, 4101 Resevoir Road, NW, Washington, DC 20007 USA
Tel: 202-944-6000
Fax: 202-944-6166

SPECIFICATIONS

Flag: The Netherlands
Rig: Barque
Homeport: Amsterdam, The Netherlands
Normal cruising waters: Worldwide
Sparred length: 185'
LOA: 150'
LOD: 143'
LWL: 132'
Draft: 12'
Beam: 24'
Rig height: 109'
Freeboard: 4'
Sail area: 11,000 square feet
Tons: 303 GRT
Hull: Steel

EUROPA

Europa was launched in Hamburg, in 1911. Her construction had been ordered by the city of Hamburg for use as a lightship. In the seventies she was bought by a German from Rendsburg and spent years lying at rest waiting to find out if a new owner had the financial means to pay for her costly face-lift. This new owner materialized as Harry Smit. The gutting and reconstruction of the barque *Europa* took 8 years to complete. In the years since 1994 when she recommenced sailing, *Europa* has become famous among tall ship lovers as a ship which really sails. The crew of 10 to 12 professional seafarers tries to involve the passengers as much as possible in running and sailing the ship. With the motto "anything you may, nothing you must" the ship is sailed with or without the help of the passengers, many of whom have no seafaring experience. They stand watches, take turns at steering or an lookout, make up or set sails, bake bread, scrub the decks and practise traditional seafaring/seamanship skills. For a few weeks of each year, the ship sails as the training ship of the "Enkhuizen Nautical College" which trains people as Mates and Captains of coastal and ocean sailing vessels.

Who sails: Youth trainees, individuals, families, and groups of all ages
Program type: Sail training for paying trainees; fully accredited sea education in maritime history; special expeditions; dockside interpretation during port visits
Season: Year-round
Built: 1911: Hamburg, Germany, Stülcken
Crew: 12 **Trainees-passengers:** 100 day sails, 50 overnight
Contact: Rederij Bark Europa B.V., PO Box 17402, NL-2502 CK The Hague or PO Box 17402, NL-2502 CK The Hague, The Netherlands USA
Tel: +31-70-331 7475
Fax: +31-70-354 2865
E-mail: info@barkeuropa.com
Website: www.barkeuropa.com

Photo by Lee Uran

SPECIFICATIONS

Flag: USA
Rig: Brigantine
Homeport:
Los Angeles, California
Normal cruising waters:
Southern California and offshore
islands
Sparred length: 110' 8"
LOA: 90'
LOD: 81' 7"
LWL: 72' 6"
Draft: 11'
Beam: 21' 9"
Rig height: 87' 8"
Sail area: 4,540 square feet
Tons: 99 GRT
Power: 315 HP diesel
Hull: Wood

EXY JOHNSON

The Los Angeles Maritime Institute launched the twin brigantines *Exy Johnson* and *Irving Johnson* in 2002 for the TopSail Youth Program. Named in honor of sail training pioneers and seven-time circumnavigators with youth crew aboard their three ships named *Yankee*, the TopSail program focuses on the shipboard environment as challenging, yet nurturing – encouraging exploration and self-reliance. TopSail is notably effective with youth who are not yet coping well with the demands of society and are at risk of dropping out of school and giving up. With the premise that 'school is where the kids are...' TopSail youth engage in building cooperation, courage, confidence and character through sailing and sea experiences. TopSail enriches, validates, and challenges conventional school curricula by bringing biology, math, physics, geography, history, literature and the environment to life in the real world classroom of the sea. LAMI is a volunteer-driven, youth-focused, educational 'family' organization. We welcome the skills and enthusiasm of people of all ages and all walks of life to sail with youth, to maintain our ships, and to be involved in many other ways. Tall ships and 'educationally significant' vessels are invited to let us know when they like to visit the Port of Los Angeles.

Who sails: Referred youth-at-risk and groups catering to students and adults
Program type: Educational sailing adventures for youth and adult groups
Season: Year-round
Coast Guard certification: Sailing School Vessel (Subchapter R), Passenger vessel (Subchapter T)
Contact: Captain Jim Gladson, President, Los Angeles Maritime Institute, Berth 84, Foot of Sixth Street, San Pedro, CA 90731 USA
Tel: 310-833-6055
Fax: 310-548-2055
Website: www.LAMITopSail.org

Flag: Canada
Rig: Brigantine
Homeport: Ottawa, Ontario, Canada
Normal cruising waters:
Great Lakes and East Coast
(summer), Caribbean (winter)
Sparred length: 110'
LOD: 82'
LOA: 62'
Draft: 6'
Beam: 24' 6"
Rig height: 80'
Freeboard: 8'
Sail area: 4,000 square feet
Tons: 124 GRT
Power: 235 HP diesel
Hull: Fiberglass on steel

FAIR JEANNE

Designed and built in 1982 by the Late Captain Thomas G. Fuller, *Fair Jeanne* was first sailed as a private yacht. Captain Fuller was one of Canada's most decorated WWII naval war heroes, earning the name "Pirate of the Adriatic". His wartime experience taught him the value of instilling confidence and resourcefulness in our youth while at sea. More than 100,000 nautical miles and 22 years later *Fair Jeanne* is now in service as a sail training vessel for Bytown Brigantine, a non-profit charitable organization dedicated to providing adventure through the time honored traditions inherent in square rigged sailing. During the summer months we provide programs for youth 14-19 years old, and during the spring and fall we also provide programs for school groups, adults, and Elderhostel. As *Fair Jeanne* glides toward her 25th anniversary, plans are underway for a jubilee voyage down the Mississippi to the Gulf of Mexico and beyond for her first trip south in 6 winters.

Who sails: Middle school, high school, college, adults, Elderhostel
Program type: Sail training for paying trainees; overnight voyages; sea education in maritime history with formal organizations and as informal, in-house programming; dockside interpretation
Season: Spring, summer and fall (winter sailing in 2006/2007)
Designer: Captain Thomas G. Fuller
Built: 1982: Ottawa, Ontario, Canada, T. G. Fuller
Certification: Sailing School Vessel, inland/near coastal
Crew: 6 high school and university officers **Trainees-passengers:** 50 day sails, 24 overnight
Contact: Bytown Brigantine, Inc., 2700 Queensview Drive, Ottawa, Ontario K2B 8H6 Canada
Tel: 613-596-6258
Fax: 613-596-5947
E-mail: tallshipinfo@tallshipsadventure.org
Website: www.tallshipsadventure.org

Flag: Sweden
Rig: Schooner
Homeport: Karlskrona, Sweden
Sparred length: 129'
Draft: 13' 9"
Beam: 23'
Hull: Steel

Photo and Text by Thad Koza

FALKEN

Falken and her sister ship *Gladan* are twin schooners built in 1947, the same yard and according to the same plans. Differentiated only by their sail numbers, these two vessels train future officers of the Swedish royal navy as they have since their commissioning.

Program type: Sail training vessel of the Swedish royal navy
Built: 1947
Contact: Embassy of Sweden, 1501 M Street, NW, Suite 900, Washington, DC 20005-1702 USA
Tel: 202-467-2600
Fax: 202-467-2699

FAME

SPECIFICATIONS

Flag: USA
Rig: Chebacco schooner
Homeport: Salem, MA
Sparred Length: 70'
LOA: 60'
LOD: 52'
LWL: 49'
Freeboard: 5'
Draft: 6'4"
Beam: 15'
Rig Height: 70'
Sail Area: 1200 square feet
Tons: 29 GRT
Power: 160 HP diesel
Hull Material: White Oak

Fame is a replica of the successful Salem privateer from the War of 1812. The original *Fame* was a Chebacco-style fishing schooner that was converted to privateering at the outbreak of war. She was one of the first American privateers to put to sea, and one of the first to bring back a prize. She captured 21 vessels both British merchantmen and American smugglers before being lost in the Bay of Fundy in 1814. Her captured crew was involved in the infamous Dartmoor prison riot of 1815. Our *Fame* is a traditional double-sawn-frame vessel, framed and planked in native white oak by Harold Burnham of Essex, MA in 2003. *Fame* is now based at Pickering Wharf in Salem, where she carries the paying public on 90-minute cruises upon historic Salem Sound. For much more information on *Fame*, please visit our website at www.SchoonerFame.com.

Who Sails: Individuals of all ages, school groups elementary through college, private and corporate charters
Program Type: Sail training for paying trainees; sea education in maritime history; passenger day sails; dockside interpretation (Example: Scientific or living history educational programs, sail training, corporate team building, day sails and overnight sailing adventures)
Season: May through October
Designer: H. A. Burnham
Built 2003: Essex, MA, H.A. Burnham
Coast Guard certification: Sailing School Vessel
Crew: 2 **Trainees-passengers:** 40 Day sails
Contact: Captain Mike Rutstein Pennant Enterprises 73 Middleton Road, Boxford, MA 01921, USA
Tel: 978- 729-7600
Fax: 978- 561-3021
E-mail: SchoonerFame@aol.com
Website: www.SchoonerFame.com

SPECIFICATIONS

Flag: USA
Rig: Topsail schooner
Homeport: Dundalk, Maryland
Normal cruising waters:
Chesapeake Bay,
East Coast of US
Sparred length: 47'
LOD: 40'
LWL: 30'
Draft: 4'
Beam: 10'
Sail area: 1,000 square feet
Tons: 57 GRT
Power: 25 HP diesel
Hull: Fiberglass

FAREWELL

Peter Van Dine designed *Farewell* and traded the design with Andy Merrill for guitar lessons for he and his wife. Over a two-year period Andy built *Farewell* in his backyard in Annapolis, MD and launched her in 1972. *Farewell* was home to Andy and his family until 1982. Her second owner purchased *Farewell* in 1994 to use as a coastal sail training vessel for her three pre-teen sons. In 1996, she and the three boys cruised from Annapolis, MD to Camden, ME. In early 1999 her present owners, Captain Linda Meakes and her husband, Mike, purchased *Farewell*. During the past few years, they have participated in several maritime festivals and celebrations, including the homecoming of the USS *Constellation*, the Baltimore Preakness Schooner Race, and the Leukemia & Lymphoma Society Bridge to Bridge race. They also continued the tradition of competing in the Great Chesapeake Bay Schooner Race, placing no less than third with stiff competition in very close races. Future plans include participating in various educational programs to promote sail training and maritime traditions and history.

Who sails: Groups and individuals of all ages
Program type: Sail training for paying trainees; sea education in maritime history; passenger day sails and overnight passages; dockside interpretation
Season: May through October
Designer: P. Van Dine
Built: 1972: Andy Merrill
Crew: 6
Contact: Captain Linda Meakes, 4414 Falls Bridge Drive, Unit K, Baltimore, MD 21211 USA
Tel: 410-235-3415
E-mail: mgmeakes@kinchhelp.com
Website: www.geocities.com/schoonerfarewell

SPECIFICATIONS

Flag: USA
Rig: Brig
Homeport:
Gloucester, Massachusetts
Sparred length: 72'
LOA: 55'
LWL: 49'
Draft: 6'
Beam: 18'
Rig height: 55'
Sail area: 3,000 square feet
Hull: Wood

FORMIDABLE

Formidable is inspected by the Coast Guard and permitted to carry up to 49 passengers on day trips. They offer an extensive day charter schedule, including fund-raising for charities.
Formidable is rigged as a brigantine. Her main mast carries the spanker and her foremast carries square sails, fore tops'l, and fore course, as well as several jibs and stays'ls.

Program type: Day sails including fund raising trips for nonprofit organizations; military reenactments
Contact: Captain Keating Wilcox, Longmeadow Way, Box 403, Hamilton, MA 01936-0403 USA
Tel: 866-921-9674
Fax: 978-468-1954
E-mail: kwillcox@shore.net
Website: www.tallshipformidable.com

SPECIFICATIONS

Flag: USA
Rig: Square Topsail Sloop
Homeport:
South Haven, Michigan
Normal cruising waters:
Upper Great Lakes
Sparred Length: 101'
LOD: 56' 3"
Draft: 8' 9"
Beam: 16' 10"
Rig Height: 82'
Sail area: 3,180 square feet
Power: Diesel
Tons: 49.2 GRT
Hull: Wood

FRIENDS GOOD WILL

"We have met the enemy and they are ours..." -Commander Oliver Hazard Perry, U.S.N., Battle of Lake Erie, September 10, 1813. This famous dispatch, dashed off within an hour after the great guns fell silent, went on to reference a merchant sloop turned Man-o-War. That sloop was *Friends Good Will*. The Michigan Maritime Museum is launching a replica of this fateful vessel. Scarano Boatbuilding, Inc. of Albany, New York, designed and built *Friends Good Will*, to be rigged and sailed by Museum volunteers. The vessel serves as an historic flagship for the preservation of traditional maritime skills. The Michigan Maritime Museum is developing programs and curriculum, utilizing its Padnos Boat Shed as a rig shop and its ample exhibit space so to assist in educating members, visitors, school groups of all ages and special tours about Michigan's maritime history and culture. Combining these resources with dockside interpretation and a day sail program throughout the summer, *Friends Good Will* employs traditional materials and skills to keep Michigan's rich maritime heritage alive.

Who Sails: Museum members, school groups, individuals and families
Program Type: Sail Training for museum members and crew; passenger day sails; dockside interpretation, historical reenactment at home port and during port visits; education in history, geography, navigation, marine science for school groups of all ages. Affiliated with Sea Scout Ship #5191, South Haven, Michigan.
Design: Scarano Boatbuilding, Inc.
Built: 2004: Albany, NY, Scarano Boatbuilding, Inc.
Crew: 13 **Trainees-passengers:** 28 day sails
Coast Guard certification: Passenger Vessel (Subchapter T)
Contact: Dr. Barbara Kreuzer, Executive Director, Michigan Maritime Museum, 260 Dyckman Avenue, South Haven, Michigan 49090 USA
Tel: 269-637-8078
Fax: 269-637-1594
Email: barbara@michiganmaritimemuseum.org
Website: www.MichiganMaritimeMuseum.org

FRIENDSHIP

SPECIFICATIONS

Flag: USA
Rig: Full-rigged ship
Homeport: Salem, Massachusetts
Normal cruising waters:
Massachusetts Bay, Buzzards Bay
Sparred length: 171'
LOA: 116'
LOD: 104'
LWL: 99'
Draft: 11' 3"
Beam: 30'
Rig height: 112'
Freeboard: 10'
Sail area: 9,409 square feet
Tons: 99 GRT
Power: Twin 300 HP diesels
Hull: Wood

Friendship, a full size replica of a Salem East Indiaman built for the National Park Service and berthed at Salem Maritime National Historic Site in Salem, Massachusetts, was launched in August 1998. Although she represents a specific vessel built in Salem in 1797, she is typical of a class of commercial carriers commonly employed in both the East India and transatlantic trades during the early years of the new American republic. *Friendship's* historic predecessor is credited with 15 voyages to the Far East, South America, Mediterranean, and northern Europe. She had the misfortune of being taken as a prize of war by the Royal Navy on a return voyage from Archangel, Russia, in 1812. Sold by the British government in 1813, her ultimate fate remains a mystery. Today's *Friendship* is built from wood laminates and solid timbers and was designed as a passenger carrying and sail training vessel while exhibiting the look and function of an historic vessel. While the National Park Service completes her remaining rigging, *Friendship* is accessible to the public for dockside tours.

Who sails: When fully certified, *Friendship* will welcome all age groups through school programs as well as general public on day sails and weekly programmed trips and elderhostel training with Coast Guard and Navy cadets will be part of formal offerings.
Program type: Dockside interpretation as an historic site exhibit; informal sea education in maritime history
Season: Spring, summer, fall
Designer: Bay Marine, Inc., Barrington, RI
Built: 1998: Port of Albany, NY 1999-2000: Salem, MA, Dion Yacht Yard & USS Constitution riggers
Crew: 5 **Trainees-passengers:** 20 day sails
Coast Guard certification: Sailing School Vessel (Subchapter R) pending, Passenger Vessel (Subchapter T) pending
Contact: Colleen Bruce, Project Manager, Salem Maritime National Historic Site, 174 Derby Street, Salem, MA 01915 USA
Tel: 978-740-1694
Fax: 978-740-1685
E-mail: colleen_bruce@nps.gov
Website: www.salemweb.com/frndship/

SPECIFICATIONS

Flag: USA
Rig: Brigantine
Homeport: Mackeral Cove, Maine
Sparred length: 74'
LOA: 47'
LOD: 53'
Draft: 7'
Beam: 14'
Rig height: 65'
Freeboard: 5'
Tons: 40 GRT
Power: 175 HP diesel
Hull: Wood

FRITHA

Built in New Zealand in 1985, *Fritha* reached Bermuda in May of 2000. There she met up with the Tall Ships 2000® fleet arriving from Europe. From Bermuda, *Fritha* raced to Charleston, South Carolina as part of ASTA's Bermuda to Charleston Race. She then cruised in company up the Eastern Seaboard to Boston, Massachusetts, where she participated in Sail Boston 2000. She completed the voyage with her arrival in Mackeral Cove, Maine, only a few nautical miles from her place of origin, the drawing board of her designer, Murray Petterson. *Fritha* is available for sail training charters on a weekly basis for groups of up to six. She is also available for special events.

Who sails: Groups and individuals of all ages; private charters
Program type: Sail training for paying trainees; private charters; special event appearances
Designer: Murray Petterson
Built: 1985: New Zealand, McMullan and Wing
Coast Guard certification: Uninspected vessel (6-passengers)
Crew: 3 **Trainees-passengers:** 12 day sails, 6 overnight
Contact: Phillip Fuller, Captain/owner, 304 Chestnut Street, N. Andover, MA 01845 USA
Tel: 918-685-0061
Fax: 978-258-6808
E-mail: lbpomeroy@aol.com

Flag: Canada
Rig: Gaff Ketch
Homeport: Vancouver, Canada
Normal cruising waters: West Coast British Columbia, Alaska (summer), West Coast of North
Sparred length: 64'
LOD: 48'
LWL: 48'
Draft: 9'
Beam: 19'
Rig height: 44'
Freeboard: 5'
Sail area: 2,000 square feet
Tons: 43 GRT
Power: 160 HP Diesel

GAIA

Gaia is a 60-foot classic gaff ketch, originally built in 1921 as a North Sea sailing trawler without an engine. She worked the North Sea until 1939 when a 10 hp engine was installed! During World War II, she was involved in the Dunkirk evacuation of Allied troops captured and left to rot by the Germans while smuggling refugees from Norway to the Shetland Islands. The previous owners purchased her in 1975 and commenced a complete yacht conversion lasting three years, then sailed *Gaia* all across Europe, North and South America for 25 years. She was purchased in Venezuela and sailed via the Panama Canal to Vancouver, Canada where she has started another chapter – the star attraction of Time of Yore Sailing's tall ship adventures! Sailing programs are all-inclusive featuring the timeless skills of seafaring along with the opportunity to explore the pristine wilderness of the beautiful B.C. coast in the summer season. Winter adventure sailing destinations include the coasts of America, Mexico, Central America through the Panama Canal to Colombia.

Program type: Informal in-house programming, Maritime History
Season: April to October (summer), October to March (winter)
Designer: Colin Archer
Built: 1921, Bohuslan, Sweden
Coast Guard certification: Canadian Coast Guard Certified
Crew: 3 **Trainees-passengers:** 10
Contact: Anil Chowdhary, President, Time of Yore Sailing, 343 Churchhill Avenue, New Westminister, B.C. V3l4P5, Canada
Tel: 604-521-7564
E-mail: info@timeofyore.com
Website: www.timeofyore.com

Flag: USA
Rig: Barquentine, three-masted
Homeport:
Philadelphia, Pennsylvania
Normal cruising waters:
Delaware River and the
Atlantic Coast
Sparred length: 178'
LOA: 150'
LOD: 140'
LWL: 133'
Draft: 17'
Beam: 27' 9"
Rig height: 100'
Sail area: 8,910 square feet
Tons: 299 GRT
Power: Diesel
Hull: Wood

GAZELA PHILADELPHIA

The century-old *Gazela Philadelphia* was built as a Grand Banks fishing vessel. She is one of many Portuguese ships that fished for cod there for hundreds of years. Now owned and operated by the Philadelphia Ship Preservation Guild, a nonprofit organization, the *Gazela* sails as a good-will ambassador for the City of Philadelphia, the Commonwealth of Pennsylvania, and the Ports of Philadelphia and Camden, New Jersey. A new initiative is the maritime education of Philadelphia's disadvantaged youth. *Gazela* and her volunteer crew have also taken part in the filming of *Interview with the Vampire*, the documentary *The Irish in America*, and *The Widow of St. Pierre*. *Gazela* is maintained and sailed by a very active and knowledgeable volunteer group participating in maintenance and sail training activities throughout the year. After 25 hours of work on the vessel, a volunteer is eligible for a crew position on the next available voyage.

Who sails: Volunteers who support the maintenance of the ship
Program type: Sail training for crew and apprentices; sea education based on informal in-house programming; dockside interpretation during out-port visits
Built: 1883: Cacihas, Portugal, major rebuild 1901: Setubal, Portugal
Crew: 2 **Trainees-passengers:** 35 (volunteer)
Contact: Philadelphia Ship Preservation Guild, 801 S. Columbus Blvd., Philadelphia, PA 19147-4306 USA
Tel: 215-238-0280
Fax: 215-238-0281
E-mail: office@gazela.org
Website: www.gazela.org

GERONIMO

SPECIFICATIONS

Flag: USA
Rig: Sloop
Homeport:
Newport, Rhode Island
Normal cruising waters:
North Atlantic and Caribbean
Sparred length: 69' 8"
LOA: 69' 8"
LOD: 68'
LWL: 53' 11"
Draft: 6' 8" – 13' 5"
Beam: 18' 7"
Rig height: 85' 6"
Sail area: 2,091 square feet
Freeboard: 5'
Tons: 53 GRT
Power: Diesel
Hull: Fiberglass

The sailing vessel *Geronimo* sails year round between the Canadian maritime and the greater Carribean. Trainees are taught Nautical Science and Oceanography/Marine Biology while on board. During the academic year, *Geronimo* carries students from St. George's School on six-week long voyages. During these trips, the students stand watch, learn the intricacies of handling a modern sailing vessel and conduct research on sea turtles working in conjunction with the Archie Carr Center for Sea Turtle Research University of Florida, Gainsville. In the summer months, the vessel makes 3 shorter trips along the east coast. Summer trainees range in age from high school to adult.

Who sails: High school students through adults
Program type: Marine/nautical science
Season: Year-round
Designer: Ted Hood Design Group
Built: 1998: Portsmouth, RI, New England Boatworks
Coast Guard certification: Sailing School Vessel (Subchapter R)
Crew: 2 **Trainees-passengers:** 8
Contact: Captain Deborah Hayes, Program Director, St. George's School, 372 Purgatory Road, PO Box 1910, Newport, RI 02840 USA
Tel: 401-842-6702
Fax: 401-842-6696
E-mail: Deborah_Hayes@stgeorges.edu
Website: www.sailgeronimo.org

Flag: Sweden
Rig: Schooner
Homeport: Karlskrona, Sweden
Sparred length: 129'
Draft: 13' 9"
Beam: 23'
Hull: Steel

Photo and text by Thad Koza

GLADAN

Gladan and her sister ship *Falken* are twin schooners built in 1947, in the same yard and according to the same plans. Differentiated only by their sail numbers, these two vessels train future officers of the Swedish royal navy as they have since their commissioning.

Program type: Sail training vessel of the Swedish royal navy
Built: 1947
Contact: Embassy of Sweden, 1501 M Street, NW, Suite 900, Washington, DC 20005-1702
Tel: 202-467-2600
Fax: 202-467-2699

SPECIFICATIONS

Flag: USA
Rig: Gaff topsail schooner, two-masted
Homeport: Biloxi, Mississippi
Normal cruising waters: Northern Gulf of Mexico
Sparred length: 76'
LOA: 65'
LOD: 50'
LWL: 47'
Draft: 4' 10"
Beam: 17'
Sail area: 2,400 square feet
Freeboard: 4' 6"
Tons: 21 GRT
Power: 4-71 Detroit diesel
Hull: Wood - Juniper

GLENN L. SWETMAN

The *Glen L. Swetman* is the first of two replica Biloxi oyster schooners built by the Biloxi Schooner Project under the auspices of the Maritime and Seafood Industry Museum. She is available for charter trips in the Mississippi Sound and to the barrier islands, Cat Island, Horn Island, and Ship Island. Walk-up day sailing trips are made when she is not under charter. Groups can learn about the maritime and the seafood heritage of the Gulf Coast and about the vessels that began Biloxi's seafood industry. The *Glen L. Swetman* is an integral part of the museum's Sea and Sail Summer Camp, and sailing classes are also offered through local colleges. *Glen L. Swetman* also accommodates weddings, parties, and Elderhostel and school groups.

Who sails: Groups and individuals of all ages
Program type: Sail training for volunteer and paying trainees; sea education in maritime history, marine science, and ecology for college students and adults in cooperation with accredited institutions, organized groups, and as informal in-house programming; children's summer camp; private charters
Season: Year-round
Designer: William Holland
Built: 1989: Biloxi, Mississippi, William T. Holland
Coast Guard certification: Passenger vessel (Subchapter T)
Crew: 3 **Trainees-passengers:** 49 day sails
Contact: Maritime and Seafood Industry Museum of Biloxi, PO Box 1907, Biloxi, MS 39533 USA
Tel: 228-435-6320
Fax: 228-435-6309
E-mail: schooner@maritimemuseum.org
Website: www.maritimemuseum.org

Flag: Colombia
Rig: Barque, 3-masted
Homeport: Cartagena, Colombia
Normal cruising waters:
Worldwide
Sparred length: 249' 4"
LOA: 212'
LOD: 189'
LWL: 184'
Draft: 14' 9"
Beam: 34' 9"
Rig height: 126' 4"
Sail area: 15,075 square feet
Freeboard: 21' 7"
Tons: 934 GRT
Power: Twin 256 HP KV
Hull: Steel

GLORIA

Built in Bilbao, Spain for the Colombian Navy in 1966, the three masted barque *Gloria* is used as a school ship for the cadets of the Colombian Naval Academy. She carries a compliment of 150 men and women, ranging from enlisted to midshipmen and officers. The cruises are aimed at training officers in their third year at the Naval Academy, to implement their academic knowledge in the areas of star navigation, seamanship, leadership and teambuilding. *Gloria* is a proud goodwill ambassador of the Colombian navy. During her service has made 46 cruises, navigating over 500,000 nautical miles, visiting 143 different ports around the world.

Who sails: Midshipmen, enlisted and officers of the Colombian Navy
Program type: Sail training vessel of the Colombian Navy
Season: Year-round
Designer: Sener
Built: 1969: Bilbao, Spain, A. T. Celaya
Coast Guard certification: Colombian Naval Vessel
Crew: 69 **Trainees-passengers:** 80 students
Contact: Commander Sergio Uribe Cáceres, Naval Operations Director, Navy of Colombia, Avenida El Dorado Carrera 52 CAN., Bogotá, D.C., Cundinamarca, 01-110 Colombia
Tel: 751-266-0189 or 751-266-0288
Fax: 751-266-0448
E-mail: jemnm3@armada.mil.co
Website: www.armada.mil.co

SPECIFICATIONS

Flag: Germany
Rig: Barque
Homeport: Kiel, Germany
Normal cruising waters: Worldwide
Sparred length: 293'
Draft: 15' 6"
Beam: 39'
Sail Area: 21,140 square feet
Hull: Steel

GORCH FOCK II

Built from the same plans and in the same shipyard (Blohm & Voss in Hamburg, Germany) as the original, *Gorch Fock II* boasts contemporary safety features and the latest navigational equipment. She is an eminent replacement for her namesake (now the training vessel *Tovarishch* from Ukraine). Since her launch in 1958, *Gorch Fock II* has logged thousands of nautical miles in her twice-yearly voyages and has hosted more than ten thousand cadets for training cruises. The barque is named for a popular German writer of sea stories, Hans Kinau (1880 – 1916), who used the pseudonym Gorch Fock (fock means "foresail" in German). Kinau became part of the romantic mythology of the sea when he perished aboard the cruiser Weisbaden, which was sunk during the Battle of Jutland on 31 May 1916. The training vessel of the German navy, *Gorch Fock II* is a proud symbol of Germany's distinguished sailing and shipbuilding traditions.

Program type: Sail training vessel of the German navy.
Built: 1958: Hamburg, Germany, Blohm & Voss
Crew: 73 **Trainees-passengers:** 200
Contact: Embassy of the Federal Republic of Germany, 4645 Reservoir Road, NW, Washington, DC 20007 USA
Tel: 202-298-8140
Fax: 202-298-4249

SPECIFICATIONS

Flag: USA
Rig: Topsail Schooner
Homeport: Oriental,
North Carolina
Normal cruising waters:
Caribbean, West and North
Atlantic, Great Lakes
Sparred length: 75'
LOA: 60'
LOD: 57'
LWL: 49'
Draft: 8'
Beam: 16'
Rig height: 75'
Sail area: 3,000 square feet
Freeboard: 5'
Tons: 42 GRT
Power: 140 HP Yanmar
Hull: Fiberglass

GRAND NELLIE

Owner operated *Grand Nellie* provides tall ship sailing experience for beginner to advanced sailors of all ages and abilities. Participation in all aspects of vessel operation is encouraged to allow passengers and trainees to gain experience and increase their abilities while on board. Offshore and multiple day voyages provide participants the opportunity to be an integral part of sail handling, navigation, and watch keeping. Designers Parker Marean III and Russel Woodin of Boothbay, Maine, balanced traditional Maine schooner lines with modern technology for comfort, safety, and performance in creating the classic schooner *Grand Nellie*. On deck, *Grand Nellie* is free of clutter, providing plenty of room to move about. Below deck, the open interior is beautifully appointed with cherry and maple custom woodwork. *Grand Nellie* participates in festivals, special events, and races throughout the Caribbean and Western Atlantic. *Grand Nellie* is the two-time winner of the TALL SHIPS CHALLENGE® Race Series.

Who sails: Groups, families, and individuals of all ages
Program type: Oceans international, Sail training for paying trainees; sea education in cooperation with accredited institutions and other organized groups; dockside interpretation; participation in special events and festivals
Season: Year-round
Designer: Parker Marean III and Russel Woodin
Built: 1998: Meritt, North Carolina, Custom Steel Boats
Coast Guard certification: Passenger vessel (Subchapter T)
Crew: 6 **Trainees-passengers:** 6 day sails, 6 overnight
Contact: Captains Ellen and Jeff Troeltzsch, Schooner *Grand Nellie*, PO Box 468, Oriental, NC 28571 USA
Tel: 252-249-0290
Fax: 252-249-0945
E-mail: ellen@grandnellie.com
Website: www.grandnellie.com

GUAYAS

SPECIFICATIONS

Flag: Ecuador
Rig: Barque
Homeport: Guayquil, Ecuador
Normal cruising waters: Worldwide
Sparred length: 257'
LOA: 221'
LOD: 218'
LWL: 184'
Draft: 15' 4"
Beam: 34' 9"
Sail area: 15,784 square feet
Power: Diesel
Hull: Steel

Guayas was built in the Celaya Shipyard in Bilbao, Spain. She is named after the Chief of Huancavilcas, a native culture in the Ecuadorian coastal region. Commissioned in 1977, the *Guayas* is proud to serve as a goodwill ambassador for the Ecuadorian Navy. The ship carries a complement of 16 officers, 43 midshipmen, and 94 enlisted men, including the ship's band. During a cruise, considered one semester at the Ecuadorian Naval Academy, midshipmen apply – in a very challenging environment – theoretical principals of navigation, seamanship, and other subjects learned in the classroom.

Who sails: Ecuadorian Naval Academy cadets
Program type: Sail training for Ecuadorian Naval Academy cadets
Season: Year-round
Designer: Celaya
Built: 1976: Bilbao, Spain, Celaya Shipyard
Coast Guard certification: Ecuadorian Naval Vessel
Crew: 76
Contact: Naval Attaché, Embassy of Ecuador, 2535 15th Street NW, Washington, DC 20009 USA
Tel: 202-265-7674
Fax: 202-667-3482

SPECIFICATIONS

Flag: USA
Rig: Viking faering boat
Homeport: Oakley, Maryland
Normal cruising waters:
East Coast and Chesapeake Bay
LOA: 21'
Draft: 1'
Beam: 5'
Rig height: 10'
Sail area: 80 square feet
Freeboard: 1'
Tons: 200 lbs
Hull: Wood

GYRFALCON

Gyrfalcon is a copy of the faering (four-oared boat) buried with the Gokstad ship in Norway in the 9th century. She was built by the boat-building program at the Hampton Mariner's Museum (now the North Carolina Maritime Museum), in Beaufort, North Carolina, under the direction of Geoffrey Scofield. *Gyrfalcon* is often seen at cultural, waterfront, community, and boat festivals, historic reenactment events, and school demonstrations. She also participates in living history events in concert with the Markland Medieval Mercenary Militia's Viking reenactment camps, where the public enjoys the spectacle of crews, dressed in costume and armor, offering historic interpretation. As an enticement to school children and adults to discover more about the Viking Age, *Gyrfalcon* often spends off-season time on display at area libraries and schools. The *Gyrfalcon*, and her consort *Sae Hrafn* are both owned and operated by the Longship Company, Ltd., a member-supported, nonprofit educational association.

Who sails: School groups from elementary through college; individuals of all ages
Program type: Sail training for volunteer crew and apprentices; sea education in maritime history based on informal-in-house programming; dockside interpretation
Season: March to November
Designer: Traditional Norse design
Built: 1981: Beaufort, NC, Hampton Mariners Museum (now the North Carolina Maritime Museum)
Coast Guard certification: Uninspected vessel
Crew: 4 **Trainees-passengers:** 3
Contact: Longship Company, Ltd., 21924 Oakley Road, Avenue, MD 20609 USA
Tel: 301-390-4089
E-mail: longshipco@hotmail.com
Website: www.wam.umd.edu/~eowyn/longship/

SPECIFICATIONS

Flag: USA
Rig: Full-rigged ship
Homeport: Albany, New York
Normal cruising waters:
East Coast and Great Lakes
Sparred length: 95'
LOA: 65'
LOD: 64' 3"
LWL: 84'
Draft: 8' 5"
Beam: 17' 6"
Rig height: 78'
Sail area: 2,757 square feet
Freeboard: 10' 5"
Tons: 112 GRT
Power: Diesel
Hull: Wood

HALF MOON

The replica ship *Half Moon* (*Halve Maen*) was launched on June 20, 1989, to draw attention to the exploration and colonization of the Mid-Atlantic States. The 1609 voyage of the original *Halve Maen,* under the command of Henry Hudson, led to the first European settlements by the Dutch in what are now the states of New York, Pennsylvania, New Jersey, Connecticut, and Delaware. In 1614, the Dutch named the area "Nieu Nederlandt." Since her launch, the replica *Half Moon* has visited over 40 ports along the eastern seaboard and the Great Lakes. She has been boarded by over 100,000 visitors and participated in port festivals and a yearly New Netherland Festival. The ship's design is based on original Dutch East India Company documents, including the resolution of 1608 ordering the original ship's construction and Juet's Journal. Hudson sailed the *Halve Maen* up the Hudson River as far as present-day Albany in 1609. The *Half Moon's* program offers the public both an active sail training program and instruction on the history of New Netherland. Thus, the crew is trained in both historical presentation and ship handling.

Who sails: Schools groups from elementary through high school; individuals of all ages
Program type: Sail training and maritme history based on informal programs; dockside interpretation
Designer: Nicholas S. Benton
Built: 1980:Albany, NY, The New Netherland Museum
Coast Guard certification: Attraction Vessel
Crew-trainees-passengers: 7-12 day sails, 8-15 overnight
Contact: The New Netherland Museum and Half Moon Visitors Center, P.O. Box 10609, Albany, NY 12201 USA
Tel: 518-443-1609
Website: www.newnetherland.org

SPECIFICATIONS

Flag: USA
Rig: Gaff topsail schooner, two-masted
Homeport: : Islesboro, Maine
Normal cruising waters: North Atlantic Ocean and Caribbean Sea, Canada to South America
Sparred length: 131'
LOA: 95'
LOD: 90'
LWL: 85'
Draft: 9' 7"
Beam: 24'
Rig height: 91'
Sail area: 4,200 square feet
Tons: 94 GRT
Power: 220 HP diesel
Hull: Wood

HARVEY GAMAGE

Owned by the Ocean Classroom Foundation, the schooner *Harvey Gamage* sails on programs of education under sail for the youth of America. Programs range from a 4 month semesters-at-sea to week-long programs with schools and youth groups. Trainees sail the ship and learn traditional seamanship skills under the captain and crew, and they explore maritime subjects with the onboard academic staff. The Ocean Classroom program is a semester-at-sea for qualified high school students, fully accredited by Proctor Academy. The voyage covers more than 4,000 nautical miles, connecting South American shores to the Canadian Maritimes. Students live and work as sailors on a true voyage of discovery, while they study maritime history, maritime literature, marine science, applied mathematics, and navigation. Ocean Classroom is offered Fall, Spring, and summer terms. Other programs include SEAmester (a complete semester-at-sea for college credit), OceanBound (for high school and college students), and Summer Seafaring Camp (for teens age 13 – 16). The Ocean Classroom Foundation also owns and operates the schooners *Spirit of Massachusetts and Westward.*

Who sails: Individuals and school groups from middle school through college; affiliated institutions include Proctor Academy, Long Island University, Center for Coastal Studies, Hurricane Outward Bound School, and other schools
Program type: Traditional seamanship training combined with accredited academic studies in maritime subjects
Season: Year-round
Designer: McCurdy & Rhodes
Built: 1973: South Bristol, ME, Harvey Gamage Shipyard
Coast Guard certification: Sailing School Vessel (Subchapter R), Passenger vessel (Subchapter T)
Crew: 8-11 including faculty **Students:** 27 overnight
Contact: Bert Rogers, Director, Ocean Classroom Foundation, Inc., 23 Bay Street, Watch Hill, RI 02891 USA
Tel: 800-724-7245 or 401-596-4582 **Fax:** 401-596-4583
E-mail: mail@oceanclassroom.org
Website: www.oceanclassroom.org

SPECIFICATIONS

Flag: USA
Rig: Square topsail schooner, two-masted
Homeport: Miami, Florida
Sparred length: 85'
LOA: 68'
LOD: 65'
LWL: 62'
Draft: 6'
Beam: 17' 9"
Rig height: 64'
Sail area: 2,200 square feet
Freeboard: 8'
Tons: 47 GRT
Power: 140 HP diesel
Hull: Steel

HERITAGE OF MIAMI II

The *Heritage of Miami II* is an 83-foot square topsail schooner that is modern in materials and construction but traditional in style. Built specifically for crossing wide expanses of open water, she has a wide, spacious deck that provides ample room for working the sails, lounging in the sun, and sleeping in the evening. Her shoal draft makes even small islands accessible while her long bowsprit, topmasts, and yards allow extra sails for speed between them.

Heritage of Miami II's travels take her from her Miami home base down through the coral reefs of the Florida Keys to Garden Key and the famous Fort Jefferson in the Dry Tortugas. Sea Explorer cruises last for six days and five nights. Co-winner of the 1999 ASTA Sail Training Program of the Year, her professional captain and crew help the Explorers experience the life of the sea: setting and furling sails, manning the helm, and even catching, cleaning, and cooking fish. The program offers a unique opportunity to explore a part of the Florida Keys while enjoying a hands-on sailing experience.

Who sails: School groups from elementary through college as well as individuals
Program type: Sail training for crew, apprentices, and paying trainees; sea education in maritime history and ecology in cooperation with accredited schools and colleges and other organized groups; passenger day sails and overnight passages; dockside interpretation
Season: Year-round
Designer: Merritt Walters
Built: 1988: Norfolk, VA, Howdy Bailey
Coast Guard certification: Passenger Vessel (Subchapter T)
Contact: Captain Joseph A. Maggio, The Schooner Heritage of Miami, Inc., 3145 Virginia Street, Coconut Grove, FL 33133 USA
Tel: 305-442-9697
Fax: 305-442-0119
E-mail: heritage2@mindspring.com
Website: www.heritageschooner.com

SPECIFICATIONS

Flag: USA
Rig: Dipping lug
Homeport:
Aberdeen, Washington
Normal cruising waters:
Grays Harbor, Puget Sound,
Western Washington
Sparred length: 26'
LOA: 25'
LOD: 25'
LWL: 25'
Draft: 20'
Beam: 7'
Rig height: 16'
Sail area: 316 square feet
Freeboard: 20"
Tons: 3,800 LBS
Hull: Wood

HEWITT R. JACKSON

On May 12, 1792 Captain Robert Gray sailed his ship, *Columbia Rediviva*, over the bar of the "Great River of the West" and named it Columbia's River in honor of his ship. Captain Gray never would have entered that river had it not been for the information he received from the first American vessel to enter the river, *Columbia's* longboat. Unnamed and unheralded, ship's boats were the workhorses of the 16th to 19th century. Powered by either oars or sails, these versatile seaworthy craft carried all manner of cargo from ship to shore and back again. Grays Harbor Historical Seaport Authority built two 18th-Century ship's longboat reproductions in 1993. Noted maritime historian and artist Hewitt R. Jackson, who worked closely with naval architect Stewart Hoagland and Seaport Director Les Bolton to ensure both historical accuracy and the meeting of specific program needs, painstakingly researched the design for the Seaport longboats. Powered by ten oars or up to a three-masted dipping lugsail rig, these versatile vessels are ideal for exploring the protected inland waterways of Washington. Programs are customized to the needs and interests of specific groups.

Who sails: Students in grades elementary through college and groups and individuals of all ages
Program type: Sail training for volunteer and paying crew and trainees in cooperation with accredited institutions and other organized groups; sea education in maritime history, marine science, and ecology; passenger day sails; dockside interpretation
Designer: Stewart Hoagland, Hewitt Jackson Built: 1993: Aberdeen, WA, Grays Harbor Historical Seaport Authority
Coast Guard certification: Sailing School Vessel (Subchapter R)
Crew: 2 **Trainees-passengers:** 8 – 13 day sails
Contact: Les Bolton, Executive Director, Grays Harbor Historical Seaport, PO Box 2019, Aberdeen, WA 98520 USA
Tel: 800-200-LADY (5239)
Fax: 360-533-9384
E-mail: ghhsales@techline.com

HIGHLANDER SEA

SPECIFICATIONS

Flag: USA
Rig: Gaff topsail schooner
Homeport: Port Huron, Michigan
Normal cruising waters:
Great Lakes and
Eastern Seaboard
Sparred length: 154'
LOA: 116'
LOD: 126'
LWL: 100'
Draft: 14'
Beam: 25' 6"
Rig height: 131'
Sail area: 9,728 square feet
Freeboard: 3' 8"
Tons: 140 GRT
Power: Twin Detroit diesel,
8V-92, 350 HP each
Hull: White oak

Dedicated to showcasing the marine lore of Port Huron, Michigan and the Great Lakes region, Acheson Ventures, LLC purchased *Highlander Sea* for her new role as Port Huron's flagship ambassador. The ship was repatriated to the US in April 2002. Originally christened *Pilot*, she served 47 years as a Boston Harbor pilot ship. In the 1970s, she was purchased to circumnavigate the globe, got as far as Fiji and was sold. Her next owner renamed her *Star Pilot* and obtained US Coast Guard Certification as a school-ship. In 1998 Secunda Marine Services acquired the ship in San Diego, sailed her to Nova Scotia, Canada, renamed her *Highlander Sea* and refit her extensively to train young seafarers. Today, *Highlander Sea* offers opportunities for character development, teamwork, and community citizenship for the people of Port Huron, in particular its youth, through leadership and training. The ship rests in Port Huron, sails the Great Lakes and Eastern Seaboard, and is available for public tours, educational programs, and special events.

Who sails: Enthusiastic individuals age 16 and up
Program type: Sail training opportunities for volunteer crew or trainees; sea education in maritime history and ecology in cooperation with accredited institutions and other organized groups; overnight passages and passenger day sails; dockside interpretation
Season: April to November
Designer: W. Starling Burgess
Built: 1924: Essex, MA, J. F. James and Son
Coast Guard certification: Passenger vessel (Subchapter T)
Crew: 12 **Trainees-passengers:** 12 day sails, 12 overnight
Contact: Mary Russel, Highlander Sea, 600 Fort Street, Port Huron, MI 48060 USA
Tel: 810-966-0900 x205
Fax: 810-966-0990
E-mail: highlandersea@achesonventures.com
Website: www.achesonventures.com

SPECIFICATIONS

Flag: USA
Rig: Skipjack/sloop
Homeport: Potomac River, Maryland
Normal cruising waters: Chesapeake Bay
Sparred length: 70'
LOA: 54'
LOD: 48'
LWL: 45'
Draft: 4'8"
Beam: 16'
Rig height: 65'
Sail area: 1,850 square feet
Tons: 8 GRT
Power: 150 HP diesel; yawl boat
Hull: Wood

H. M. KRENTZ

One of the last skipjacks to be built, and still commercially dredging oysters during the winter months (November – March), the *H. M. Krentz* offers day sails on the Chesapeake's Eastern Shore waters near St. Michaels, Maryland from April through October. Get the feel of a true working vessel and learn about the history of the working fleet of sailing vessels on the Chesapeake Bay. Experience dragging for oysters, and then explore the ecology and economic development of the Chesapeake region through discussing the past and present status of this once abundant natural resource. What we can learn about ourselves and about our surrounding world through sailing is what makes the present the greatest age of sail. By working with the technologies and traditions of the past, perhaps we can have a better vision for the future. Since 1972, Captain Ed Farley has been a commercial oysterman and has worked to preserve several of the working skipjacks; since 1985, he has been sharing his life experience with school children, business leaders, politicians and family groups.

Who sails: School groups from elementary through college as well as families and individuals of all ages
Program type: Sail training for professional and volunteer crew/trainees; sea education in marine science, maritime history and ecology as informal in-house programming; dockside interpretation while in port
Season: Mid-April to late October
Designer: Krentz/Skipjack
Coast Guard certification: Passenger vessel (Subchapter T)
Crew: 1 **Trainees-passengers:** 32
Contact: Captain Ed Farley, Chesapeake Skipjack Sailing Tours, LLC, PO Box 582, St. Michaels, MD 21663 USA
Tel: 410-745-6080
E-mail: hmkrentz@bluecrab.org
Website: www.oystercatcher.com

SPECIFICATIONS

Flag: USA
Rig: Ketch-rigged pulling boat
Normal cruising waters:
Maine Coast, Puerto Rico,
Florida Keys
Sparred length: 30'
LWL: 28'
Draft: 18"
Beam: 8'
Rig height: 20'
Sail area: 366 square feet
Freeboard: 2'
Hull: Wood

HURRICANE

Built exclusively for Outward Bound's second school in the United States, and modeled after traditional whaling vessels and Coast Guard rescue boats, the Hurricane Island ketch-rigged pulling boat is an ideal training vessel. Safe, seaworthy, and fun to operate, these rugged, 30-foot open boats are excellent for exploring tough to reach spots in shallow water. The Hurricane Island Outward Bound School has built its reputation teaching sailing on the East Coast and internationally for 40 years, primarily using this fleet of 22 traditional wooden boats, as well as historic schooners such as *Westward, Tenacious*, and *Roseway*. Living as student-crew, participants rotate responsibilities, learning to sail and navigate, as well as developing teamwork and leadership skills. From its headquarters in Rockland, ME the school runs educational expeditions in 14 locations from Maine to the Florida Keys, as well as internationally. Outward Bound is a nonprofit educational organization that offers more than 750 Wilderness courses through our 4 wilderness schools in the US.

Who sails: Individuals and groups 15 and older, coed; families 14 and older; corporations and organizations
Program type: Sail training and seamanship, taught to encourage growth, discovery and life enhancement
Designer: Cyrus Hamlin, Kennebunk, ME
Built: 1965 - 1988: Maine Coast
Crew: 2 **Trainees-passengers:** 12
Contact: Hurricane Island Outward Bound School, 75 Mechanic Street, Rockland, ME 04841USA
Tel: 800-341-1744
Fax: 207-594-8202
E-mail: admissions@hurricaneisland.org
Website: www.hurricaneisland.org or www.outwardbound.org

SPECIFICATIONS

Flag: USA
Rig: Gaff schooner, two-masted
Homeport: Suttons Bay, Michigan
Normal cruising waters: Grand Traverse Bay, Lake Michigan
Sparred length: 77'
LOA: 61' 6"
LOD: 61' 6"
LWL: 53'
Draft: 7'
Beam: 17'
Rig height: 66'
Sail area: 1,800 square feet
Freeboard: 4'
Tons: 41 GRT
Power: 130 HP diesel
Hull: Steel

INLAND SEAS

The *Inland Seas* Education Association (ISEA) was created in 1989 to teach culturally diverse students from throughout the state of Michigan, the Midwest and beyond about the science and heritage of the Great Lakes. ISEA's award-winning experiential educational programs are designed for students in grades 5 – 12 and are modified for learners of all ages. More than 60,000 participants have experienced the Great Lakes Schoolship Program, including students from over 140 Michigan communities. Summer shipboard experiences for all ages include astronomy, history, and science programs on Grand Traverse Bay and Lake Michigan. The goal of every ISEA program is: to encourage young people to pursue academic interests related to the Great Lakes, particularly the sciences; and, to provide enhanced public understanding and stewardship of the Great Lakes for future generations. The heart of the Schoolship Program is the work of 200 dedicated and professionally trained volunteers who donate nearly 8,000 hours annually aboard the School ship.

Who sails: School groups and individuals of all ages
Program type: Sail training for volunteer and paying trainees; sea education in marine science, maritime history, and ecology for students from elementary through college, adults, and at-youth risk; dockside interpretation during port visits
Season: May through early October
Designer: Charles W. Wittholz, Woodin & Marean
Built: 1994: Palm Coast, FL, Treworgy Yachts
Coast Guard certification: Passenger Vessel (Subchapter T)
Crew: 5 **Trainees-passengers:** 30 day sails, 10 overnight
Contact: Thomas M. Kelly, Executive Director, Inland Seas Education Association, PO Box 218, Suttons Bay, MI 49682 USA
Tel: 231-271-3077 **Fax:** 231-271-3088
E-mail: isea@greatlakeseducation.org
Website: www.greatlakeseducation.org

SPECIFICATIONS

Flag: USA
Rig: Brigantine
Homeport: Los Angeles, California
Normal cruising waters: Southern California and offshore islands
Sparred length: 110' 8"
LOA: 90'
LOD: 81' 7"
LWL: 72' 6"
Draft: 11'
Beam: 21' 9"
Rig height: 87' 8"
Sail area: 4,540 square feet
Tons: 99 GRT
Power: 315 HP diesel
Hull: Wood

IRVING JOHNSON

Designated the 'Official Tall Ships and Maritime Ambassadors of the City of Los Angeles' the *Irving Johnson* sails with twin brigantine *Exy Johnson* in the TopSail Youth Program of the Los Angeles Maritime Institute. Purpose-built by LAMI to serve youth, the brigantines are named in honor of Captain Irving and Electa 'Exy' Johnson, sail training pioneers and seven-time circumnavigators with youth crew. Built to last 100 years, the state-of-the-art brigantine design is based on TopSail founder Captain Jim Gladson's decades of experience with adolescent education and youth sail training programs. TopSail Youth Program is an education and adventure experience aboard a tall ship consisting of day sails, voyages, or both, all designed to provide youth with real-life challenges that develop knowledge, skills and attitudes needed to live healthy, productive lives. TopSail enriches, validates, and challenges conventional school curricula by bringing sciences, math, geography, history, literature and the environment to life in the real world classroom of the sea. LAMI is a youth-focused organization whose volunteer-based family is known for our friendly welcome to visiting tall ships and shipmates who let us know they'd like to visit us in the Port of Los Angeles.

Who sails: Referred youth-at-risk and groups catering to students and adults
Program type: Educational sailing adventures for youth and adult groups
Season: Year-round
Coast Guard certification: Sailing School Vessel (Subchapter R), Passenger vessel (Subchapter T)
Contact: Captain Jim Gladson, President, Los Angeles Maritime Institute, Berth 84, Foot of Sixth Street, San Pedro, CA 90731 USA
Tel: 310-833-6055
Fax: 310-548-2055
Website: www.LAMITopSail.org

Flag: Poland
Rig: Barquentine
Homeport: Gdynia, Poland
Normal cruising waters:
Baltic Sea
Sparred length: 161'
LOA: 140'
LOD: 137'
LWL: 121'
Draft: 13' 9'
Beam: 26'
Freeboard: 5'
Rig height: 115'
Sail area: 377 square feet
Hull: Steel

Photo and text by Thad Koza

ISKRA

The ship took her name after a 3-masted gaff schooner, *Iskra*, which sailed under the Polish navy ensign for 50 years between 1927 and 1977. ORP *Iskra* was built in 1982 in Gdanska Shipyard. She is a 3-masted barquentine with different rigging on all three masts. The foremast has 5 square sails; main sail is gaff-rigged; and mizzen is Bermudian. The main purpose of the ship is to train Polish Naval Academy cadets on their summer practices. Every year since 1987 she has participated in the Cutty Sark Tall Ships' Races. During her years of sailing, the ship has won numerous prizes including the United Nations Peace Medal in 1990, the Cutty Sark Trophy in 1989, the Fair Play Prize in the 1999 Cutty Sark Tall Ships Race, and the Polish navy's Best Ship Prize (5 times). The letters ORP in front of her name are the abbreviation for Ship of the Republic of Poland and indicate that the ship belongs to the Polish navy. The name *Iskra* means "spark".

Who sails: Cadets of the Polish Naval Academy
Program type: Training vessel
Designer: Zygmunt Choren
Built: 1982: Gdanska Shipyard
Contact: Commanding Officer, ORP Iskra, JW 1449 ORP ISKRA, Gdynia, Wojewodztwo Pomorskie, 81-103 Gdynia 3 Poland
Tel: 48-58-626-25-54
Fax: 48-58-626-25-54
E-mail: iskra2@poczta.fm

SPECIFICATIONS

Flag: USA
Rig: Topsail schooner
Homeport: Freeport, Maine
Normal cruising waters: Worldwide
Sparred length: 113'
LOD: 89'
LWL: 74'
Draft: 10'
Beam: 22'
Rig height: 105'
Sail area: 5,000 square feet
Tons: 96 GRT
Power: diesel/electric
Hull: Steel

ISLAND ROVER

The *Island Rover* is a 113-foot topsail schooner of William Peterson Design. This steel schooner is currently under construction at Flying Point, Freeport, Maine at the site of the *Island Rover* Foundation home office; a non-commercial shipyard with much volunteer labor although future paid shipwright labor is anticipated. The planned voyage range will be all ocean and the schedules will be consistent with the planned research and educational missions of the foundation. The missions include educational opportunities in multi-age level sail training, informing the vessels visitors at every opportunity as to the origin of the materials constituting the vessels construction, promotion of the industrial concepts of: Reduce, Reuse, Repair, Refurbish, Re-utilize, Re-manufacture and Recycle as a means to conserve natural resources and protect the environment, provide a platform from which professional marine oceanographic research can be conducted, promote environmental consciousness and awareness of the environmental impact of modern societies activities on the marine eco-systems of the world.

Who sails: Groups and individuals of all ages
Season: Year-round
Designer: William Peterson, Murray Peterson Associates, South Bristol, ME
Built: Under construction; Flying Point, Freeport, ME
Crew: 6
Contact: Captain Harold E. Arndt, Island Rover Foundation, Flying Point, 93 Maquoit Drive, Freeport, ME 04032 USA
Tel: 207-865-6621
E-mail: capt.harold@islandrover.org
Website: www.islandrover.org

Flag: USA
Rig: Schooner
Homeport: Rockland, Maine
Normal cruising waters: New England
Sparred length: 120'
LOD: 90'
Draft: 7' (centerboard up)
Beam: 23'

J. & E. RIGGIN

This traditional sailing vessel was built as an oyster dredger in 1927, and is now a National Historic Landmark. The Schooner *J. & E. Riggin* is a family run business. The captain, Jon Finger, has almost two decades of professional experience on the water from Maine to the Mediterranean. His wife and the cook on board, Annie Mahle, also holds her captains license and is a trained chef. Windjamming is the best of both worlds: adventure and relaxation. Sail where the wind and tide take you and experience freedom from everyday noises and distractions. Throw itineraries to the wind, anchor in a different harbor every night, and even enjoying a traditional lobster bake on the beach, Maine-style! The sight of lighthouses, pink-granite islands and colorful sunrises, the smell of fresh bread just out of the wood stove or freshly brewed coffee from the wood stove, all are part of your trip on our windjammer. From May to October twenty-four people join us as our guests for a week of sailing, sightseeing and nature-watching. Our quiet adventures travel from Boothbay, Maine to Bar Harbor, Maine.

Who sails: Groups and individuals of all ages
Program type: Sail training for paying trainees; passenger day sails; group charters
Built: 1927: Dorchester, NJ
Coast Guard certification: Passenger Vessel (Subchapter T)
Crew: 6 **Trainees-passengers:** 24
Contact: Captains Jon Finger and Anne Mahle, Schooner J. & E. Riggin, 136 Holmes Street, Rockland, ME 04841 USA
Tel: 800-869-0604
Fax: 207-594-4921
Email: info@riggin.com
Website: www.riggin.com OR www.mainewindjammer.com

SPECIFICATIONS

Flag: USA
Rig: Bugeye ketch
Homeport: Bridgeport, CT
Normal cruising waters: Long Island Sound
Sparred length: 65'
LOA: 55'
LOA: 47'
LWL: 47'
Draft: 3'
Beam: 14' 6"
Rig height: 49'
Freeboard: 2' 6"
Sail area: 1,200 square feet
Tons: 14 GRT
Hull: Wood

JOHN E PFRIEM

The *John E. Pfriem* is a classic Chesapeake Bay bugeye ketch design built in Gloucester, Massachusetts in 1964. She operates as a marine environmental education vessel sailing the waters of Long Island Sound from April through November.

Program type: Sail training for crew and apprentices; sea education in marine science and ecology in cooperation with accredited institutions; dockside interpretation
Season: April through November
Designer: Russell Grinnell
Built: 1964: Gloucester, MA, Russell Grinnell
Crew: 2-3 **Trainees-passengers:** 22 day sails
Contact: The Aquaculture Foundation, 525 Antelope Trail, Shelton, CT 06484 USA
Tel: 203-372-4406
Fax: 203-372-4407
E-mail: tmerritt@pcnet.com

SPECIFICATIONS

Flag: USA
Rig: Ship, three-masted
Homeport: Mystic, Connecticut
Sparred length: 118' 6"
LOA: 100' 8"
Draft: 12'
Beam: 25' 3"
Rig height: 98' 6"
Tons: 213 GRT
Hull: Iron

Photo by Russell A. Fowler

JOSEPH CONRAD

For over 50 years young people have come to Mystic Seaport, our nation's leading maritime museum to learn to sail and live on board the tall ship *Joseph Conrad*. Each morning, campers tackle the wind and current of the Mystic River and then set off for an active afternoon investigating the Museum's unique exhibitions. After a late-day sailing session, some "R and R" and dinner, campers spend their evenings with new friends, stargazing in a planetarium, climbing the rigging of the *Conrad* or enjoying a lively sea music sing-a-long. The *Joseph Conrad* program is open to individual boys and girls and organized groups ages 10 – 15. Groups must have one adult leader per 10 participants. No prior experience is required for beginner sessions, only a desire to participate and learn. Intermediate sessions are for those who have attended a previous beginner session or have had sailing experience. All must hold current Red Cross swimmers certification or its equivalent.

Who sails: Individuals and organized groups ages 10 – 15
Program type: Sail training; dockside visitation for school groups and individuals
Season: June – August
Designer: Burmeister and Wain
Built: 1882: Copenhagen, Denmark, Burmeister & Wain
Contact: Waterfront, Preservation and Programs Department, Mystic Seaport, PO Box 6000, Mystic, CT 06355-0990 USA
Tel: 860-572-0711
Fax: 860-572-5355
Website: www.mysticseaport.org/sailing

SPECIFICATIONS

Flag: Spain
Rig: Topsail schooner, 4-masted
Homeport: Cadiz, Spain
LOA: 305' 6"
Draft: 23' 7"
Beam: 42' 7"
Rig height: 164'
Power: GM358 Diesel
Hull: Iron

JUAN SEBASTIAN DE ELCANO

The official training vessel for the midshipmen and ensigns of the Spanish navy, *Juan Sebastian de Elcano* was launched in 1927 and delivered to the Spanish navy in 1928. Her hull is made of iron, and she has four masts, each named after other training ships which preceded her (*Blanca*, *Almansa*, *Asturias*, and *Nautilus*). She is named in honor of *Juan Sebastion de Elcano*, captain of Ferdinand Magellan's last exploratory fleet. The ship also carries the *de Elcano* coat of arms– a terraqueous globe and the motto "Primus Circumdedisti Me" (first to circumnavigate me) which emperor Charles I conferred on *de Elcano* after he returned to Spain having completed Magellan's global expedition. She has sailed in more than 50 training voyages, including six circumnavigations of the globe.

Who sails: Midshipmen of the Spanish Navy
Program type: Training vessel of the Spanish Naval Academy
Designer: Nicholson, England
Built: 1927: Cadiz, Spain, Shipyard Echevarrieta y Larrinaga
Certification: Spanish Naval Vessel
Crew: 250 – 270 including midshipmen
Contact: Office of the Naval Attache, Embassy of Spain, 4801 Wisconsin Avenue, NW, 3rd Floor, Washington, DC 20016 USA
Tel: 202-244-2166
Fax: 202-362-3993
E-mail: armada@agredwas.org

SPECIFICATIONS

Flag: USA
Rig: Sloop
Homeport: Chicago, IL
LOA: 78'
LOD: 75'
LWL: 64.5'
Draft: 13'
Beam: 18'
Rig Height: 98'
Freeboard: 5'
Sail Area: 3,600 square feet
Tons: 36 GRT
Hull: Aluminum

JULIANNA

Julianna , purchased in 2002 in Algonac, Detroit has been refitted with new rigging modified from racer to racing cruising vessel. In Spring 2003 she sailed through the Great Lakes and St. Lawrence Seaway across the North Atlantic to Europe to participate in the Cutty Sark Race from Gdynia, Poland; Turku, Finland; Riga, Latvia and Travemunde, Germany and back to Gdynia. *Julianna* returned to the US across the South Atlantic to Martinique, San Juan, PR, Key West, FL, New York and back through the St. Lawrence Seaway to Chicago. After the 20,000 mile voyage, she participated in the 2004 Mackinac Race. Currently, *Julianna* is moored in Lake Michigan at Monroe Harbor in the heart of Chicago. She will be taking trainees on daily or weekly excursions between Chicago and Mackinac Island throughout the Summer and providing sail training opportunities for the public.

Who sails: 15 and up
Season: May 15 – October 15
Designer: Ron Holland
Built: 1984: Sturgeon Bay, WI, Palmer-Johnson
Crew: 3 **Trainees-passengers:** Up to 22 trainees
Coast Guard Certification: Un-inspected, Yacht-documented
Contact: Isidore P. Ryzak, President, Polish Yachting Association of North America, Inc. 942 W. Montrose Ave, Chicago, Illinois 60613 USA
Tel: 773-334-2615 or 847-922-5627
E-mail: ipryzak@comcast.net

SPECIFICATIONS

Flag: USA
Rig: Gaff topsail schooner
Homeport: Sausalito, California
Normal cruising waters: San Francisco Bay and California Coast
Sparred length: 86'
LOA: 67'
LOD: 65'
LWL: 53'
Draft: 7' 6"
Beam: 18'
Freeboard: 4'
Sail area: 1,436 square feet
Tons: 63 GRT
Power: 9M 671 diesel
Hull: Cold-molded mahogany

KA'IULANI

Call of the Sea, an educational non-profit organization based in San Francisco Bay, operates a variety of educational programs aboard Schooner *Ka'iulani* which range from coastal voyaging to three hour sails within the Bay. She is a modern replica of an 1850s Pacific Coast gaff topsail schooner. Designed for long distance ocean cruising and to sail around Cape Horn, she was built to the highest standards of safety and craftsmanship. Schooner Ka'iulani is a noble representative of the trading vessels that plied the California Coast in the 1800s. Call of the Sea's programs connect people of all ages to the sea through programs described on our website: www.callofthesea.org. *Ka'iulani* is available for collaborative programs with educational partners as well as private charters and public sails.

Who sails: School groups from elementary through college, as well as individuals and families
Program type: Day sails for 4th/5th graders and others; passenger day sails
Designer: WIB Crealock Built: 1984: Coaster Boat Works, San Diego, CA
Coast Guard certification: Passenger Vessel (Subchapter T)
Crew: 4 - 5 **Trainees-passengers:** 49 day sails, 12 overnight
Contact: Captain Ken Neal-Boyd, Executive Director, Call of the Sea, 3020 Bridgeway #278, Sausalito, CA 94965 USA
Tel: 415-331-3214
Fax: 415-331-1412
E-mail: info@callofthesea.org
Website: www.callofthesea.org

Flag: Japan
Rig: Barque, 4-masted
Homeport: Tokyo, Japan
Sparred Length: 361'
Draft: 22'
Beam: 46'
Hull: Steel

Photo and text by Thad Koza

KAIWO MARU & NIPPON MARU

These twin barques were completed in 1984 and 1989, respectively, for the Institute of Sea Training in Japan to replace their predecessors, Kaiwo Maru and Nippon Maru, sail training built in the 1930s. Designed for sail training and built by Sumitomo Heavy Industries at the Uraga dockyards, the twin barques exemplify Japan's proud marine design and shipbuilding heritage. Both carry a complement of 190: 70 officers and permanent crew and a cadet contingent of 120. Both carry and inventory of 36 sails, and when sailing before the wind, some 30,000 square feet of sail fly from the yards. One innovation found on these modern training vessels is actually highly traditional. Each vessel carries a graceful figurehead on her bow. They are the sisters Ranjo (on *Nippon Maru*) and Konjo (on *Kaiwo Maru*) who exemplify traditional Japanese womanhood. Both their names mean deep blue sea.

Built: 1984, Uraga Dockyards, Sumitomo Heavy Industries
Crew: 70 **Trainees-passengers:** 120
Contact: National Institute for Sea Training, 5-57 Kitanakadori, Naka-ku, Yokohama, 231-0003 Japan
Tel: 81-45-211-7302
Fax: 81-45-211-7317
E-mail: mail@kohkun.go.jp
Website: www.kohkun.go.jp

Photo and text by Thad Koza

KALIAKRA

SPECIFICATIONS

Flag: Bulgaria
Rig: Barquentine
Homeport: Varna, Bulgaria
Sparred length: 159'
Draft: 11'
Beam: 27'
Hull: Steel

Completed in 1984, *Kaliakra* trains future officers for the Bulgarian navy and is a sister ship to *Iskra*. Her home port is Varna on the Black Sea, although she has been a frequent participant in European and American tall ship gatherings. As initially rigged, only four yardarms crossed her foremast because of variations in deck thickness that affected the height of the foremast. Since her refitting in 1992, however, she carries five yardarms in her barquentine configuration. Her figurehead is a stylized version of a Bulgarian mythological figure.

Program type: Training vessel of the Bulgarian Navy
Built: 1984
Contact: Embassy of the Republic of Bulgaria, 1621 22nd Street NW, Washington, DC 20008 USA
Tel: 202-387-7969
Fax: 202-234-7973

SPECIFICATIONS

Flag: USA
Rig: Full-rigged ship
Homeport: Wilmington, Delaware
Normal cruising waters: Mid-Atlantic and Northeast
Sparred length: 141'
LOA: 93'
LOD: 91'
LWL: 89' 2"
Draft: 12' 5"
Beam: 24' 11"
Freeboard: 8'
Sail area: 7,600 square feet
Tons: 168 GRT
Power: 2 Caterpillar 3208 @ 180 HP ea
Hull: Wood

KALMAR NYCKEL

The *Kalmar Nyckel*, the tall ship of Delaware, is a re-creation of the first Swedish colonial settlement ship to arrive in America in 1638, which established the colony of New Sweden in what is now Wilmington, Delaware. Launched in the fall of 1997, commissioned in May of 1998, and USCG certified in June of 2000, this ornately carved 17th Century Dutch pinnace sails the Northeast and Mid-Atlantic regions seasonally, carrying out her mission of education and goodwill. She transforms Delaware's history into hands-on educational opportunities for children through adults, from teaching fourth and sixth graders history and physics to conducting her bi-annual volunteer crew sail training. She provides economic development opportunities, private charters both underway and dockside, public sails and public tours, and statewide marketing initiatives on a national scale, serving as Delaware's tall ship ambassador. A professional captain and mates and a volunteer crew man the *Kalmar Nyckel*.

Who sails: School groups from elementary through college, as well as individuals and families
Program type: Sail training for volunteer and paying trainees; dockside interpretation during port visits
Designer: Tom Gillmer
Built: 1997: Wilmington, Delaware, Allen C. Rawl
Coast Guard certification: Passenger Vessel (Subchapter T)
Crew: 8 **Trainees-passengers:** 49 day sails
Contact: Kalmar Nyckel Foundation, 1124 East Seventh Street, Wilmington, DE 19711 USA
Tel: 302-429-7447
Fax: 302-429-0350
E-mail: info@kalnyc.org
Website: www.kalmarnyckel.org

SPECIFICATIONS

Flag: Russia
Rig: Barque, four-masted
Homeport: Kalingrad, Russia
Normal cruising waters:
Western European waters (summer)
Southern European waters (winter)
Sparred length: 376'
LOA: 346'
LOD: 329'
LWL: 311' 6"
Draft: 19'
Beam: 46'
Rig height: 176'
Freeboard: 27' 9"
Sail area: 36,380 square feet
Power: twin 600 HP diesels
Hull: Steel

KRUZENSHTERN

Kruzenshtern was built as *Padua* in 1927 in Bremerhaven, Germany. The sister ship to *Peking*, she is the last of the "Flying P" liners still under sail. These vessels were engaged in the grain trade from Australia to Europe. In 1933 *Kruzenshtern* sailed from her homeport of Hamburg to Port Lincoln in Australia in only 67 days. At the end of World War 11 she was handed to the USSR and converted into a sail training ship. Since 1990, up to 40 trainees of all ages have been welcomed onboard to sail along with the Russian students of the Baltic Academy in Kalingrad, Russia, learning the ropes, manning the helm, or climbing the rigging to set more than 30,000 square feet of sail. No previous experience is necessary. *Kruzenshtern* is supported by Tall Ship Friends, a nonprofit organization in Hamburg, Germany. The goals of Tall Ship Friends are to promote sail training on square-riggers, to contribute to the further existence of these beautiful ships, and to provide an unforgettable experience for the participants. Members of Tall Ship Friends receive the quarterly Tall Ships News (English/German) and a personal sailing log.

Who sails: Groups and individuals of all ages
Program type: Sail training for paying trainees; fully accredited sea education in traditional seamanship
Built: 1927: Bremerhaven, Germany, J.C. Tecklenborg
Certification: Special Purpose (School Vessel), Russia
Crew: 45-70 **Trainees-passengers:** 250 day sails, 60 overnight
Contact: Wulf Marquard, Managing Director, Tall Ship Friends Germany, Schweriner Sir. 17, Hamburg, D22143 Germany
Tel: 49-40-675 635 97
Fax: 49-40-675 635 99
E-mail: tallshipl@aol.com
Website: www.tallship-friends.de

SPECIFICATIONS

Flag: USA
Rig: Pungy schooner
(gaff rigged), two-masted
Homeport: Baltimore, Maryland
Normal cruising waters:
Chesapeake and Delaware Bays,
East Coast between Maryland
and Maine
Sparred length: 104'
LOD: 72'
LWL: 64' 3"
Draft: 7'
Beam: 22'
Rig height: 85'
Freeboard: 3'
Sail area: 2,994 square feet
Tons: 60 GRT
Power: twin 80 HP diesels

LADY MARYLAND

Lady Maryland is an authentic pungy schooner, an elegant boat designed to haul cargo, fish, dredge for oysters, and carry luxury items quickly from port to port on Chesapeake Bay and along the Atlantic Coast. Instead of carrying watermelons and oysters, her mission today is to provide students with the opportunity to experience sailing a historic vessel while studying history, sailing, seamanship, marine science, and ecology on her traditional waters from Maryland to Maine. The Living Classrooms Foundation has developed a flexible educational program that can fit the needs of a variety of school and community groups. More than 50,000 students participate in LCF programs each year. The *Lady Maryland* operates educational day experiences for 32 trainees and extended live-aboard sail training and marine science programs for up to 14 people.

Who sails: Student and other organized groups, individuals, and families
Program type: Sail training with paying trainees; sea education in marine science, maritime history, and ecology for school groups from elementary school through college as well as adults
Season: March through November
Designer: Thomas Gilmer
Built: 1986: Baltimore, Maryland, G. Peter Boudreau
Coast Guard certification: Passenger Vessel (Subchapter T)
Crew: 6 day sails, 8 overnight **Trainees-passengers:** 32 day sails, 12-14 overnight
Contact: Living Classrooms Foundation, 802 South Caroline Street, Baltimore, MD 21231-3311 USA
Tel: 410-685-0295
Fax: 410-752-8433
Website: www.livingclassrooms.org

SPECIFICATIONS

Flag: USA
Rig: Brig
Homeport: Aberdeen, Washington, Grays Harbor
Normal cruising waters: Washington, West Coast of North America
Sparred length: 112'
LOA: 87'
LOD: 66' 9"
LWL: 58'
Draft: 11'
Beam: 24'
Rig height: 89'
Freeboard: 6'
Sail area: 4,400 square feet
Tons: 99 GRT
Power: diesel
Hull: Wood

LADY WASHINGTON

As a privateer during the American Revolution, the original *Lady Washington* fought to help the colonies gain their independence from England. In 1788, she became the first American vessel to visit the West Coast of North America, opening trade between the colonies and the native peoples of the Northwest Coast. Built at Grays Harbor Historical Seaport in Aberdeen, Washington, and launched in 1989 as a Washington State Centennial project, the reproduction *Lady Washington* sails the waters of Washington State and the West Coast of North America as the tall ship ambassador for the state of Washington. With a busy year-round sailing schedule, *Lady Washington* regularly tours the West Coast, providing shipboard education programs for schools in 89 port communities in Washington, Oregon, California, British Columbia, and Alaska. More than 15,000 school children visit *Lady Washington* each year to learn about the rich and colorful maritime heritage of our nation. Crew are paid professionals and volunteer trainees.

Who sails: School groups from elementary school through college, individuals, and families
Program type: Sail training for crew, apprentices, and paying trainees; sea education in maritime history in cooperation with accredited institutions based on informal, in-house programming; passenger day sails, overnight passages, and family camps; dockside interpretation
Season: Year-round
Designer: Ray Wallace
Built: 1989: Aberdeen, Washington, Grays Harbor Historical Seaport Authority
Coast Guard certification: Passenger Vessel (Subchapter T)
Crew: 12 **Trainees-passengers:** 48 day sails, 8 overnight
Contact: Les Bolton, Grays Harbor Historical Seaport, PO Box 2019, Aberdeen, WA 98520 USA
Tel: 800-200-LADY (5239)
Fax: 360-533-9384
E-mail: ghhsa@techline.com
Website: www.ladywashington.org

SPECIFICATIONS

Flag: USA
Rig: Gaff topsail schooner, two-masted
Homeport:
New York City, New York
Normal cruising waters:
Northeast United States
Sparred length: 129'
LOD: 83'
LWL: 71'
Draft: 11'
Beam: 21'
Rig height: 91'
Sail area: 5,017 square feet
Tons: 52 GRT
Power: Twin 85 HP diesels
Hull: Wood

LETTIE G. HOWARD

The *Lettie G. Howard* is a Fredonia model-fishing schooner, a type of vessel once widely used along the Atlantic seaboard from Maine to Texas. She was built in 1893 at Essex, Massachusetts, where the majority of the schooners for the fishing fleets of Gloucester, Boston, and New York were produced. She operated out of Gloucester for her first eight years. The fishing would have been done with hand lines set either from the vessel's deck or from small boats called dories. The *Howard* was similar to the schooners that carried their Long Island and New Jersey catches to New York City's Fulton Fish Market. In 1901, the *Howard* was purchased by Pensacola, Florida, owners for use off Mexico's Yucatan Peninsula. Completely rebuilt in 1923, she was fitted with her first auxiliary engine a year later. She remained in the Gulf of Mexico until 1968, when she was sold to the South Street Seaport Museum. The *Lettie G. Howard* was designated a National Historic Landmark in 1988. Between 1991 and 1993 the museum completely restored her to her original 1893 appearance, while outfitting her to accommodate trainees on educational cruises.

Who sails: School groups, Elderhostel, individual adults, and families
Program type: Sail training for volunteer and paying trainees; sea education in marine science, maritime history, and ecology in cooperation with accredited institutions and other groups
Built: 1893: Essex, MA, A. D. Story (restored at South Street Seaport Museum in 1993)
Coast Guard certification: Sailing School Vessel (Subchapter R)
Crew: 7 Trainees-passengers: 14 overnight
Contact: South Street Seaport Museum, 207 Front Street, New York, NY 10038 USA
Tel: 212-748-8596
Fax: 212-748-8610
Website: www.southstseaport.org

SPECIFICATIONS

Flag: Argentina
Rig: Full-rigged ship
Homeport: Buenos Aires, Argentina
Sparred length: 356"
LOD: 317'
LWL: 263'
Draft: 21' 9"
Beam: 45' 3"
Freeboard: 15'
Rig height: 147' 6"
Sail area: 28,545 square feet
Power: Two 1,200 HP diesel engines
Hull: Steel

LIBERTAD

The frigate A.R.A. *Libertad* was initiated as a training ship in 1963 for the Argentine Navy. As a training ship, her mission is to enhance the maritime knowledge and cultural background of her midshipmen while integrating them to life at sea and instructing them on the fundamentals of the art of sailing. *Libertad* also serves as a floating ambassador representing the Argentine Republic establishing professional and friendly ties with navies around the world while preparing her cadets academically, physically and spiritually. In 1966 *Libertad* established the world record for speed crossing the North Atlantic sailing from Cape Race (Canada) to Dursey Island (Ireland) in six days and 21 hours. The International Sail Training Association (ISTA) officially recognized her record, and *Libertad* flies a pennant commemorating this achievement. Her figurehead was made by a Spanish sculptor and depicts Liberty, for which the ship is named. *Libertad* has sailed the seven seas and participates in regattas and port visits around the world.

Who sails: Cadets from the Military Naval School (20 – 23)
Program type: Naval training vessel
Season: May through December
Designer: Astilleros y Fabricas Navales del Estado (AFNE)
Built: 1960 (launched 1956): Rio Santiago (BA), Argentina, Astilleros y Fabricas Navales del Estado (AFNE)
Crew: 150 **Trainees-passengers:** 150
Contact: Argentine Naval Attache Office, Embassy of Argentina, 630 Indiana Avenue, NW, Washington, DC 2004 USA
Tel: 202-626-2164
Fax: 202-626-2180
E-mail: MICassain@argnavattache-usa.org
Website: www.argnavattache-usa.org or www.ara.mil.ar

SPECIFICATIONS

Flag: USA

Rig: Gaff topsail schooner

Homeport: Boston, Massachusetts (summer), Key West, Florida (winter)

Normal cruising waters: East Coast US

Sparred length: 80'

LOA: 64'

LOD: 61'

LWL: 53'

Draft: 7'

Beam: 17'

Rig height: 65'

Freeboard: 5'

Sail area: 1,744 square feet

Tons: 50 GRT **Power:** diesel

Hull: Steel

LIBERTY

Liberty is modeled on early 1800s coastal schooners used by New England fisherman and as cargo vessels along the East Coast to the Florida Keys. She is based in Key West, where she offers three two-hour sails each day. *Liberty* is kept "shipshape and Bristol fashion" and is available for charter day and evening for every occasion.

Who sails: School groups from elementary through high school, individuals, and families
Program type: Passenger day sails and overnight passages; corporate and private charters
Designer: Charles Wittholz
Built: 1993: Palm Coast, FL, Treworgy Yachts
Coast Guard certification: Passenger Vessel (Subchapter T)
Crew: 3 day sails, 4 overnight **Trainees-passengers:** 49 day sails, 8 overnight
Contact: Gregory E. Muzzy, President, The Liberty Fleet of Tall Ships, Hilton Resort & Marina, Key West, FL 33040 USA
Tel: 305-295-0095
Fax: 305-292-6411
E-mail: info@libertyfleet.com
Website: www.libertyfleet.com

SPECIFICATIONS

Flag: USA
Rig: Gaff topsail schooner
Homeport: Boston, MA (summer),
Key West, FL (winter)
Normal cruising waters: East
Coast US
Sparred length: 125'
LOD: 86'
LWL: 76'
Draft: 8'(min.), 13'(max.)
Beam: 25'
Rig height: 78'
Freeboard: 5'
Sail area: 4,300 square feet
Tons: 99 GRT
Power: Diesel
Hull: Steel

LIBERTY CLIPPER

The *Liberty Clipper* is a replica of the mid-19th century Baltimore Clippers famous for their fast passages around Cape Horn on their way to California and other Pacific ports. The *Liberty Clipper* operates in Boston Harbor during the summer and, with the schooner *Liberty*, in Key West, Florida during the winter. *Liberty Clipper* is available for charter on day and evening cruises for up to 110 passengers. Her spacious decks and on-board hospitality create an ambiance under sail that will meet the expectations of the most discriminating clients. In addition to a variety of high quality charter opportunities, during the summer months, the *Liberty Clipper* offers the Liberty Classroom program for Boston area youth groups. *Liberty* Classroom is a sail training and harbor education program designed to give trainees an introduction to essential topics in seamanship, safety, and Boston's maritime history. Much of the *Liberty* Classroom curriculum is based on active participation in the operation of the vessel, allowing one to master the first two skill levels in the ASTA Training Logbook. For those interested in extended trips, *Liberty Clipper* offers a limited number of berths for the passage between Boston and Key West in the spring and fall.

Who sails: School groups from elementary through high school, individuals, and families
Program type: Passenger day sails and overnight passages; corporate and private charters
Designer: Charles Wiftholz
Built: 1983: Warren, RI, Blount Marine Corporation
Coast Guard certification: Passenger Vessel (Subchapter T)
Crew: 5 day sails, 10 overnight **Trainees-passengers:** 115 day sails, 24 overnight
Contact: Gregory E. Muzzy, President, The Liberty Fleet of Tall Ships, 67 Long Wharf, Boston, MA 02210 USA
Tel: 617-742-0333
Fax: 617-742-1322
E-mail: info@libertyfleet.com
Website: www.libertyfleet.com

SPECIFICATIONS

Flag: UK
Rig: Barque, three-masted
Homeport: Southampton, United Kingdom
Normal cruising waters: United Kingdom (summer), Canary Islands (winter)
Sparred length: 180'
LOA: 140' 5"
LOD: 133'
LWL: 121' 5"
Draft: 13' 6"
Beam: 29' 6"
Rig height: 108'
Freeboard: 6' 8"
Sail area: 11,030 square feet
Tons: 368 GRT
Power: Twin 260 HP
Hull: Steel

LORD NELSON

The 180-foot, three-masted barque *Lord Nelson* was built in 1986 for the Jubilee Sailing Trust to encourage integration between able-bodied and physically disabled people by offering them the opportunity to experience the excitement of tall ship sailing together. Voyages last from 4 to 11 days, departing from a wide variety of ports and sailing in the English Channel and the North and Irish Seas. A winter season of voyages based in the Canary Islands is also available. Above deck the ship's equipment enables physically disabled crew to work alongside their able-bodied crewmates. Features include power steering, wide decks to accommodate wheelchairs, a speaking compass, powered lifts between decks, and Braille marking. Below are specially designed wheelchair-accessible cabins, showers, and heads. Voyages are open to anyone between the ages of 16 to 70+ with or without sailing experience. 20 people with physical disabilities, including eight wheelchair users, serve alongside an equal number of able-bodied people. There is a permanent crew of 10 including a medically trained person and a cook.

Who sails: Physically disabled and able-bodied people, aged 16 to 70+
Program type: Sail training for paying trainees; integration of physically disabled and able-bodied people through the medium of tall ship sailing
Designer: Colin Mudie
Built: 1986: Wivenhoe, UK, James W. Cook & Co., Ltd.
Certfication: Lloyds 10Oal A1
Crew: 10 **Trainees-passengers:** 40
Contact: Mrs. Lindsey Neve, Jubilee Sailing Trust, Jubilee Yard, Hazel Road, Woolston, Southampton, Hampshire S019 7GB, United Kingdom
Tel: 44-23-8044-9108
Fax: 44-23-8044-9145
E- mail: jst@jst.org.uk
Website: www.jst.org.uk

LYNX

SPECIFICATIONS

Flag: USA
Rig: Square topsail schooner
Homeport:
Newport Beach,CA
Sparred Length: 122'
LOA: 78'
LOD: 76'
LWL: 72'
Draft: 8' 6"
Beam: 23'
Freeboard: 3' 6"
Sail Area: 4,669 square feet
Power: Cat 3306B - 290 HP
Hundested Variable Pitch
Propeller
Hull: Wood

The square topsail schooner *Lynx* has been designed and built to interpret the general configuration and operation of a privateer schooner or naval schooner from the War of 1812, the original *Lynx* being a "letter of marque" Baltimore Clipper commissioned during the opening days of the war. Serving effectively as a blockade-runner and offensive weapon of war, she was among the first ships to defend American freedom. Dedicated to all those who cherish the blessings of America, *Lynx* sails as a living history museum, providing inspiration and resolve at this time in our nation's history. She is fitted with period ordnance and flies flags and pennants from the 1812 era. To complement her historic character, the *Lynx* crew members wear period uniforms and operate the ship in keeping with the maritime traditions of early 19th Century America. *Lynx* also operates as a sail training vessel to serve as a classroom for the study of historical, environmental, and ecological issues. In addition, she undertakes "cruises of opportunity" that lead to personal growth and awareness through the experience of life at sea aboard a traditional sailing vessel. *Lynx* is guided by the maxim, "Be Excellent to Each Other and To Your Ship."

Who sails: School groups from elementary age through college; individuals and families
Program type: Sail training for volunteer and paying trainees; sea education in maritime history in cooperation with accredited institutions and other organized groups; passenger day sails and overnight voyages; dockside interpretation
Designer: Melbourne Smith - International Historical Watercraft Society
Built: Rockport, ME, Rockport Marine; launched July 28, 2001 in Rockport, ME
Coast Guard certification: Passenger Vessel (Subchapter T)
Crew: 5 **Trainees-passengers:** 40 day sails, 6-8 overnight
Contact: Woodson K. Woods, Executive Director, Woods Maritime LLC, 509 29th Street, Newport Beach, CA 92663 USA
Tel: 914-723-7814
Fax: 914-723-7815
E-mail: nkwoods@privateerlynx.org
Website: www.privateerlynx.org

MABLE

SPECIFICATIONS

Flag: USA
Rig: Ketch w/ sprit rigged mainsíl and dipping lug mizzen
Homeport: Vineyard Haven, MA
Normal cruising waters: Near coastal, New York to Maine
Sparred Length: 35'
LOA: 28'
LWL: 25'
Freeboard: 2'
Draft: 18'
Beam: 8'11"
Rig Height: 23' 6"
Sail Area: 350 sq. ft.
Power: Sail and oars
Hull: Lapstrake Cedar on Oak Frames

Vineyard Voyagers, Inc. provides opportunities for adventure to young people on Martha's Vineyard, residents and visitors alike, ages 12-21. The Maritime Studies Program helps teenagers learn to build traditional wooden boats for expeditions in New England waters. *Mable* is our first expedition vessel, designed and built in Vineyard Haven by Myles Thurlow at age 18, a striking example of what a young person can accomplish when encouraged and supported in the pursuit of a passionate interest. Reminiscent of Nomansland fishing boats common in Vineyard waters a century ago, *Mable* sailed to New York and up the Hudson River with a crew of 7 teenagers on her maiden voyage to the 2003 Clearwater Revival. Her summer programs range from daysails to a week on expedition at sea following a week of boatbuilding. The current project is construction of a pair of 32' Cornish pilot gigs for a new community rowing program.

Who Sails: All ages with a focus on local youth ages 12-21
Program Type: Maritime Studies combining wooden boat building and sail training
Sailing Season: May-November
Designer: Myles Thurlow
Built: 2002: Vineyard Haven
Crew: 2 **Trainees-passengers:** 6
Contact: Sidney Morris, Executive Director, Vineyard Voyagers, Inc., HC 61 Box 124, 16 Knight Lane, Edgartown, MA 02539 USA
Tel: 774-563-0200
Fax: 508-627-6659 (by arrangement)
E-mail: info@vineyardvoyagers.org
Website: www.vineyardvoyagers.org

MADELINE

SPECIFICATIONS

Flag: USA
Rig: Gaff topsail schooner, two-masted
Homeport: Traverse City, Michigan
Normal cruising waters: Upper Great Lakes
Sparred length: 92'
LOA: 55' 6"
LWL: 52'
Draft: 7' 7"
Beam: 16' 2"
Rig height: 71'
Freeboard: 2' 2"
Sail area: 2,270 square feet
Tons: 42 GRT

The *Madeline* is a reconstruction of a mid-19th-century schooner, typical of the trading schooners that once sailed the upper Great Lakes. Launched in 1990, the modern *Madeline* was built over period of five years by volunteers of the Maritime Heritage Alliance (MHA), using traditional meth-ods and materials. From her homeport, Traverse City, Michigan, she has sailed with her volunteer crew on all five Great Lakes, visiting over 60 ports with dock-side tours and historical interpretation. *Madeline* is the State of Michigan's official tall ship and is designated as the City of Traverse City's goodwill ambassador. *Madeline's* dockside programs bring visitors on board to learn about schooners and Great Lakes history first-hand. Crewmembers, trained as historical interpreters, share their knowledge of history, marlinespike skills, and wooden boat building. School programs with special hands-on activities are also available. The Maritime Heritage Alliance, a nonprofit organization, fosters the study and practice of upper Great Lakes' maritime history. MHA programs, focusing on building and operating indigenous crafts, include crew training, traditional boat carpentry, and other wooden boat maintenance skills.

Who sails: Trained crew members of the Maritime Heritage Alliance; Madeline is associated with the Association for Great Lakes History
Program type: Adult sail training and maritime history
Designer: Kenneth (Bob) Core
Built: 1990: Traverse City, MI, Maritime Heritage Alliance
Coast Guard certification: Uninspected Vessel
Crew: 9
Contact: Mr. Richard Brauer, President of the Board, Maritime Heritage Alliance, 322 Sixth Street, Traverse City, MI 49684 USA
Tel: 231-946-2647
Fax: 231-946-6750
E-mail: mhatc@bignetnorth.net
Website: www.traverse.com/maritime

Flag: USA
Rig: Staysail schooner, three masted
Homeport: Kaneohe Bay, Hawaii
Normal cruising waters: Hawaiian Islands
Sparred length: 96'
LOA: 85'
LOD: 75'
Draft: 8'
Beam: 20'
Rig height: 65'
Freeboard: 5'
Sail area: 2,000 square feet

MAKANI OLU (Gracious Wind)

The *Makani Olu* is owned and operated by the Marimed Foundation which has been involved in sail training since its inception in 1988. In July 2001 Marimed Foundation purchased the sail training ship in Florida and spent five months doing a major refit to prepare the private vessel for sail train-ing in Hawaiian waters. The 96-foot, three-masted staysail schooner arrived in Kaneohe Bay in March 2002 and began service with Marimed's Kailana Youth Program. The *Makani Olu (Gracious Wind)* is the primary experiential educational component of the Kailana Program. Special-needs adolescents sail the ship year round in Hawaiian waters. From its base on Oahu, the *Makani Olu* makes six-day trips throughout the Hawaiian chain. Cadets from the Kailana Program learn marine skills, navigation and team building. They participate in service learning projects at ports of call. In addition to providing the key component of the Kailana Program, the *Makani Olu* is available for group sail training and team building to youth, families and community organizations of all kinds. Day, weekend and six-day sail training trips are available.

Who sails: Groups and individuals of all ages
Program type: Sail training for paying trainees; fully accredited sea education in marine science, maritime history, and ecology, as well as service learning, in cooperation with accredited institutions and other organized groups, and as informal in-house programming
Season: Year-round
Designer: Thomas Kolvin
Built: 1998: St. Augustine, FL, Schrieber
Coast Guard certification: Sailing School Vessel (Subchapter R)
Crew: 5 **Trainees-passengers:** 30 day sails, 20 overnight
Contact: Matthew Claybaugh, Ph.D., President and CEO Marimed Foundation, 45-021 Likeke Place, Kaneohe, HI 96744 USA
Tel: 808-236-2288 **Fax:** 808-235-1074
E-mail: kailana@marimed.org
Website: www.marimed.org

SPECIFICATIONS

Flag: USA
Rig: Ketch
Homeport: Dover, DE
Normal Cruising Waters: Worldwide
LOA: 43'
Draft: 6'
Beam: 13'
Rig height: 55'
Freeboard: 5'
Tons: 27 GRT
Power: 75 HP Yanmar
Hull: Fiberglass

MAKULU II

Reach the World is an organization that uses technology and travel to bring the world into underprivileged classrooms. RTW's mission is to connect students and teachers in high-needs schools with online journeys that have the power to bring the world into the classroom, making learning come alive. Since 1998, RTW has operated three online journeys: the world circumnavigations of *Makulu*, a 43-foot ketch. On board, five crewmembers serve as eyes and ears in foreign ports for RTW's students, most of whom are elementary and middle school-age students in New York Cityís poorest public schools. RTW's crewmembers fill the following positions on board: Captain, First Mate, Curriculum Director, Field Curriculum Coordinator, and Science Coordinator. Crewmembers work full-time and receive an annual stipend for their service. The third world circumnavigation of *Makulu* departed from New York City in December 2004 and is set to conclude in June 2007.

Who sails: Full-time crewmembers, generally with a background in education. Age range tends to be early 20s through early 30s.
Program type: Digital Education
Season: Year-round
Designer: Sparkman & Stephens
Built: 1979: Nautorís Swan, Finland
Coast Guard certification: Sailing School Vessel (Subchapter R), Passenger Vessel (Subchapter T) Oceanographic Research Vessel (Subchapter U), Moored Attraction Vessel, Un-inspected Small Passenger Vessel (Subchapter C, no more than 6 passengers)
Crew: 5 **Trainees-passengers:** Total capacity is 6 persons.
Contact: Heather Halstead, Executive Director, Reach the World, 329 E 82nd Street, New York, NY 10028 USA
Tel: 212-288-6987 **Fax:** 212-517-7284
E-mail: rtwinfo@reachtheworld.org
Website: www.reachtheworld.org

Flag: USA
Rig: Staysail schooner
Homeport: Seattle, Washington
Normal cruising waters: Pacific
Northwest, Canada, and Alaska
Rig: Staysail schooner
Sparred length: 65'
LOA: 60'
LOD: 65'
LWL: 50'
Draft: 5' (min.) 8' (max.)
Beam: 16'
Rig Height: 65'
Freeboard: 5'
Sail area: 1,545 square feet
Tons: 38 GRT
Power: Diesel
Hull: Composite

MALLORY TODD

Named for Captain Mallory Todd, who served as master on American vessels during the Revolutionary War, the *Mallory Todd* is a modern 65-foot schooner built in the classic style. Designed for long distance voyages, she has sailed the West Coast from Mexico to Alaska for 18 years. When at homeport in Seattle, she relieves the tedium of long-term cancer treatment with recreational outings for hospital patients and their caregivers under the auspices of the nonprofit Sailing Heritage Society. These trips are open to anyone between 18 and 80 with or without sailing experience. Together, part time volunteers, trainees, and professionals get the job done. Hands on tending the sails, steering, scrubbing, navigating, fishing, or clamming, each contributes where a need fits their abilities. Schooner *Mallory Todd* also offers corporate and private charters that provide a unique and delightful venue for business or recreational activities-be it exclusive executive meeting or picnic outing.

Who sails: All ages for volunteers, paying trainees, and apprentices
Program type: Sail training for crew, volunteers, trainees, and apprentices; sea education based on programmed and day to day events; passenger day sails for corporate team building or recreational events
Designer: Perry & Todd
Built: 1981: Seattle, WA
Coast Guard certification: Passenger Vessel (Subchapter T)
Crew: 2 **Trainees-passengers:** 25 day sails, 6 overnight
Contact: Captain George Todd, Sailing Heritage Society, 10042 NE 13th Street Bellevue, WA 98004 USA
Tel: 425-451-8160
Fax: 425-451-8119
E-mail: george@sailingheritage.org
Website: www.sailseattle.com

SPECIFICATIONS

Flag: USA
Rig: Gaff topsail schooner, two-masted
Homeport: Traverse City, Michigan
Normal cruising waters: Great Lakes
Sparred length: 114'
LOD: 77'
LWL: 65'
Draft: 7' (min.) 11' (max.)
Beam: 21'
Rig height: 77'
Freeboard: 6'
Sail area: 3,000 square feet
Tons: 82 GRT
Power: 150 HP diesel
Hull: Steel

MANITOU

Owned and operated by Traverse Tall Ship Co., LLC, the schooner *Manitou* is one of the largest sailing vessels on the Great Lakes. This replica of a 19th century "coaster" can accommodate 24 overnight guests and 62 passengers for day excursions. *Manitou* is fully certified by the US Coast Guard and offers day sails on Grand Traverse Bay, Lake Michigan. In addition, join us for an adventurous overnight as part of our "Floating Bed & Breakfast." Awake in the morning to hot coffee and fresh baked muffins from the galley before sitting down to a full breakfast prepared from scratch on the wood stove. In conjunction with Inland Seas Education Association *Manitou* operates the Schoolship Program, which provides an environmental, historical, and sail training education for students during the spring. The schooner offers partial as well as private charter service to family, company, and motor coach groups.

Who sails: School groups; individual, family, and corporate groups for day sails and bed & breakfast
Program type: Sail training for crew; sea education in marine science, maritime history and ecology; individual and group day sails; "Floating Bed & Breakfast"
Season: May to October
Designer: Woodin & Marean
Built: 1982: Portsmouth, NH, Roger Gagnon Steel Ship Company
Coast Guard certification: Passenger Vessel (Subchapter T)
Crew: 5 **Trainees-passengers:** 56 day sails, 24 overnight
Contact: Captain Dave McGinnis, Traverse Tall Ship Co., LLC, 13390 SW Bay Shore Drive, Traverse City, MI 49684 USA
Tel: 231-941-2000
Fax: 231-941-0520
E-mail: info@tallshipsailing.com
Website: www.talishipsailing.com

SPECIFICATIONS

Flag: Canada
Rig: Gaff schooner
Homeport: Victoria, British Columbia
Normal cruising waters: British Columbia & Alaska coasts
Sparred Length: 92'
LOA: 77'
LOD: 75'
LWL: 59'
Draft: 11'
Beam: 15'
Rig height: 96'
Freeboard: 5'
Sail area: 3,300 square feet
Tons: 40.75 GRT
Power: 260 HP diesel
Hull: Wood

MAPLE LEAF

The *Maple Leaf* is a 92-foot classic wooden schooner with a rich history of operation along the North Pacific Coast. Launched in 1904 as a private yacht she was overbuilt with large timbers of the finest local wood, details glinted with gold and bronze, and she even boasted new-fangled 'electric' lights. A second life in the middle of the century as a halibut schooner on the North Pacific saw *Maple Leaf* out-fish every other boat in the fleet. *Maple Leaf* fished another 20 years and then underwent an award-winning, six-year restoration and was re-launched in 1986. Since 1988 *Maple Leaf* has been part of the Royal Canadian Sea Cadets sail training program. While experiencing the opportunity to sail the beautiful British Columbia coast, cadets gain an appreciation for the age-old traditions of sailing a tall ship and the inherent life and leadership skills that come from meeting new challenges. In addition to youth sail training, *Maple Leaf* offers 5 to 11 day ecotourism adventures on the B.C. and Alaska coasts. The trips explore the coast's natural and cultural history. *Maple Leaf* is also available for private charter. Her beautiful form and maple-leaf-painted main sail are known and loved up and down the coast.

Who sails: Sea cadets (sail training) and charter guests
Program type: Youth sail training / Eco-tourism
Season: Sail Training: April, July, August Eco-tourism: April, May, June, September, October
Designer: William Watts
Built: 1904: Vancouver, British Columbia, Canada
Certification: Inspected passenger carrying vessel, Home Trade 3
Crew: 5 **Trainees-passengers**: 30 day sails, 18 overnight **Adult eco-tourism guests:** 9
Contact: Kevin J. Smith, Mapleleaf Adventures, 2087 Indian Crescent, Duncan, B.C., V9L 5L9 Canada
Tel: 250-746-0906 (outside North America), 888-599-5323 (inside North America)
E-mail: mapleleaf@mapleleafadventures.com
Website: www.mapleleafadventures.com

Flag: Canada
Rig: Brig
LOA: 101'
LWL: 79'
Draft: 10'
Beam: 22'

ASTA

MARY DARE

The Brig *Mary Dare*, an armed merchantman, was built in Bridport, Dorset, England in 1842 for Captain Robert Hatson Dare, to sail from London, England, via Cape Horn, to Lima Peru and California. In September 1846 Captain Dare sold this vessel to the Hudson's Bay Company who sailed the vessel to Victoria, British Columbia, via Cape Horn and Hawaii, where she continued to work on the Pacific Coast of the United States and Canada during the time when, despite the treaty of 1846, the border dispute between England and America was still a fresh issue. The vessel was returned to England in 1854 and was sold into the collier trade. Early in the morning of December 16, 1857 the *Mary Dare*, under the command of Captain Taylor, was sailing from Seaham in Yorkshire to London with 150 tons of coal. Twenty miles into the voyage she was struck by the vessel *Adonis* and sank. In view of the *Mary Dare's* strong connection with the Pacific Ocean, The Pacific Sail Training Association has been researching the history of this vessel and plans to build a replica. We are currently talking to universities about partnering in their academic program, and consulting civic governments regarding potential building sites.

Program type: The Pacific Sail Training Association aims to provide professional and experienced supervision, so that young persons may have the opportunity to develop physical, mental, social and leadership skills by means of experiencing the challenges that accompany living and working together on a sailing vessel at sea
Contact: Pacific Sail Training Association, 6260 Riverdale Drive, Richmond, BC V7C 2B9 Canada
E-mail: sailtraining@shaw.ca
Website: www.pacificsailtraining.com

SPECIFICATIONS

Flag: USA
Rig: Gaff topsail schooner, two-masted
Homeport: Camden, Maine
Normal cruising waters:
Mid-Coast and Downeast Maine
Sparred length: 125'
LOA: 92'
LOD: 90'
LWL: 81'
Draft: 7' 6"
Beam: 22'
Rig height: 102'
Freeboard: 5'
Sail area: 5,000 square feet
Tons: 86 GRT
Hull: Wood

MARY DAY

Built in 1962 by Harvey Gamage, *Mary Day* combines the best aspects of the New England centerboard coaster with modern design thinking. *Mary Day* operates out of Camden, Maine, in the windjammer trade from late May to early October. She carries 30 passengers on weeklong vacation cruises in mid-coast Maine. *Mary Day* is a pure sailing vessel. She has no engine and depends on a small yawl boat when winds fail. She has a large and powerful rig and exhibits out-standing sailing abilities. *Mary Day* carries a professional crew of six, including captain, mate, cook, two deckhands, and one galley hand. The galley and one deck posi-tion are considered entry-level posi-tions, and a great many sailing profes-sionals have started out or gained valuable experience on board the schooner *Mary Day*.

Who sails: Individuals and families
Program type: Sail training for crew and apprentices; passenger overnight passages; dockside interpretation in homeport
Season: May to October
Designer: H. Hawkins
Built: 1962: South Bristol, ME, Harvey Gamage Shipyard
Coast Guard certification: Passenger Vessel (Subchapter T)
Crew: 7   **Trainees-passengers:** 49 day sails, 29 overnight
Contact: Captains Barry King and Jen Martin, Penobscot Windjammer Company, PO Box 798, Camden, ME 04843 USA
Tel: 800-992-2218
E-mail: captains@schoonermaryday.com
Website: www.schoonermaryday.com

SPECIFICATIONS

Flag: USA
Rig: Brigantine
Homeport: Beaufort, North Carolina
Normal cruising waters: North Carolina (summer) Caribbean (winter)
Sparred length: 52'
LOA: 36'
LWL: 32'
Draft: 7'
Beam: 12' 5"
Rig height: 55'
Freeboard: 3'
Sail area: 900 square feet
Tons: 18 GRT

MEKA II

The *Meka II* has an overall length of 54-feet and is a half-scale replica of an 18th century, two masted pirate brigantine. Captain Horatio Sinbad built the *Meka II* in Detroit, Michigan and launched her in 1967, first cruising the Great Lakes. In 1970 she found her way to the high seas through the St. Lawrence Seaway and has since earned the respect of many high seas adventurers for her sail training and historical educational voyages, following in the wake of great pirates and privateers. The *Meka II*, Captain Sinbad, and his crew are active participants in reenactments of historical context and tall ship events throughout the east coast, Bahamas, Jamaica, and Cayman Islands. The *Meka II's* homeport is Beaufort, NC where locals and tourists take pride and part in her ongoing efforts to preserve historical heritage.

Who sails: Groups and individuals of all ages
Program type: Sail training for paying trainees; sea education and maritime history, as informal in-house programming; overnight passages; dockside interpretation
Designer: Captain Sinbad & Gerald White, Westlawn
Built: 1967: Detroit, MI, Captain Sinbad
Coast Guard certification: Uninspected Vessel
Contact: Captain Horatio Sinbad, Pirate Privateer, PO Box 705, Beaufort, NC 28516 USA
Tel: 252-728-7978
E-mail: Sinbad@mail.clis.com
Website: www.pirate-privateer.coms

SPECIFICATIONS

Flag: USA
Rig: Gaff topsail schooner, two-masted
Homeport: Biloxi, Mississippi
Normal cruising waters: Coastwise Gulf of Mexico
Sparred length: 78'
LOA: 78'
LOD: 50'
LWL: 43'
Draft: 5' 10"
Beam: 17'
Sail area: 2,499 square feet
Tons: 24 GRT
Power: 4-71 Detroit diesel
Hull: Wood

MIKE SEKUL

The *Mike Sekul* is one of the two Biloxi oyster schooner replicas built as part of the Biloxi Schooner Project under the auspices of the Maritime and Seafood Industry Museum. She was launched in April of 1994 as part of the effort to preserve the maritime and seafood industry of the Mississippi Gulf Coast. Money for construction and fitting out of the *Mike Sekul* and her sister ship, *Glenn L. Swetman*, has come from donations and fundraising events. The *Mike Sekul* is available for charter for two-and-a-half hours, half-day, and full-day trips in the Mississippi Sound and to the barrier islands, Cat Island, Horn Island, and Ship Island. Walkup day sailing trips are made when she is not under charter. Groups of up to 45 passengers learn about the maritime and seafood heritage of the Gulf Coast and about the vessels working in Biloxi's seafood industry. Sailing classes are offered through local colleges and the museum's Sea and Sail Adventure summer camp. Wedding parties, Elderhostel, and school groups are also accommodated.

Who sails: Elementary students through college age, adults, and families; affiliated institutions include William Carey College, Seashore Methodist Assembly, J.L. Scoff Marine Education Center, and Mississippi State University
Program type: Sail training for paying and volunteer trainees; sea education in marine science, maritime history, and ecology in cooperation with accredited institutions and organized groups and as informal, in-house programming
Season: Year-round
Designer: Neil Covacevich
Built: 1994: Biloxi, Mississippi, Neil Covacevich
Coast Guard certification: Passenger Vessel (Subchapter T)
Crew: 3 **Trainees-passengers:** 45 day sails - Age: 15+
Contact: Robin Krohn, Executive Director, Maritime and Seafood Industry Museum of Biloxi, PO Box 1907, Biloxi, MS 39533 USA
Tel: 228-435-6320 **Fax:** 228-435-6309
E-mail: schooner@maritimemuseum.org
Website: www.maritime museum.org

SPECIFICATIONS

Flag: USA
Rig: Sloop
Homeport: Baltimore, Maryland
Normal cruising waters:
Baltimore Harbor
Sparred length: 69'
LOD: 45' 3"
Draft: 3'
Beam: 15' 7"
Rig height: 58'
Freeboard: 2'
Sail area: 1,450 square feet
Tons: 10 GRT
Hull: Wood

MINNIE V

The skipjack *Minnie V*, built in Wenona, Maryland, was used to dredge oysters on the Chesapeake Bay for many years. The vessel was rebuilt by the City of Baltimore in 1981 and is now owned and operated by the Living Classrooms Foundation. The Foundation uses the vessel for educational programs and as a tourist attraction offering interpretive tours of the historic port of Baltimore. While on board the *Minnie V*, students learn about the oyster trade, its importance to the economy of Maryland, and the hard life of a waterman as they relive history by raising the sails on one the Chesapeake's few remaining skipjacks.

Who sails: School groups from middle school through college; individuals and families
Program type: Sea education in marine science, maritime history, and ecology in cooperation with accredited schools, colleges, and other organized groups; passenger day sails; dockside interpretation
Season: April through October
Built: 1906: Wenona, MD, Vetra
Coast Guard certification: Passenger Vessel (Subchapter T)
Crew: 2 **Trainees-passengers:** 24
Contact: Christine Truett, Director of Education Living Classrooms Foundation, 802 South Caroline Street, Baltimore, MD 21231-3311 USA
Tel: 410-685-0295
Fax: 410-752-8433
Website: www.livingclassrooms.org

SPECIFICATIONS

Flag: Russia
Rig: Full-rigged ship
Homeport: St. Petersburg, Russia
Normal cruising waters: West and southwest European
Sparred length: 345' 9"
LOA: 328'
LOD: 300' 9"
LWL: 254'
Draft: 18'
Beam: 44' 9"
Rig height: 149'
Freeboard: 34' 6"
Sail area: 29,997 square feet
Tons: 2,856 GRT
Power: Twin 570 HP diesels
Hull: Steel

Photo by Thad Koza

MIR

Mir is regarded by many as the fastest Class A sail training ship in the world. She was the overall winner of the 1992 Columbus Race and the winner of the Cutty Sark Tall Ship Races in 1996, 1997, and 1998 under the command of Captain Victor Antonov. *Mir* was launched in 1989 at the Lenin shipyard in Gdansk, Poland, the builders of five more of the M 108 type ships: *Dar Mlodziezy, Pallada, Khersones, Druzhba*, and Nadezhda. *Mir* is the school ship of the Makaroz Maritime Academy in St. Petersburg, Russia, training future navigators and engineers for the Russian merchant fleet. Since 1990 up to 60 trainees of all ages are welcomed on board to sail along with the Russian students, learning the ropes, manning the helm, or climbing the rigging to set the sails. No previous experience is necessary. *Mir* is supported by Tall Ship Friends, a nonprofit organization in Hamburg, Germany. The goals of Tall Ship Friends are to promote sail training on square-riggers, to contribute to the further existence of these beautiful ships, and to provide an unforgettable experience for the participants. Members of Tall Ship Friends receive the quarterly Tall Ships News (English/German) and a personal sailing log.

Who sails: Students and individuals of all ages. Affiliated with Tall Ship Friends clubs in France, UK, Switzerland, Austria, Ireland, and Italy
Program type: Sail training for paying trainees; fully accredited sea education in traditional seamanship; dockside interpretation during port visits
Designer: Z. Choren
Built: 1987; Gdansk, Poland, Stocznia Gdanska
Certification: Russian registered Sailing School Vessel
Crew: 45-70 **Trainees-passengers:** up to 250 day sails, 60 overnight
Contact: Wulf Marquard, Managing Director, Tall Ship Friends Germany Schweriner Str. 17, Hamburg, D22 143, Germany
Tel: 49-40-675 635 97 **Fax:** 49-40-675 635 99
E-mail: tallshipl@aol.com
Website: www.tallship-friends.de

Photo by Thad Koza

MIRCEA

SPECIFICATIONS

Flag: Romania
Rig: Barque
Homeport: Constanta, Romania
Sparred length: 328'
LOA: 266'
LOD: 241' 6
LWL: 203'
Draft: 18'
Beam: 39' 6"
Rig height: 144'
Freeboard: 8'
Sail area: 18,837 square feet
Tons: 1320 GRT
Power: 1,100 hp Diesel
Hull: Steel

Mircea is the flagship and the training vessel of the Romanian Naval Forces. The last of a quartet of sailing school ships built in Blohm & Voss Shipyard, Hamburg, Germany, in the 1930s, *Mircea* and her sister ships became the models for sailing vessels built during the last three decades. During overhaul concluded in 2002 *Mircea* has been equipped with modern navigation and communication devices that made her up-to-date despite the 65 years of age.

Who sails: Students and cadets of the Romanian Naval Academy and Romanian Petty Officer School
Program type: Schoolship for the Romanian Naval Forces' cadets
Built: 1938: Hamburg, Germany, Blohm & Voss Shipyard
Crew: 65 **Trainees-passengers:** 120
Contact: Public Affairs Officer, Romanian Naval Academy, Fulgerului Street, Constanta, Romania 900218
Tel: +40 241 643040
Fax: +40 241 643096
E-mail: relpub@navedo.anmb.ro
Website: www.anmb.ro

SPECIFICATIONS

Flag: Canada
Rig: Gaff schooner
Homeport: Ivy Lea, Ontario, Canada
Sparred length: 100'
LOA: 84'
LOD: 83'
Draft: 10'
Beam: 20' 1"
Rig height: 92'
Sail area: 3,668 square feet
Tons: GRT
Power: 3306 Cat diesel
Hull: Wood

MIST OF AVALON

The *Mist of Avalon* began her life in 1967 as the motor vessel Liverpool Bay. She was built of strong native timber, and by the skilled hands of shipwrights of MacLean Shipbuilding, Mahone Bay, Nova Scotia, Canada. Her captain and crew worked the banks off Nova Scotia and Newfoundland, fishing for the cod that was her reason for being. After 20 years working in the harsh environment of the North Atlantic, with fish stock declining and her machinery and equipment well past their prime, this once proud vessel was left abandoned at a Halifax pier in 1987. Another five years of neglect added to her decline, but under layers of old paint and algae, behind the rotting timber and planks, was a gracious schooner hull waiting to return her to the sea. In 1992 she began a new life as the *Mist of Avalon*, named for the mystic Celtic island of rebirth. She was brought from Nova Scotia to her new homeport at Holiday's Afloat Museum in Ivy Lea, Ontario, Canada in the summer of 1993. There work continued on the conversion from motor vessel to fully rigged tall ship in the tradition of the late 19th century Grand Banks schooners.

Who sails: Groups and individuals of all ages
Program type: Sail training for paying trainees, corporate & social events, festivals, boat shows, tall ship events. Passenger day sails and overnight passages
Built: 1967: Mahone Bay, Nova Scotia, Canada, MacLean Shipbuilding
Crew: 3 **Trainees-passengers:** 8
Contact: George Mainguy, 29 Ivy Lea Road, Lansdowne, Ontario KOE 1LO Canada
Tel: 613-659-2736
E-mail: mistofavalon@1000island.net
Website: www.mistofavalon.ca

SPECIFICATIONS

Flag: USA
Rig: Gaff-rigged schooner
Homeport: Mystic, Connecticut
Normal cruising waters: Southeast New England
Sparred length: 110'
LOA: 83'
LOD: 83'
LWL: 78'
Draft: 7' 6" (min.) 13' (max.)
Beam: 25'
Rig height: 90'
Freeboard: 7'
Sail Area: 3,000 square feet
Tons: 100 tons
Power: 175 hp diesel
Hull Material: Steel

MYSTIC WHALER

Built in 1967 and rebuilt in 1993, the *Mystic Whaler* carries passengers and trainees on a variety of cruises, ranging from 3 hours to 5 days. In April, May, and early June, the schooner joins Clearwater on the Hudson River, for environmental education programs. Sailing from Mystic, CT throughout the summer months, the *Mystic Whaler* offers great sailing opportunities for both novice and experienced passengers. Three-hour Lobster Dinner Cruises are popular as are the 5-hour Day sails, or try an overnight of 2, 3 or 5 days. In September and October, the *Mystic Whaler* travels to Baltimore Maryland for two weeks of 3-day overnight sails and to participate in the Great Chesapeake Bay Schooner Race. Some of the overnight cruises have special interest extras such as lighthouse tours, sea music and full moon cruises. Two-week apprenticeship programs run throughout the season (June-September).

Who sails: School groups from elementary school through college, as well as individuals and families ages 5 and up
Program type: Sail training for crew and apprentices; sea education in maritime history and ecology based on informal programming with organized groups such as Scouts; passenger day sails and overnight passages
Season: March through November
Designer: "Chub" Crockett
Built: 1967: Tarpon Springs, Florida, George Sutton
Coast Guard certification: Passenger Vessel (Subchapter T)
Crew: 5 **Trainees-passengers:** 65 day, 34 overnight
Contact: Captain John Eginton Mystic Whaler Cruises, Inc. PO Box 189, Mystic, CT 06355-0189 USA
Tel: 800-697-8420
Fax: 860-536-4219
E-mail: mysticwhaler@earthlink.net
Website: www.mysticwhaler.com

Rig: Ship
Homeport: Vladivostok, Russia
LOA: 359'
Draft: 21.5'
Hull: Steel

NADEZHDA

The *Nadezhda*, the name is Russian word for "hope", is the last of 6 "DAR –class" full-rigged ships that were built in the Gdansk shipyard in the 1980s. *Nadezhda* was completed in 1990, and delivered and commissioned to the Far Eastern State Maritime Academy in Vladivostok, Russia in 1991.

Built: 1990
Coast Guard certification: Passenger Vessel (Subchapter T)
Contact: FESMA (Far Eastern Maritime Academy), 50a Verkhneportovaya St., Vladivostok, 690059 Russia
E-mail: fesma@ints.vtc.ru

SPECIFICATIONS

Flag: USA
Rig: Brig
Homeport: Erie, Pennsylvania
Normal cruising waters: Coastwise and Great Lakes
Sparred length: 198'
LOA: 123'
LOD: 116'
LWL: 110'
Draft: 11'
Beam: 32' 6"
Rig height: 121'
Sail area: 11,600 square feet
Tons: 162 GRT
Power: Twin 200 HP diesels
Hull: Wood

NIAGARA

The US Brig *Niagara* was built in 1988 as a reconstruction of the warship aboard which Oliver Hazard Perry won the Battle of Lake Erie in 1813 during the War of 1812. Her mission is to interpret War of 1812 history, promote the Commonwealth of Pennsylvania and the Erie Region, and preserve the skills of square-rig seafaring. The present *Niagara* has auxiliary power and modern navigation equipment, but lacks modern amenities such as warm water, showers and privacy. She is sailed by a crew of 18-20 professionals supplemented by 20 volunteers willing to live under Spartan conditions such as hammock berthing and living out of a duffel bag. Volunteers do not need to have experience, but a minimum sign-on of three weeks is required. During "home summers" (odd numbered years) there are typically two day sails per week from early May to late September/early October, with a short voyage of three to four weeks sometime in the season. In the even years, the ship is away from seven to eighteen weeks on voyages to ports in the Great Lakes, US East Coast, and Canadian Maritimes. When not on extended voyages, she makes her home at the Erie Maritime Museum in Erie, Pennsylvania.

Who sails: School groups from middle school through college, as well as individuals and families
Program type: Sail training for crew and apprentices; sea education based on informal, in-house programming; dockside interpretation
Designer: Melbourne Smith
Built: 1988: Erie, PA
Coast Guard certification: Uninspected Vessel and Attraction Vessel
Crew: 40
Contact: Captain Walter P. Rybka, Pennsylvania Historical and Museum Commission, 150 East Front Street, Suite 100, Erie, PA 16507 USA
Tel: 814-452-2744
Fax: 814-455-6760
E-mail: sail@brigniagara.org
Website: www.brigniagara.org

Flag: USA

Rig: Schooner

Homeport: Morehead City & Beaufort, North Carolina

Normal cruising waters: Chesapeake Bay

Sparred length: 82'

LOD: 65' "

LWL: 60'

Draft: 5'

Beam: 20'

Rig height: 55'

Sail area: 2,000 square feet

Freeboard: 6'

Tons: 45 GRT

Power: Twin diesels

Hull: Steel

NIGHTHAWK

Built in 1980 as a replica of a 19th-century coastal schooner, *Nighthawk* sails the waters of the Chesapeake Bay and its tributaries from April 1 through November 1 each season. She voyaged to the Caribbean, Mexico, and South America prior to arriving in Baltimore in 1986. *Nighthawk* operates as a private charter vessel as well as offering basic sail training to local school and scout groups. Docked in the historic Fells Point section of Baltimore's Inner Harbor, the *Nighthawk* and her captain and crew provide an ideal opportunity for character and team building through hands-on exploration. *Nighthawk* is also available for wide variety of corporate and private charters and celebrations, as well as public excursions. "Murder Mystery" and other theme cruises are featured. The captain performs weddings onboard and catering is available.

Who sails: Passengers of all ages

Program type: Day charters with a historical sailing theme

Season: April 1st through September

Designer: Haglund

Built: 1980; Florida, Haglund Schooner Company

Coast Guard certification: Passenger Vessel (Subchapter T), Lakes, Bays, Sounds and Inland waters

Crew: 4 (50 ton Master with Sail endorsement) and 3 deck hands **Trainees-passengers:** 48 day sails, 6 overnight

Contact: Dawn M. Skene, Owner, P.O. Box 126 Beaufort, NC 28516 USA

Tel: 252-241-1775

Fax: 410-327-7245

E-mail: syrensvixen@aol.com (boat) or sirenmacloki@aol.com (personal)

SPECIFICATIONS

Flag: Brazil/USA
Rig: 15th century caravel redondo
Homeport:
Nuevo Vallarta, Mexico
Sparred length: 92'
LOA: 68'
LOD: 65'
LWL: 58'
Draft: 7'
Beam: 18'
Rig height: 54'
Sail area: 1,919 square feet
Freeboard: 5'
Tons: 37 GRT
Power: 128 HP diesel
Hull: Wood

NINA

The *Nina* is a historically accurate replica of a 15th century caravel. John Sarsfield, the leading authority on caravels, was designer and builder until his death halfway through the project. Jonathon Nance, a noted British designer and archaeologist, finished the vessel and designed the sail plan and rig. She was built in Valenca, Bahia, Brazil, using only traditional tools and techniques of the 15th century. Her mission today is to educate the public on the "space shuttle" of the 15th century, and over one million students and teachers have visited the *Nina* since her completion in 1992. Starting in November 2004 the *Nina* will be in Nuevo Vallarta, Mexico taking passengers on 2-hour day sails. The ship is available for filming and charters. Look for our new caravel coming to the Cayman Islands in winter 2005.

Who sails: families and individuals of all ages
Program type: Day sailing
Designer: John Sarsfield/Jonathon Nance
Built: 1988-1991: Valenca, Brazil, John Sarsfield/Jonathon Nance/Ralph Eric Nicholson
Coast Guard certification: Attraction Vessel
Crew: 6 **Trainees-passengers:** 50 day sails
Contact: Morgan P. Sanger, Captain/Director, Columbus Foundation, Box 305179, St. Thomas, VI 00803
Tel: 284-495-4618
Fax: 284-495-4616
E-mail: columfnd@surfbvi.com
Website: www.thenina.com

Flag: Canada
Rig: Gaff rigged staysail schooner
Homeport:
Midland, Ontario, Canada
Normal cruising waters:
Southern Georgian Bay
Sparred length: 60'
Draft: 6' 3"
Beam: 13' 6"
Rig height: 60'
Sail area: 1,265 square feet
Hull: Fiberglass over triple
planked wood

NISKA

Niska was built on the Chippewa-Ojibway Reserve in Rama, Ontario. Hence the name *Niska*, ("Neis Kah" the language of the Cree of James Bay) means the bird known as the Canada Goose. *Niska* is an adaptation of the 1850s clipper schooners of the East Coast of Canada and the United States. As well as strength, her designer/owner has paid extreme attention to details on this sleek, elegant, handcrafted ship: From the traditional clipper bow which enables her to swim smoothly and maintain a dry foredeck to the hand carved trailboards on the bow and quarter badges at the stern. The sails were developed by her designer/owner as well, and were built at the same loft as the sails for the original *Bluenose* in Lunenburg, Nova Scotia. Even the ends of the spars are traditionally painted red to protect the ship from "evil spirits." She is set apart by the 11-foot tall Canada Goose in full flight on her main sail. *Niska* is able to accommodate 12 passengers for day sails or 4 passengers for overnight passages.

Who sails: School Groups and individual 12 years of age and older
Built: 1974 – 1985: Ontario, Canada, Heiko Bank
Contact: Contact: Captain Heiko Bank, PO Box 124, Cumberland Beach, Ontario L0K 1G0 Canada
Tel: 705-330-9930
Fax: 705-689-6344
E-mail: neiskah1@yahoo.ca
Website: www.geocities.com/neiskah1

SPECIFICATIONS

Flag: USA
Rig: Gaff schooner, 2-masted
Homeport: Norfolk, Virginia
Normal cruising waters: East Coast from Canada to the Gulf of Mexico
Sparred length: 59'
LOA: 51'
LOD: 51'
LWL: 48'
Draft: 6' 6"
Beam: 15' 3"
Rig height: 50'
Sail area: 1,700 square feet
Freeboard: 4' 6"
Tons: 38 GRT
Power: Diesel
Hull: Steel

NORFOLK REBEL

Captain Lane Briggs' "tugantine" is a favorite flagship for sail-assisted working vessels and is credited with a 1984 circumnavigation of Virginia." The *Norfolk Rebel* is a familiar site to all involved in sail training and tall ships events up and down the Chesapeake. In 2000 she participated in Tall Ships 2000®, traveling as far as Halifax, Nova Scotia from her homeport of Norfolk, Virginia. In 2001 she participated in the TALL SHIPS CHALLENGE® series in the Great Lakes. A long-time supporter of sail training, Captain Lane Briggs was the 2001 recipient of the ASTA Lifetime Achievement Award.

Who sails: Individuals of all ages
Program type: Sail training for crew and apprentices; sea education in local maritime history and ecology based on informal, in-house programming; dockside interpretation
Season: Year-round
Designer: Merritt N. Walter
Built: 1980: Howdy Bailey, Norfolk, Virginia
Crew: 3 day sails, 6 overnight **Trainees-passengers:** 3
Contact: Captain Lane Briggs, Owner/Master, Rebel Marine Service, Inc., 1553 Bayville Street, Norfolk, VA 23503 USA
Tel: 804-588-6022 **Fax:** 804-588-7102
E-mail: tugantine@aol.com
Website: www.schoonerman.com/rebel.htm

Flag: USA
Rig: Viking longship (single square sail)
Homeport: Wilmington, Delaware
Normal cruising waters:
Chesapeake Bay, Delaware River, Jersey Shore, New York Bay, Hudson River, and Long Island Sound
Sparred length: 40'
LOD: 32'
LWL: 30'
Draft: 3'
Beam: 9'
Rig height: 30'
Sail area: 297 square feet
Freeboard: 3'
Tons: 2 GRT
Power: 19 HP Volvo Penta diesel sail drive
Hull: Fiberglass

NORSEMAN

Built in 1992, the *Norseman* offers people a glimpse of Viking culture and reminds everyone of the first discovery of North America by Europeans; Leif Ericson and his fellow Vikings, who sailed from Greenland in about the year 1000 to explore the new lands to the west. Crewmembers appear in full Viking costume, share their interests in Viking culture and their Scandinavian heritage, and practice their sailing and rowing skills. Over the years the *Norseman* has appeared in sailing events concentrating on the Mid-Atlantic region of the US, but traveling where invited. The organization has also traveled to Stockholm, Sweden, St. Petersburg, Russia, and Newfoundland, Canada. The *Norseman's* operating season runs from March to November. The earlier months are devoted to cleanup and training, and the majority of the events are held in the summer months. Training is provided year-round and the crewmembers bring Viking history to local schools off-season. The Leif Ericson Day celebration, held every October 9, is the organizations "main event", and is held in Philadelphia, Pennsylvania.

Who sails: Students and individuals of all ages
Program type: Sail training for volunteer crew and apprentices; sea education in maritime history relevant to Viking period; dockside interpretation during port visits
Designer: Applecraft, Inc.
Built: 1992: Isle of Man, UK, Applecraft, Inc.
Crew: 7-12 **Trainees-passenger:** 7-12
Contact: Marty Martinson, President or Dave Segermark, Captain, Leif Ericson Viking Ship, Inc., 4919 Township Line Rd. #303, Drexel Hill, PA 19026-5017 USA
Tel: Marty Martinson: 610-566-8065   Dave Segermark) 410-275-8516
Fax: 410-275-2633
E-mail: info@vikingship.org
Website: www.vikingship.org

NORTH WIND

SPECIFICATIONS

Flag: USA
Rig: Staysail schooner
Homeport: Philadelphia, Pennsylvania
Normal cruising waters: Delaware and Chesapeake Bays
LOA: 75'
LOD: 57'
LWL: 47'
Draft: 8'
Beam: 16'
Rig height: 70'
Freeboard: 5'
Sail area: 1,457 square feet
Tons: 40 GRT
Power: Volvo diesel
Hull: Steel

Philadelphia City Sail, Inc. is a nonprofit educational organization that inspires Philadelphia area youth to value themselves and their education, with a focus on reaching underserved populations. Through sailing and maritime topics, students gain hands-on experiences while learning about the environment, science, mathematics, and maritime arts. Philadelphia City Sail empowers youth to think critically and act responsibly as they expand their worldview.

Who sails: Middle through high school students and individuals of all ages
Program type: Sail training for Philadelphia youth in the maritime arts and sciences
Designer: Woodin and Marin
Built: 1995: Treworgy Yachts, FL
Crew: 3 - 5 **Trainees - passengers:** 30 day sails, 12 overnight
Coast Guard certification: Passenger Vessel (Subchapter T)
Contact: Michele Raymond, Executive Director or Brett Hart, Captain, Philadelphia City Sail, 475 N. 5th Street, Philadelphia, PA 19123 USA
Tel: 215-413-0451
Fax: 215-422-0737
E-mail: brett@citysail.org
Website: www.citysail.org

SPECIFICATIONS

Flag: UK
Rig: Schooner, two-masted
Normal cruising waters: Eastern Caribbean
Sparred length: 115'
LOA: 88'
LOD: 73'
LWL: 65'
Draft: 9'
Beam: 20'
Rig height: 92'
Sail area: 4,600 square feet
Freeboard: 5'
Tons: 70 GRT
Power: 210 HP diesel
Hull: Steel

OCEAN STAR

Launched in 1991 as the school ship for Ocean Navigator Magazine, *Ocean Star* now sails under the banner of Sea-mester programs as a college level semester voyage. Sea-mester programs offer 20, 40 and 80-day semesters aboard that are based on principles of experiential and adventure education. Learning through interaction and practical activities, the primary academic foci of oceanography, marine science, communication, and leadership skills development are brought from the textbook into real-life application. Under the guidance of professional staff, our students earn college credits for both academic and vocational activities, while piloting *Ocean Star* throughout the islands of Lesser Antilles. Along the way the crew visit up to 20 individual Caribbean islands, undertaking research and service projects with local government and private organizations while simultaneously working toward certificates in sailing and scuba diving. No experience is necessary. Programs are available to high school seniors, high school graduates, and college-aged students.

Who sails: 12th grade high school students (fall semester), high school graduates and college age students (fall, spring, and summer)
Program type: Experiential education semesters for high school graduates and college students; accredited academics with sail and scuba training; service projects and adventure travel
Designer: Bill Peterson
Built: 1991: Norfolk, VA, Marine Metals
Crew: Crew: 4   **Trainees-passengers:** 14
Contact: Sea-mester Programs, PO Box 5477, Sarasota, FL 34277 USA
Tel: 941-924-6789 or 800-317-6789
Fax: 941-924-6075
E-mail: info@seamester.com
Website: www.seamester.com

SPECIFICATIONS

Flag: Canada
Rig: Marconi rigged ketch
Homeport: Esquimalt, British Columbia, Canada
LOA: 102'
LOD: 91'
LWL: 19'
Draft: 10'
Beam: 19'
Rig height: 67' 8"
Sail area: 15,700 square feet
Freeboard: 6' 8" (forward) 4' 9" (aft)
Power: 261 HP Detroit Diesel

HMCS ORIOLE

The oldest commissioned ship in the Canadian Navy has a pedigree that goes back to 1880 when George Gooderham sailed the first *Oriole* as the flagship of the Royal Canadian Yacht Club of Toronto. Gooderham, who was for several years Commodore of the Toronto club, built *Oriole II* in 1886 and *Oriole III* in 1909. In 1921, the last of the *Orioles* - then called *Oriole IV*, was thought to be the most majestic of all R.C.Y.C. flagships. She was started by the Toronto Dominon Shipbuilding company but due to labor problems, was completed by George Lawley & Sons, a Boston shipyard. She was launched at Neponset, Mass, June 4, 1921, commissioned *HMCS Oriole* June 19, 1952 and two years later the navy moved her to the West Coast to become a training vessel to VENTURE the Naval Officer Training Center. She was purchased by the Royal Canadian Navy in 1957. HMCS *Oriole* is both the oldest vessel and the longest serving commissioned ship in the Canadian Navy. Her distinctive red, white, and blue spinnaker displays an orange oriole.

Program type: Training vessel of the Canadian Navy
Built: 1921
Crew: 5 **Trainees-passengers:** 16
Contact: Embassy of Canada, 501 Pennsylvania Avenue, NW, Washington, DC 20001 USA
Tel: 202-682-1740
Fax: 202-682-7726

Flag: Canada
Rig: Gaff topsail schooner
Homeport: Victoria, British Columbia, Canada
Normal cruising waters: Coastal waters of British Columbia
Sparred length: 138' 7"
LOA: 115'
LOD: 108' 7"
LWL: 89' 6"
Draft: 11' 6"
Beam: 22' 2"
Rig height: 115'
Sail area: 7,564 square feet
Freeboard: 3' 7"
Tons: 175 GRT
Power: Twin diesels
Hull: Wood

Photo by Mark Kaarremaa

PACIFIC GRACE

Built over seven winters, *Pacific Grace* was launched in her homeport of Victoria, British Columbia on October 9, 1999. She replaces the *Robertson II*, one of Canada's last original Grand Banks fishing schooners, and is built along the lines of the old ship using traditional methods. After three years sailing, *Pacific Grace* embarked on a nine-month offshore voyage in 2003 which saw her travel down the west coast of North and Central America and on to exotic ports of call in the South Pacific. During the summer months of July and August 10-day trips are available to anyone aged 13 - 25. In the spring and fall shorter school programs are offered. Each year over one thousand young people participate aboard *Pacific Grace* in an experience which combines all aspects of shipboard life from galley chores to helmsmanship, with formal instruction in navigation, pilotage, seamanship and small boat handling. S.A.L.TS. is a registered charitable organization that seeks to develop through shipboard life in a Christian context, the spiritual, mental and physical potential of young people.

Who sails: Students and young adults ages 13 – 25
Program type: Sail training for paying trainees
Season: March through October
Built: 1999: Victoria, British Columbia, Canada, SALTS
Canadian Coast Guard certification: Passenger Vessel, Sailing School Vessel
Crew: 5 **Trainees-passengers:** 40 day sails, 30 overnight
Contact: Captain Martyn J. Clark, Executive Director, Sail and Life Training Society (SALTS), PO Box 5014, Station B, Victoria, British Columbia V8R 6N3 Canada
Tel: 250-383-6811
Fax: 250-383-7781
E-mail: info@salts.ca
Website: www.salts.ca

PACIFIC SWIFT

SPECIFICATIONS

Flag: Canada
Rig: Square topsail schooner, two-masted
Homeport: Victoria, British Columbia, Canada
Normal cruising waters: Coastal waters of British Columbia
Sparred length: 111'
LOA: 81'
LOD: 77' 3"
LWL: 73'
Draft: 10' 8"
Beam: 20' 6"
Rig height: 88'
Sail area: 5,205 square feet
Freeboard: 3' 6"
Tons: 98 GRT
Power: 220 HP diesel
Hull: Wood

Built as a working exhibit at Expo '86 in Vancouver, British Columbia, the *Pacific Swift* has sailed over 100,000 deep-sea miles on training voyages for young crewmembers. Her offshore travels have taken her to Australia and Europe, to remote communities on Easter and Pitcairn Islands, and to many other unusual and far-flung ports of call. When not offshore, the *Swift* provides coastal sail training programs among the cruising grounds of the Pacific Northwest, which include shorter school programs in the spring and fall, and 10-day summer trips open to anyone aged 13 to 25. Each year over one thousand young people participate in an experience, which combines all aspects of shipboard life, from galley chores to helmsmanship, with formal instruction in navigation, pilotage, seamanship, and small boat handling. Rooted in Christian values, SALTS believes that training under sail provides the human spirit a real chance to develop and mature. SALTS received the 1998 Sail Training Program of the Year Award from the American Sail Training Association.

Who sails: Individuals and groups
Program type: Offshore and coastal sail training
Season: March through October
Built: 1986: Vancouver, British Columbia, Canada, SALTS
Canadian Coast Guard certification: Passenger vessel, Sailing School Vessel
Crew: 5 **Trainees-passengers:** 35 Age: 13 – 25
Contact: Captain Martyn J. Clark, Executive Director, Sail and Life Training Society (SALTS), PO Box 5014, Station B, Victoria, British Columbia V8R 6N3 Canada
Tel: 250-383-6811
Fax: 250-383-7781
E-mail: info@salts.ca
Website: www.salts.ca

SPECIFICATIONS

Flag: USA
Rig: Cutter
Homeport: Portland, Maine
Normal cruising waters: Casco Bay, Caribbean
Sparred length: 58'
LOD: 58'
LWL: 40'
Draft: 8' 1"
Beam: 12' 4"
Rig height: 68'
Sail area: 1,308 square feet
Freeboard: 4' 4"
Tons: 24 GRT
Power: 60 HP
Hull: Aluminum

PALAWAN

Designed in 1965, built by Derecktor's for Thomas Watson as an ocean racer under the CCA rating rule, *Palawan* is a landmark in yacht design. She led the move from the full keel, with a fin and skeg configuration, though she retains the wineglass sections of more traditional boats. Olins Stephens declared her "perhaps the easiest steering boat I ever drew." Maine Maritime Academy used her in their sailing program for over 10 years, as *Omega*, and many have learned offshore sailing and buoy racing under her tutelage. *Palawan* has operated as a passenger vessel since 1988, in Portland, Maine. She serves both individuals and groups, and is easy to find at the Long Wharf, by DiMillo's Floating Restaurant. Winters may be spent in the Caribbean, with up to 6 crew aboard.

Who sails: Students, adults, and groups
Program type: Sail training with team-building activities for paying trainees; passenger day sails and overnight passages
Designer: Olin Stephen
Built: 1965: New York, New York, Derecktor
Coast Guard certification: Passenger Vessel (Subchapter T)
Crew: 2 day sails, 3 overnight **Trainees-passengers:** 24 day sails, 6 overnight
Contact: Captain Tom Woodruff, Palawan Services, Inc., PO Box 9715-240, Portland, ME 04104 USA
Tel: 207-773-2163
Fax: 207-781-8281
E-mail: palawan@nlis.net
Website: www.sailpalawan.us

Photo by Thad Koza

SPECIFICATIONS

Flag: Russia
Rig: Full-rigged ship
Homeport:
Vladivostok, Russia
Normal cruising waters:
Worldwide
Sparred length: 356' 4"
Draft: 22' 4"
Beam: 45' 9"
Hull: Steel

PALLADA

Pallada is the fifth ship of the *Dar Mlodziezy*-class built in Poland during the 1980s. Unlike her white- hulled sisters, *Pallada* has a black hull with false gunports and resembles the great Russian Barque *Kruzenshtern*. She is named for the Greek goddess Pallas Athena. She is owned by Dalryba, a conglomerate of fishing companies, and offers sail training to foreign marine-college cadets. Though her homeport is in Vladivostok, which is on the far eastern coast of Russia, *Pallada* voyages widely. She visited the West Coast of the United States in 1989 and Europe in 1991; participated in the European Columbus Regatta in 1992; completed a circumnavigation to celebrate the 500th anniversary of the Russian navy in 1996; and sailed in the 1997 Hong Kong to Osaka race. *Pallada* sails with a compliment of 143 cadets and a permanent crew of 56 officers, teachers, and professionals. With twenty-six sails and masts soaring 162 feet above the deck, *Pallada* combines traditional sail training with a modern maritime college curriculum.

Who sails: Marine-college cadets
Program type: Sail training and sea education for marine-college cadets
Season: Year-round
Designer: Zygmunt Choren
Built: 1989: Gdansk, Poland
Crew: Crew: 56   **Trainees-passengers:** 143
Contact: Evgeny N. Malyavin, Far Eastern State Technical Fisheries University, 52-B, Lugovaya Street, Vladivostok 690950 Russia
Tel: +0117 42 32 44-03-06
Fax: +011 7 42 32 44-24-32

SPECIFICATIONS

Flag: USA
Rig: Barque, four-masted
Homeport: New York, New York
Sparred length: 377' 6"
LOD: 320'
Draft: 16'
Beam: 45' 8"
Rig height: 170' 5"
Sail area: 44,132 square feet
Freeboard: 3' 6"
Tons: 3,100 GRT
Hull: Steel

PEKING

Peking was launched in 1911 at Hamburg, Germany by the Blohm & Voss shipyard. She was owned by the F. Laeisz Company of that port, who used her to carry fuel and manufactured goods to the West Coast of South America, around Cape Horn, and return to European ports with nitrate mined in northern Chile. With her four-masted barque rig, steel hull and masts, and mid-ship bridge deck, *Peking* represents the final generation of sailing ships built for world trade. Though a product of the 20th century, she still sailed in the traditional way, with few labor saving devices or safety features. Her crew followed the standard sailing vessel routine of four hours on duty and four hours off duty, around the clock, seven days a week. *Peking* was retired in 1933, when steamers using the Panama Canal took over what was left of the nitrate trade. She served as a nautical school for boys, moored on a British River, until she was acquired by the South Street Seaport Museum in 1974. She now serves as a floating dockside exhibit. Educational programs for children and young adults take place on board, with a wet lab on the ship interpreting the biology of New York harbor.

Program type: Sea education in marine science, maritime history, and ecology based on informal, in-house programming
Built: 1911: Hamburg, Germany, Blohm & Voss
Contact: South Street Seaport Museum, 207 Front Street, New York, NY, 10038 USA
Tel: 212-748-8681
Fax: 212-748-8610
Website: www.southstseaport.org

SPECIFICATIONS

Flag: USA
Rig: Gaff schooner, two-masted
Homeport: Glen Cove, New York
Normal cruising waters: Long Island Sound
Sparred length: 71'
LOA: 59'
LOD: 56'
LWL: 54'
Draft: 6'
Beam: 16'
Rig height: 60'
Freeboard: 4'
Sail area: 1,600 square feet
Tons: 40 GRT
Power: 80 HP Ford/Lehman
Hull: Steel

PHOENIX

The coastal schooner *Phoenix* was built on Long Island, New York and launched in 1984 as a replica of the type of vessels plying the waters of Long Island Sound at the turn of the century. *Phoenix* was first used as a cargo vessel between Port Jefferson, New York and Bridgeport, Connecticut, before carrying passengers over the same route for day trip excursions. In the mid-1980s the Nassau County Board of Cooperative Services used her as a platform for their marine biology public school education program. The vessel was later sold and moved to the Bahamas. In 1993 *Phoenix* returned to Long Island and was acquired by the Coastal Ecology Learning Program, a nonprofit educational corporation. C.E.L.P. offers shipboard environmental education programs for schoolchildren, families, and adults. *Phoenix* is the training ship for the Long Island US Naval Sea Cadets. The vessel is also available for private functions, children's birthday parties, corporate events, etc. *Phoenix* travels the length of Long Island Sound, offering programs throughout the region.

Who sails: Students of all ages, individuals and families
Program type: Sail training for volunteer and paying trainees; sea education in marine science, ecology, and maritime history. Affiliated with the Long Island US Naval Sea Cadets
Designer: Walter Merrit
Built: 1984: Patchogue, NY, Greg Brazier
Coast Guard certification: Passenger vessel (Subchapter T)
Crew: 3 **Trainees-passengers:** 2
Contact: Captain Dennis F. Watson, Coastal Ecology Learning Program, Inc., PO Box 473, Huntington, NY 11743 USA
Tel: 631- 85-CELP
Fax: 631-385-2357
E-mail: celp@optonline.net
Website: www.coastalecology.org

Flag: UK
Rig: Topsail schooner
Homeport: Gloucester
Normal cruising waters:
UK & Northern Europe
Sparred length: 96' 6"
LOA: 65'"
LOD: 61' 4"
LWL: 58' 4"
Draft: 7' 4"
Beam: 15' 4"
Rig height: 75' 0"
Sail area: 2,287 square feet
Freeboard: 6'
Tons: 67 GRT
Power: Volva Penta TAMD 145
Hull: Wood

PICKLE

Pickle will tour the UK in 2005 to commemorate the 'Battle of Trafalgar Bicentenary' and to celebrate 'Sea Britain 2005'. The *Pickle* has been built as a sail training vessel to a 18th century design for fast, armed top sail schooners used at that time by the British Royal Navy. They were used for carrying messages and small cargo to service the Fleet. The original HMS *Pickle* brought the sad news of Lord Nelson's death and Vice Admiral Collingwood's dispatches of the battle back to England in 1805. The 1000 mile gale ridden voyage from Cadiz to Falmouth took 9 days. During 'SeaBritain 2005' *Pickle* will take crew, mainly young people between 16 and 25 years, sailing with the Ocean Youth Trust on the 'Nelson Tour' visiting major ports and delivering the Dispatch and Nelson's Legacy to each city. After 2005 the *Pickle* will be used for sail training program activities.

Who Sails: 16 to 25 years
Program type: Sail Training
Season: April to October
Designer: Grumant
Built: 1995: Petrosawodsk, St Petersburg, Askold
Crew: 14 **Trainees-Passengers:** 10
Certification: Finland 2004, Re-registered United Kingdom 2004/5
Contact: Barry Johnson, Director, OCEAN YOUTH TRUST (OYT), 102 Ewe Lamb Lane, Bramcote, Nottingham, Nottinghamshire NG9 3JW United Kingdom
Tel: 0044 115 939 9825 & 0044 133 266 8253
Fax: 0044 133 266 8253
E-mail: office@oyteast.org.uk
Website: www.oyteast.org.uk

SPECIFICATIONS

Flag: Cook Islands
Rig: Barque, 3-masted
Homeport: Lunenburg, Nova Scotia, Canada
Normal cruising waters: Rarotonga, Cook Islands, South Pacific; worldwide. Worldwide service with refits in Lunenburg, Nova Scotia, Canada
Sparred length: 176'
LOA: 148'
LOD: 135'
Draft: 14' 6"
Beam: 24'
Rig height: 100'
Sail area: 12,450 square feet
Freeboard: 6'
Tons: 284 GRT
Power: 130'
Hull: Steel

PICTON CASTLE

The 284-ton Barque *Picton Castle* is a traditionally rigged and operated sail training ship dedicated to making voyages around the world under square sail. In the spring of 2005 the *Picton Castle* will cast off on her fourth global circumnavigation. She will return in June 2006. On this ocean odyssey, the ship and her crew will sail more than 30,000 sea miles in the trade winds across the South Pacific Ocean, Indian Ocean and South and North Atlantic Oceans, putting in at remote islands and tropical ports that include Panama, Galapagos, Pitcairn Island, Rarotonga, Fiji, Vanuatu, Bali, Madagascar, Cape Town, St. Helena, and the Lesser Antilles of the Caribbean. As a training ship all on board work, stand watch, and learn the way of a square-rigged sailing ship. Workshops are conducted in wire and rope rigging, sail making, boat handling, navigation, and practical seamanship. The ship also delivers much-needed educational material and other supplies to the remote islands she visits. In the summer after returning from the circumnavigation, the *Picton Castle* will make shorter voyages in the North Atlantic and along the coast. The *Picton Castle* is outfitted to the highest standard with safety gear and equipment. She is strong, seaworthy home afloat for young adventurers devoted to learning the art of deep-water seafaring. Learn more from the web site at www.picton-castle.com.

Who sails: Those over 18 years old on the world voyage, 16 years and up on shorter training cruises
Program type: Deep water sail training; maritime education in cooperation with various institutes and organized groups; comprehensive instruction in the arts of seafaring under sail; dockside school visits and receptions; charitable/educational medical and supply to isolated islands
Designer: Masting and rigging, decks and layout: Daniel Moreland, MM - Stability, calculations and ballasting: Daniel Blachley, NA/ME Webb Institute
Certification: Registered and certified as a Sail Training Vessel for worldwide service by the Cook Islands Ministry of Transportation
Crew: 10 **Trainees-passengers:** 40 coed
Contact: David Robinson, Barque PICTON CASTLE Voyages, PO Box 1076, Lunenburg, Nova Scotia B0J 2C0 Canada
Tel: 902-634-9984 or USA 617-515-1033 **Fax:** 902-634-9985
E-mail: info@picton-castle.com
Websites: www.picton-castle.com and www.worldwise.org

SPECIFICATIONS

Flag: USA
Rig: Snow brig
Homeport: Dana Point, California
Normal cruising waters: Point Conception to Ensenada, Mexico
Sparred length: 130'
LOD: 98'
Draft: 9'
Beam: 24' 6"
Rig height: 104'
Sail area: 7,600 square feet
Freeboard: 8'
Tons: 99 GRT
Power: Diesel
Hull: Wood

PILGRIM

The Pilgrim is a full-scale replica of the ship immortalized by Richard Henry Dana in his classic book *Two Years Before the Mast*. Owned and operated by the Ocean Institute, *Pilgrim* is dedicated to multidisciplinary education. During the school year, the Ocean Institute offers an 18-hour, award-winning living history program that offers a hands-on exploration of literature, California history, and group problem solving in which crewmembers recreate the challenge of shipboard life. Students live like sailors of the 1830s as they hoist barrels, row in the harbor, stand night watches, swab the decks, and learn to cope with a stern captain. On summer evenings, audiences are treated to the sights and sounds of the sea as the *Pilgrim's* decks come alive with theatrical and musical performances. In late summer the *Pilgrim* sails on her annual cruise with an all volunteer crew to ports along the California coast as a goodwill ambassador for the City of Dana Point. She returns in September to lead the annual tall ship parade and festival.

Who sails: Student groups and individual volunteers
Program type: Maritime living history and volunteer sail training
Season: Year-round
Designer: Ray Wallace
Built: 1945: Holbaek, Denmark, A. Nielsen
Coast Guard certification: Uninspected Vessel
Crew: 35 **Dockside visitors:** 50
Contact: Daniel Stetson, Director of Maritime Affairs Ocean Institute, 24200 Dana Point, Dana Point, CA 92629 USA
Tel: 949-496-2274
Fax: 949-496-4296
E-mail: dstetson@ocean-institute.org
Website: www.ocean-institute.org

PIONEER

SPECIFICATIONS

Flag: USA
Rig: Gaff topsail schooner, two-masted
Homeport: New York, New York
Normal cruising waters: New York Harbor, Hudson River, and Atlantic Coast
Sparred length: 102'
LOA: 65'
LOD: 65'
LWL: 58' 11"
Draft: 4' 8" (min.) 12' (max.)
Beam: 21' 6"
Rig height: 79'
Sail area: 2,700 square feet
Tons: 43 GRT
Power: Diesel
Hull: Steel

The first iron sloop built in the United States *Pioneer* is the only surviving American iron-hulled sailing vessel. Built in 1885 by the *Pioneer* Iron Foundary in Chester, Pennsylvania, she sailed the Delaware River, hauling sand for use in the iron molding process. Ten years later *Pioneer* was converted to a schooner rig for ease of sail handling. In 1966, the then abandoned vessel was acquired and rebuilt by Russell Grinnell, Jr. of Gloucester, Massachusetts. In 1970 the fully restored schooner was donated to the South Street Seaport Museum. Today historic *Pioneer* serves as a vital education platform. Students of all ages can come on history and other curricular subjects during the hands-on program. *Pioneer* also offers corporate and private charters, Elderhostel day programs, and public sails.

Who sails: School groups from elementary school through college, charter groups, museum members, and the general public
Program type: Sail training for crew and volunteers; hands-on education sails designed to augment school curriculums in history, ecology, marine science, physics, and math; corporate and private charters, Elderhostel programs, and public sails
Season: April through October
Built: 1885: Marcus Hook, PA, Pioneer Iron Works (rebuilt 1968; Somerset, MA)
Coast Guard certification: Passenger Vessel (Subchapter T)
Crew: 3
Contact: South Street Seaport Museum, 207 Front Street, New York, NY 10038 USA
Tel: 212-748-8684
Fax: 212-748-8610
Website: www.southstseaport.org

SPECIFICATIONS

Flag: USA
Rig: Brig
Homeport: Gloucester, Massachusetts
Sparred Length: 72'
Draft: 7'
Beam: 18'
Rig Height: 55'
Sail Area: 3,000 square feet
Hull: Steel

POINCARE

Poincare (pwan-car-ay) can carry up to six passengers on day trips. They offer an extensive day charter schedule, sailing from East Boston, Massachusetts, often in the company of their sister ship *Formidable*. *Poincare* is rigged as a brig and sets three square sails on each mast.

Contact: Captain Keating Wilcox, Longmeadow Way, Box 403, Hamilton, MA 01936-0403 USA
Tel: 866-921-9674
Fax: 978-468-1954
E-mail: kwillcox@shore.net
Website: www.tallshipformidable.com

SPECIFICATIONS

Flag: USA
Rig: topsail schooner
Homeport: Baltimore, Maryland
Normal cruising waters: Chesapeake Bay
Sparred length: 157'
LOD: 100'
Draft: 12' 6"
Beam: 26' 4"
Rig height: 107'
Freeboard: 6'
Sail area: 10,442 square feet
Tons: 97 GRT
Power: 2 165 hp Caterpillar Diesel engines
Hull: Wood

PRIDE OF BALTIMORE II

The *Pride of Baltimore II* is a top-sail schooner built to the lines of an 1812-era Baltimore Clipper. Owned by the State of Maryland and operated by *Pride of Baltimore*, Inc., her mission is threefold: to promote Maryland trade and tourism; to represent the goodwill of all Maryland's citizens; and to provide a unique education platform through onboard activities and the Internet for American history and marine sciences. *Pride II* is available for charter and for dockside and sailing receptions in each of her destinations. She can accommodate up to six paying passengers for hire as "working guest crew" between ports of call. Maryland's Pride maintains an international sailing schedule. She sails with two rotating professional captains and a crew of eleven. Crew positions are open to qualified individuals. The *Pride of Baltimore II* maintains an international sailing schedule.

Who sails: Minimum professional crewmember age is 18; overnight guest crew minimum age is 16. Day sail minors must be accompanied by an adult and supervised one-on-one. There's no maximum age limit on crew or passengers
Program type: Economic development venue and goodwill ambassador for the State of Maryland and Port of Baltimore
Season: Spring, Summer, Fall
Designer: Thomas C. Gillmer
Built: 1987-88: Baltimore, MD, G. Peter Boudreau
Coast Guard certification: Passenger Vessel (Subchapter T)
Crew: 12 **Trainees-passengers:** 6 paying guest crew (passengers) for overnight sails; 35 paying passengers for day sails, no trainees/no volunteers
Contact: Linda E. Christenson, Esq., Executive Director, Pride of Baltimore, Inc., 401 East Pratt Street, Suite 222, Baltimore, MD 21202 USA
Tel: 410-539-1151; toll-free 888-55-PRIDE **Fax:** 410-539-1190
E-mail: pride2@pride2.org **Website:** www.marylandspride.org

SPECIFICATIONS

Flag: United Kingdom
Rig: Brig
Homeport: Portsmouth, England
Normal cruising waters: UK, Europe, Mediterranean, Canaries, Azores and Caribbean
Sparred length: 195'
LOA: 159'
LOD: 159'
LWL: 133'
Draft: 15'
Beam: 33'
Rig height: 148'
Sail area: 12,503 square feet
Tons: 493 GRT
Power: 2x MTU 33OKW

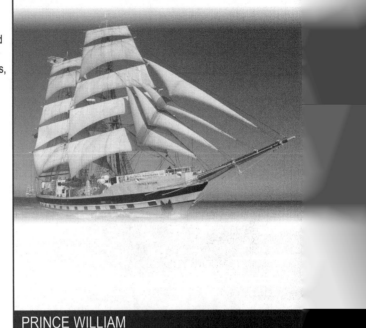

PRINCE WILLIAM

Prince William is one of the two purposely built sail training vessels owned by the Tall Ships Youth Trust. She is a 60 meter, steel hulled, square-rigged brig built in Appledore, Devon, and was launched in 2001. She is the first and only ship to proudly carry the name of the young prince. The Tall Ships Youth Trust, incorporating the Sail Training Association, is a registered charity founded in 1956 and is dedicated to the personal development of young people aged 16-25 through the crewing of tall ships. Every year over 2,000 people aged 16 to 75 from all over the world sail on either *Prince William* or her identical sister ship *Stavros S Niarchos*. *Prince William* operates all year round. In the summer months she frequents European and Mediterranean waters and during the winter she may head south for the Canaries, Azores and Caribbean. Youth voyages for 16-25 year olds last from 7-14 nights whereas 18+ voyages range from day sails to a 24 night Trans-Atlantic.

Who sails: Groups and individuals of all ages
Program type: Sail training for paying trainees
Season: Year-round
Designer: Burness, Corlett & Partners & Captain Mike Willoughby
Built: 2001: North Devon, United Kingdom, Appledore Shipbuilders
Crew: 6 Permanent and 13 Volunteer Crew **Trainees-passengers:** 44 day sails, 48 overnight
Contact: Tall Ships Youth Trust, 2A The Hard, Portsmouth, Hampshire P01 3PT England
Tel: +44 (0) 23 9283 2055
Fax: +44 (0) 23 9281 5769
E-mail: tallships@tallships.org
Website: www.tallships.org

SPECIFICATIONS

Flag: USA
Rig: Square topsail sloop
Homeport: Providence, Rhode Island
Normal cruising waters: East Coast US
Sparred length: 110'
LOA: 65"
LOD: 61'
LWL: 59'
Draft: 10'
Beam: 20'
Rig height: 94'
Sail area: 3,470 square feet
Tons: 59 GRT
Power: 170 HP diesel

PROVIDENCE

The *Providence* is a replica of one of the first ships of the American Navy. Built as a merchant ship in the 1760s. the *Providence* (ex-Katy) went on to become the first command of John Paul Jones and one of the most successful American ships to fight in the Revolutionary War. After a successful career in which she sank or captured 40 British ships, she earned the nickname "Lucky Sloop." John Paul Jones said of her "She was the first and she was the best." The Continental Sloop *Providence* is a statewide resource administered by the *Providence* Maritime Heritage Foundation and the City of *Providence*, Rhode Island. The primary mission of the *Providence* is to inspire and educate the thousands of Rhode Islanders served each year and to keep Rhode Island's rich maritime heritage alive. As Rhode Island's Flagship, the Sloop *Providence* serves youth and adults through the "Classroom Under Sail" programs, which illuminate Rhode Island's maritime history and the importance of the city of *Providence* in our nation's early development. The Sloop *Providence* also serves as the Ocean State's sailing ambassador, representing Rhode Island at waterfront festivals along the East Coast.

Who sails: School groups from elementary school through college, individuals and families
Program type: Sail training for crew and volunteers; passenger day sails; dockside interpretation at homeport and during port visits; sea education in marine science, maritime history, cadet program and more for school groups of all ages
Season: April through November
Designer: Charles W. Wittholz
Built: 1976: Melville, RI
Crew: 5-8 **Trainees-passengers:** 40 day sails, 4-6 overnight
Contact: Robert Hofmann, Executive Director, Providence Maritime Heritage Foundation, 408 Broadway, Providence, RI 02909
Tel: 401-274-7447 **Fax:** 401-828-8788
E-mail: info_sloopprovidenceri@cox.net
Website: www.sloopprovidenceri.org

SPECIFICATIONS

Flag: USA
Rig: Gaff schooner, two-masted
Homeport: New Haven, Connecticut
Normal cruising waters: Long Island Sound
Sparred length: 91'
LOA: 65'
LOD: 62'
LWL: 58'
Draft: 4' 5" - 11'
Beam: 20'
Rig height: 77'
Freeboard: 5' 2"
Sail area: 2,400 square feet
Tons: 41 GRT
Power: 135 HP diesel
Hull: Wood

QUINNIPIACK

Built in 1984 for the passenger service, *Quinnipiack* now serves as the primary vessel for Schooner Sound Learning, an organization dedicated to teaching about the ecology of Long Island Sound. Since 1975, Schooner Sound Learning has taught in classrooms, on the shores, and aboard a variety of vessels. Participants of all ages study under sail and explore the ecology of the estuary while getting an introduction to maritime heritage and seamanship. Students work alongside the crew, learning the lessons in teamwork, self-reliance, flexibility and interdependence that only sailing vessels can teach. *Quinnipiack* programs complement traditional classroom studies in sciences, mathematics, geography, history, literature, folklore, and social studies. Hands on learning activities include collection, identification, and interpretation of estuarine organisms, land use, plankton study, piloting, sail handling, seamanship, sediment analysis, water chemistry, and weather. Internships are available for high school and college students to learn the operation and care of a traditional sailing vessel while sailing as crew. The *Quinnipiack* is also available for corporate charters and special events.

Who Sails: School groups from middle school through college, individuals, and families
Program type: Sail training for crew, apprentices, and trainees; sea education in marine science, maritime history, and ecology in cooperation with accredited schools and colleges and as informal, in-house programming; dockside interpretation during port visits; passenger day sails
Season: April – November
Designer: Philip Sheldon
Built: 1984: Milbridge, ME, Philip Sheldon
Coast Guard certification: Passenger vessel (subchapter T)
Crew: 5 **Trainees-passengers:** 40 day sails, 4-6 overnight
Contact: Beth McCabe, Executive Director/ Captain Jonathan Wisch, Schooner Sound Learning, 60 South Water Street, New Haven, CT 06519 USA
Tel: 203-865-1737 **Fax:** 203-624-8816
E-mail: SSL@schoonersoundlearning.org **Website:** www.schoonersoundlearning.org

Flag: USA
Rig: Schooner
Homeport: Southwest Harbor, ME
Normal cruising waters: Maine
Sparred length: 75'
LOA: 52'
LWL: 43'
Draft: 8'
Beam: 17'
Rig height: 75'
Freeboard: 4'
Sail area: 2,500 square feet
Tons: 52 GRT
Power: 108 HP diesel
Hull: Wood

RACHEL B JACKSON

The *Rachel B. Jackson* was built in Maine and is a working replica of an 1890s coastal schooner. Her sturdily built mahogany planking, oak frames, pine decks, shining brass fittings and exotic wood cabinetry recall the workmanship of days gone by. She gives her passengers the rare opportunity to experience an authentic vessel of another era. Originally put into service as a training vessel at Mystic Seaport, the *Rachel B. Jackson* now tours the eastern seaboard from Maine to the Caribbean. She represented the State of Maine in the Tall Ships® 2000 race from Bermuda to Boston then on to Halifax, NS. The *Rachel B. Jackson* was chartered by the National Geographic Society to do whale research off the coast of the Dominican Republic and she circumnavigated the world on a 3-year adventure. The current owners, Andrew and Steven Keblinsky, along with their family, completed a two year refit in May 1999. The *Rachel B. Jackson* is United States Coast Guard Certified and Inspected to carry 30 passengers. Her USCG Licensed Master and professional crew have many years of sailing experience.

Who sails: School groups from elementary through high school; individuals and families
Program type: Sail training for volunteer and paying trainees; sea education in marine science, maritime history, and ecology in cooperation with organized groups; passenger day sails; dockside interpretation during port visits.
Designer: Burt Frost
Built: 1982: Freeport, ME, George Emery
Coast Guard certification: Passenger vessel (Subchapter T)
Crew: 3 **Trainees-passengers:** 30 day sails
Contact: Andrew Keblinsky, Downeast Sailing Adventures, LLC, x 1252, Southwest Harbor, ME 04679 USA
Tel: 207-244-7813
E-mail: downeastsail@acadia.net
Website: www.downeastsail.com

SPECIFICATIONS

Flag: USA
Rig: Yawl
Homeport: Olympia, WA
Normal cruising waters:
Puget Sound, Canada Inland
Sparred length: 44'
LWL: 30'
Draft: 6'
Beam: 11'
Rig height: 57' 6"
Sail area: 722 square feet
Tons: 15 GRT
Power: Perkins 40
Hull: Wood

RESOLUTE

Three sailors, who have all been touched by the 44 foot Annapolis Yawl *Resolute*, unknowingly had a common dream, that dream was to keep her sailing and foster education in traditional nautical skills. Last summer, John Filmer, Joe Forest and Ralph Duncan crossed paths, and the result was the establishment of the *Resolute* Sailing Foundation, a non-profit organization established to teach traditional nautical skills, maritime history and an appreciation of the marine environment. The focus will be to teach youth groups, youths at risk and students at educational institutions. Built in 1939 for the U.S. Naval Academy at Annapolis, Maryland, *Resolute* was the third of twelve such yawls built for the Navy. Over the course of 20 years, it is estimated that some 70,000 American midshipmen trained aboard these vessels. Now the Resolute Sailing Foundation will continue that rich heritage and use *Resolute* to train future leaders with this historic yawl, just as she was used to train great leaders of the past. Young people who have the opportunity to sail on her will learn to overcome their fears, acquire traditional sailing skills, develop self-confidence and learn the necessity for personal responsibility and teamwork, an experience that only the challenge of sea and sail can provide.

Who sails: High school and college age students, adults and families
Program type: Sail training for volunteer crew and paying trainees; sea education in cooperation with accredited institutions
Season: Year round
Designer: Luders
Built: 1939: Stamford, CT, Luders
Coast Guard certification:
Crew: 2 **Trainees-passengers:** 10 day sails 5 overnight
Contact: Captain John Filmore, Resolute Sailing Foundation, PO Box 88639, Steilacoom, WA 98388 USA
Tel: 253-581-6291
E-mail: entrepreneur@qwest.net
Website: www.downeastsail.com

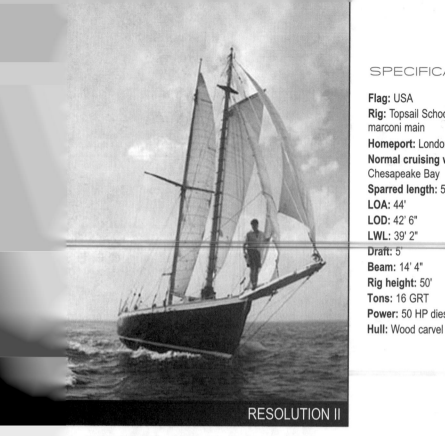

SPECIFICATIONS

Flag: USA
Rig: Topsail Schooner; gaff fore and marconi main
Homeport: Londontown, Maryland
Normal cruising waters: Chesapeake Bay
Sparred length: 50'
LOA: 44'
LOD: 42' 6"
LWL: 39' 2"
Draft: 5'
Beam: 14' 4"
Rig height: 50'
Tons: 16 GRT
Power: 50 HP diesel
Hull: Wood carvel

RESOLUTION II

Resolution II is representative of early coastal schooners of the Chesapeake Bay. She replaced her pinky schooner predecessor (*Resolution I*) in 2004 and is based at Londontown, Maryland. She sails the Chesapeake operated by Ship's Company, a maritime living history not-for-profit. SC provides period-dressed docent support for historical sites and maritime events in the Baltimore-DC-Annapolis region. SC's six sections include Circa 1800 (Navy/Marines), Civil War (Navy/Marines), singing Chanteymen, and Boat Group. *Resolution II* is a Class C tall ship and combined with historical reenactors can be engaged for dockside interpretation of circa 1800 (1775-1825), for charter, and for offshore mock cannon battles, within a day or two sail of Annapolis, Maryland. *Resolution II* and crew can interpret a wide variety of periods and roles and has two tenders (6 oar cutter / 4 oar jollyboat). Her baseline interpretation is a c.1800 armed tender despatch schooner, supporting USS *Enterprize*. Ship's Company supports activities of National Maritime Heritage Foundation to build/operate a full scale representation for youth education in Washington DC; Living Classrooms displaying Sloop of War *Constellation* in Baltimore; Hancock's Resolution farmstead; our nautical homeport Londontown; and many others.

Who sails: Ship's Company members/trainees and private or educational charters.
Program type: Living history educational programs dockside and offshore, dockside educational overnight adventures.
Season: April through November
Designer: Phil Bolger
Built: 1968: Ipswich, MA, Malanson & Sons
Coast Guard certification: Uninspected vessel
Crew: 2 to 14 including Ship's Company trainees **Trainees-Passengers:** 6 day sails, 6 overnight
Contact: Michael Bosworth, Ship's Company Boat Coordinator, Ship's Company RESOLUTION, 357 Ayr Hill Ave. NE, Vienna, VA 22180 USA
Tel: 703-864-4174 or (Captain Deathrage)703-765-8889
E-mail: michael.bosworth@verizon.net
Website: www.shipscompany.org

SPECIFICATIONS

Flag: USA
Rig: Full rigged ship
Homeport: Culver, Indiana
Normal cruising waters: Lake Maxinkuckee in Culver, Indiana
Sparred length: 65'
LOA: 54'
LOD: 50'
Draft: 5'
Beam: 13'
Rig height: 49'
Freeboard: 5'
Tons: 25 GRT
Power: Diesel

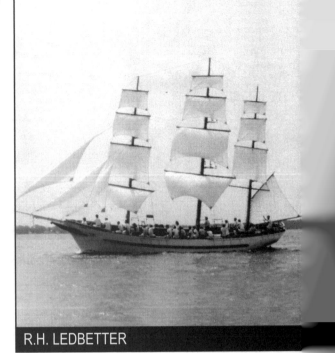

R.H. LEDBETTER

The *R.H. Ledbetter* is the flagship of the Culver Summer Naval School, located on Lake Maxinkuckee in Culver, Indiana. The three-masted square-rigger, named in honor of Georgia philanthropist and Culver alumnus Robert H. Ledbetter, was built in 1983 - 84 by the T. D. Vinette Co. of Escanaba, Michigan. Dedicated July 7, 1984, the *Ledbetter* replaced the wooden-hulled *O.W Fowler*, which had served as the flagship from 1941- 83. The masts, spars, and sails from the Fowler were used on the *Ledbetter*. Culver Summer Camps offer two simultaneous coed six-week camps from mid-June to early August (Woodcraft for ages 9-13, and Upper Camp for 13-17) and 10 two-week specialty camps from early to mid-August. Administered by The Culver Educational Foundation, which also operates the Culver Academy, the camps use the facilities of the 1,800-acre wooded campus along the north shore of Indiana's second-largest lake.

Who sails: Students and Alumni of Culver Academy
Program type: Sail training for students of Culver Academy; sea education in cooperation with organized groups such as the American Camping Association; dockside interpretation while in home port
Designer: Marine Power
Built: 1984: Escanoba, MI, T. D. Vinette
Contact: Anthony Mayfield, Director, Culver Summer Camps, 1300 Academy Road, RD# 138, Culver, IN 46511 USA
Tel: 800-221-2020
Fax: 574-842-8462
E-mail: mayfiea@culver.org
Website: www.cuiver.org

SPECIFICATIONS

Flag: USA
Rig: Gaff schooner, two-masted
Homeport: Weehawken,
New Jersey
Normal cruising waters:
Hudson River, New York Harbor,
Sandy Hook Bay,
Long Island Sound
Sparred length: 80'
LOA: 75'
LOD: 60'
LWL: 50'
Draft: 5'
Beam: 18' 6"
Rig height: 50'
Freeboard: 4'
Sail area: 1,800 square feet
Tons: 45 GRT
Power: Diesel
Hull: Wood

RICHARD ROBBINS

The *Richard Robbins* is a genuine two-masted, gaff-rigged schooner with canvas sails. She was built entirely of white oak and yellow pine in 1902, just after the Spanish American War. She has a long and colorful history, beginning with her launching at Greenwich, New Jersey, near Cape May. She sailed for many years with a fleet of schooners dredging for oysters in Delaware Bay. She was owned by the Robbins family until 1967, when she was sold and taken to Rockland, Maine where she entered the charter trade. In 1978 she went to Lake Champlain, offering week-long sailing vacations. In 1984 she returned to New Jersey and now sails from Weehawken, where she offers sail training, corporate dinner charters, Sunday brunch sails, and private birthday parties. She is a registered historic tall ship and participated in Operation Sail 1986, and Operation Sail 1992 and OpSail 2000. Share in the sense of wonder and discovery felt by Sir Henry Hudson from the deck of an authentic sailing ship!

Who sails: Students of all ages, individuals, families, clubs, corporations
Program type: Sail training for groups arranging a private charter - ecologists and scientists can be included for an additional cost; dinner parties for fundraisers, corporations, and individuals - sea chantey singers available at an additional cost
Designer: William Parsons
Built: 1902: Greenwich, NJ, Greenwich Marine Piers and Railway
Coast Guard certification: Passenger Vessel (Subchapter T)
Crew: 3 **Trainees-passengers:** 49 day sails, 20 overnight
Contact: Captain Alan Jadro, Classic Sail Windjammer Co., Inc., PO Box 459, Madison, NJ 07940 USA
Tel: 973-966-1684

SPECIFICATIONS

Flag: USA
Rig: Brigantine
Homeport: Woods Hole, Massachusetts
Normal cruising waters: Worldwide
Sparred length: 134' 6"
LOA: 119'
LWL: 87' 6"
Draft: 13'
Beam: 26' 6"
Sail area: 8,200 square feet
Power: Caterpillar 3408, 455 HP
Hull: Steel

ROBERT C. SEAMANS

SEA'S newest vessel, launched in the spring of 2001, was built at JM Martinac Shipbuilding in Tacoma, Washington. Designed by Laurent Giles of Hampshire, England, the 134-foot steel brigantine is the most sophisticated sailing research vessel ever built in the United States. Improvements in design and equipment, including a wet/dry laboratory and a large library, classroom, and computer laboratory, will enhance the SEA academic program. The new vessel is conducting SEA Semesters in the Pacific with cruise tracks including Hawaii, Costa Rica, Alaska, and Tahiti.

Who sails: Educators and students who are admitted by competitive selection; Over 150 colleges and universities award credit for SEA programs
Program type: Marine and maritime studies including oceanography, nautical science, history, literature, and contemporary maritime affairs. SEA programs include SEA Semester (college level, 12 weeks long, 17 credits), SEA Summer Session (college level, 8 weeks long, 12 credits), and SEA Seminars for high school students and K-1 2 teachers. All programs include a seagoing component on board one of the sailing school vessels
Season: Year-round
Designer: Laurent Giles, Hampshire, England
Built: Tacoma, WA, JM Martinac Shipbuilding
Coast Guard certification: Sailing School Vessel (Subchapter R)
Crew: 6 professional mariners and 4 scientists **Passengers-Trainees:** Up to 25 in all programs
Contact: Sea Education Association, Inc., PO Box 6, Woods Hole, MA 02543 USA
Tel: 508-540-3954 **Fax:** 508-540-0558
E-mail: admissions@sea.edu **Website:** www.sea.edu

SPECIFICATIONS

Homeport: Bronx, New York
Normal cruising waters:
Bronx River
Rig: 10-14' to 21' traditional
Whitehalls and one Cape Cod
Oyster Skiff

Rocking the Boat

Rocking the Boat is a boatbuilding and on-water education program based out of the southwest Bronx, New York City. Through a hands-on alternative approach to education and youth development, Rocking the Boat addresses the need for inner city youth to achieve practical and tangible goals, relevant to both everyday life and future aspirations. This process allows high school students to acquire practical, academic, and social skills. Rocking the Boat runs programming in both boatbuilding and environmental science, coordinating three after school and summer programs in each discipline annually, working directly with over 150 students, all of whom receive high school credit. During the process of building a traditional wooden boat, Rocking the Boat students create something not only beautiful, but practical in their own lives, bridging urban and natural life within their neighborhoods. This approach is mirrored in the on-water education program through direct focus on Bronx River habitat monitoring and restoration and through maritime skills programming. Both programs allow students opportunities to gain a deeper awareness of their own abilities and possibilities in the natural and urban world. Volunteers are always welcome to help out in every aspect of Rocking the Boat.

Who Sails: Rocking the Boat students (high school age)
Program Type: Traditional wooden boatbuilding and on-water maritime skills and environmental science programming for high school aged students
Season: Year Round
Designer: John Gardner Built/Year: 1998 to present, The Bronx Builder: Rocking the Boat students
Contact: Adam Green, Executive Director, Rocking the Boat, Inc., 60 East 174th Street, Bronx, NY 10452 USA
Tel: 718- 466-5799
Fax: 718-466-2892
E-mail: shop@rockingtheboat.org
Website: www.rockingtheboat.org

SPECIFICATIONS

Flag: USA
Rig: Schooner
Homeport: Belfast, Maine
Normal cruising waters:
Penobscot Bay (summer)
Caribbean (winter)
Sparred length: 137'
LOA: 112'
LOD: 112'
LWL: 90'
Draft: 14'
Beam: 25'
Rig height: 84'
Freeboard: 51'
Sail area: 5,600 square feet
Tons: 250 GRT
Power: 400 HP diesel
Hull: Wood

ROSEWAY

The World Ocean School is an internationally focused nonprofit, nonsectarian organization dedicated to providing challenging educational programs for youth by fostering an appreciation for, and obligation to, community and relationships; developing a deep commitment to ethical values and cultivating an expanded world view. The World Ocean School provides programs aboard the schooner *Roseway* for an international mix of students ages 15-21. Programs focus on studies in marine ecology, maritime history, stewardship, seamanship, ethical decision making, and community service. The 137-foot *Roseway* was built in 1925 in Essex, Massachusetts as a private fishing yacht. She was purchased by the Boston Pilots Association in 1941, where she received a bronze plaque in honor of her exemplary wartime service during World War II. The *Roseway* was the last pilot schooner in the United States when she was retired in 1973. In 1974, the *Roseway* was taken to Maine to serve in the Windjammer trade. In September 2002 she was donated to the World Ocean School. Today, after 78 years of service, she is one of the last Grand Banks schooners built in Essex, and a registered U.S. National Historic Landmark.

Who sails: Middle school through college students; individuals of all ages
Program: Sea education in ethical decision-making and community service in ports in cooperation with accredited institutions and other organized groups and as informal in-house programming; dockside interpretation during port visits
Season: Year-round
Designer: John F. James & Sons
Built: 1925: Essex, MA, John F. James & Sons
Coast Guard certification: Passenger Vessel (subchapter T)
Crew: 6
Contact: Abby Kidder, President, World Ocean School, PO Box 701, Camden, ME 04843 USA
Tel: 207-236-7482 **Fax:** 207-236-8257
E-mail: wos@worldoceanschool.org
Website: www.worldoceanschool.org

SPECIFICATIONS

Flag: USA
Rig: Gaff-rigged square topsail ketch
Homeport: San Francisco, California
LOA: 73'
LOD: 51'
LWL: 36'
Draft: 6'
Beam: 14' 6"
Rig height: 65'
Power: Perkins diesel
Hull: Wood, Mahogany

ROYALISTE

PRIVATEER is a nonprofit group with an interest in living history through sail training and reenactments of maritime events. Our present focus is primarily but not limited to the restoration, maintenance, and campaigning of the sailing vessel *Royaliste*, a replica 1755 gaff-rigged. square tops'l ketch commissioned as a dispatch gunship. Presently lying on her hook in San Francisco Bay, she currently engages in acts of 'piracy' as well as ship's greetings, mock sea. battles, and unique special events, including fireworks celebrations, "Pirate Circuses", and sail training with a privateer's flair...Quick under sail, she is an exhilarating step into the past, always a fun-filled adventure of salt and spray. Since the *Royaliste* enjoys a rather active historical reenactment schedule, an adventure on her decks at these events yields memories by the seabag full, with crew barking orders, fife and drums beat to quarters, and the smell of gunpowder watts across the bulwarks. For a taste of 'piratical' history. sail-training as a privateer, or at a dockside tour complete with a compliment of scallywags, consider visiting the *Royaliste* as a 'port of call' on your next tour of duty,'

Who sails: Groups and individuals of all ages
Program: "Period" sail training, 1755 rig
Season: Year-round
Designer: James Rosborough Built: 1969: Nova Scotia, Arthur Theriault
Coast Guard certification: Attraction Vessel / USCG Passenger Vessel (Subchapter T) pending
Crew: 5
Contact: Gary Bergman, Privateer, Inc., 1001 Bridgeway #645, Sausalito, CA 94965 USA
Tel: 415-331-3967
E-mail: orcaboat@sbcglobal.net

SPECIFICATIONS

Flag: New Zealand
Rig: Gaff rigged schooner
Homeport:
Whangarei, New Zealand
Normal cruising waters:
Worldwide
Sparred length: 85'
LOD: 60'
Draft: 6'
Beam: 16'
Sail area: 3,000 square feet
Power: 180 HP Ford diesel
Hull: Steel

R. TUCKER THOMPSON

R. Tucker Thompson started building the traditional gaff-rigged schooner *R. Tucker Thompson* in the late 1970s as a project to embody the best features of a traditional design, married to the materials of today. After Tucker's death, the *R. Tucker Thompson* was completed by Tucker's son, Tod Thompson, and Russell Harris. The ship was built in Mangawhai, New Zealand and launched in 1985. Her design is based on the Halibut schooners of the North West American coast which were considered fast, sea kindly, and easily manned. Most of her voyages take place during winter seasons of the years. During summer she operates as a day charter ship and has carried over 60,000 visitors around the Bay of Islands. The ship has taken part in five film productions. The ship's current survey is class seven foreign vessel which means that she can carry passengers around the coast of New Zealand as well as off shore. She has been built and maintained to the highest standards and is professionally manned and equipped to go anywhere in the world at any time. In 2002 she voyaged to Korea for Sail Korea 2002 and onwards to the Pacific Coast of the United States where she participated in the TALL SHIPS CHALLENGE® Pacific Coast 2002 Series.

Who sails: Individuals and groups of all ages
Season: Year-round
Built: 1985: Mangawhai, New Zealand, Tod Thompson and Russell Harris
Crew: 15 **Trainees-passengers:** 45 day sails
Contact: Russell Harris, PO Box 42, Opua Post Office, Opua 0255 New Zealand
Tel: +64-9-402-8430
Fax: +64-9-402-8565
E-mail: r.tucker@clear.net.nz

SPECIFICATIONS

Flag: USA
Rig: Viking longship
Sparred Length: 40'
LOA: 35'
LWL: 34'
Freeboard: 1.5'
Draft: 2'
Beam: 9'.6"
Rig Height: 25'
Sail Area: 320 square feet
Tons: 3 GRT
Power: 12 oars (12' Spruce)
Hull Material: Cedar and Oak

SAE HRAFN

Sae Hrafn (Sea Raven) will serve as a replacement vessel for the *Fyrdraca*. She is designed as a small coastal raiding vessel; an intermediate size between the Ralsweik ships and the Skuldelev Wreck 5 coastal defense ship. In our new ship, the Longship Company will explore the lost arts of early medieval sailing, navigation and seamanship. We plan to sail the *Sae Hrafn* once or twice a month on training cruises for our regular crew and guests/trainees, and plan to sail her on overnight voyages to further explore the living conditions of the Viking age. We will also participate in various waterfront cultural activities in the Chesapeake Bay region. Like our other vessels, the *Sae Hrafn* will be involved in filming for the History Channel and other educational media, and take part in various living history demonstrations in concert with the Markland Medieval Mercenary Militia. *Sae Hrafn*, and her consort, the *Gyrfalcon*, are both owned and operated by the Longship Company, Ltd., a member supported nonprofit educational organization. Occasional Viking raids on various fraternal and educational organizations may also, from time to time, be used to supplement our financial resources.

Who Sails: Grade school through adult
Program Type: History and research
Built: 2004: Kerry Eikenskold, Inyokern, CA
Crew: 8-18 **Trainees-passengers:** 6-12
Contact: Bruce Blackistone, President, Longship Company, LTD. 21924 Oakley Road, Avenue, Maryland 20609 USA
Tel: 301-390-4089
E-mail: longshipco@hotmail.com
Website: www.longshipco.org

Flag: Portugal
Rig: Barque
Homeport: Lisbon, Portugal
Normal cruising waters:
Worldwide
Sparred length: 293' 6"
Draft: 17'
Beam: 39' 6"
Hull: Steel

SAGRES

Sagres II sails under the Portuguese flag as a naval training ship. She was built in 1937 at the Blohm & Voss shipyard in Hamburg, Germany, and is virtually a sister ship to *Eagle*, *Mircea*, *Tovarishch*, and *Gorch Fock II*. Originally named *Albert Leo Schlageter*, she served under American and Brazilian flags before being acquired by Portugal in 1962. At that time she replaced the first *Sagres*, which was built in 1896 as the Rickmer Rickmers. The original *Sagres* has now been restored and serves as a museum ship in Hamburg, Germany. The name *Sagres* derives from the historic port that sent forth many famed Portuguese explorers and navigators. It served as the home and base for Prince Henry the Navigator (1394-1460). His court in *Sagres* was responsible for the geographic studies and practical explorations that made Portugal master of the seas in the early 15th century. A bust of Prince Henry serves as the figurehead on the bow of *Sagres II*, and the ship is easily identified by the traditional Portuguese crosses of Christ (Maltese crosses) that mark the square sails on her fore- and mainmasts.

Who sails: Cadets of the Portuguese Navy
Program type: Training vessel for the Portuguese Navy
Season: Year-round
Built: 1937: Hamburg, Germany, Blohm & Voss Shipyard
Contact: Portuguese Defense and Naval Aftaché, Embassy of Portugal, 2310 Tracy Place, Washington, DC 20008 USA
Tel: 202-234-4483
Fax: 202-328-6827
E-mail: ponavnir@mindspring.com

SAMANA

SPECIFICATIONS

Flag: USA
Rig: Ketch
Homeport: Portland, Maine
Normal cruising waters: Gulf of Maine to Nova Scotia (summer) Caribbean (winter)
Sparred length: 63'
LOD: 53'
LWL: 45'
Draft: 7'
Beam: 16'
Rig height: 85'
Freeboard: 4'
Sail area: 1,500 square feet
Tons: 34 GRT
Power: Ford Lehman
Hull: Steel

The School of Ocean Sailing operates in the North Atlantic Ocean off the coast of Maine, offering courses in offshore ocean sailing and ocean navigation in a live-aboard setting. *Samana* is a modern, well-found, romantic, beautiful, fast, and very seakindly vessel. Built in 1975 in The Netherlands, she has circumnavigated the globe and completed several noteworthy offshore passages. Captain Larry Wheeler and Letty Wheeler are professional teachers with more than 25 years of classroom teaching experience and over 10 years of sail training experience. Based in Portland, Maine, courses span the Maine coast and reach the coastline of Nova Scotia. The curriculum is a rich blend of technical skills, confidence building, and common sense coupled with a spirit of adventure and romance. The school offers courses in Advanced Ocean Sailing and Navigation, Celestial Navigation, and Offshore Passage Making. In each course, the trainees handle all offshore sailing operations. All instruction is delivered by mature and professional, Coast Guard-licensed teachers.

Who sails: Individuals of all ages
Program type: Sail training for paying trainees; ocean sailing, celestial navigation, offshore passage making
Designer: Van de Wiele
Built: 1975: The Netherlands
Crew: 3 **Trainees-passengers:** 6
Contact: Captain Larry Wheeler, School of Ocean Sailing, PO Box 7359, Portland, ME 04112 USA
Tel: 207-871-1315 or 888-626-3557
Fax: 207-871-1315
E-mail: svsamana@nlis.net
Website: www.sailingschool.com

SPECIFICATIONS

Flag: Russia
Rig: Barque, 4-masted
Homeport: Murmansk, Russia
Normal cruising waters:
Worldwide
Sparred length: 386'
Draft: 27'
Beam: 48'
Hull: Steel

SEDOV

Sedov is the world's largest tall ship still in service and was one of the last barques built for deepwater cargo carrier service from South America and Australia to the German ports of Bremen and Hamburg. Constructed in 1921 as *Magdalene Vinnen* in Kiel, Germany, she sailed for the Bremen firm of F. A. Vinnen, hence her name. Following the German commercial tradition, she was christened in honor of one of the owner's female family members. After being sold to the shipping conglomerate Norddeutscher Lloyd in 1936, she was renamed *Kommodore Johnson* and served as a sail training vessel. After World War II she was appropriated by the Russian Ministry of Fisheries and was renamed for the Soviet polar explorer and oceanographer Georgij *Sedov* (1877 – 1914). *Sedov* is the largest square-rigger still in service from the days of deepwater cargo sailing. She is 10 feet longer than the other giant Russian barque, *Kruzenshtern*. Besides her physical statistics, such as masts that rise 184 feet above the deck and a length of 386 feet, *Sedov* boasts its own bakery, workshop, and first-aid station. When her 37 sails – covering an area of some 44,000 square feet. *Sedov* is a magnificent portrait of sail power.

Who sails: Students of the Murmansk State Technical University
Program type: Sail training vessel
Designer: 1921: Friedr. Krupp, A.G. Germaniawerft, Kiel, Germany
Crew: 70 crew, 120 cadets
Trainees-passengers: 50 guest passengers
Contact: Murmansk State Technical University
Website: http://eng.mstu.edu.ru/

Flag: USA
Rig: Gaff Schooner, 2-masted
Homeport: Cape Charles, Virginia
Normal cruising waters:
Chesapeake Bay
Sparred length: 65'
LWL: 40'
Draft: 5' 6"
Beam: 14'
Rig Height: 55'
Freeboard: 4'
Sail area: 1,544 square feet
Tons: 26 GRT
Power: 66 HP Yanmar diesel
Hull: Steel

SERENITY

The *Serenity* is a two-masted, gaff-rigged schooner designed by Tom Colvin and built by Custom Steel Boats in 1986. The Low Sea Company purchased her in the spring of 2000 and brought her to Cape Charles, on Virginia's Eastern Shore. *Serenity* is USCG certified to carry 34 passengers. The Low Sea Company offers day sails and group charters designed to foster an understanding and appreciation of the maritime history and ecology of the Chesapeake Bay. *Serenity* sails out of historic Cape Charles, located on the Eastern Shore of Virginia, 10 miles from the mouth of the Chesapeake Bay. *Serenity* can accommodate 4 passengers/trainees for overnight charters.

Who sails: Individuals and groups of all ages
Program type: Sail training for crew and apprentices; sunset sails and eco-tour charters for groups and individuals of all ages
Season: April to November in Chesapeake Bay; Winter in Caribbean
Designer: Tom Colvin
Built: 1986: Arapaho, NC, Custom Steel Boats
Coast Guard certification: Passenger Vessel (Subchapter T)
Crew: 2 or 3 **Trainees-passengers:** 34 day sail, 4 overnight
Contact: Laura and Greg Lohse, Owners, Low Sea Company, 505 Monroe Avenue, Cape Charles, VA 23310 USA
Tel: 757-710-1233
E-mail: sailserenity@msn.com
Website: www.schoonerserenity.com

SPECIFICATIONS

Flag: Sultanate of Oman
Rig: Barquentine
Homeport: Muscat, Oman
Sparred length: 171'
Draft: 15'
Beam: 28'
Hull: Wood

Photo and text by Thad Koza

SHABAB OF OMAN

Built in Scotland in 1971 as a sail training vessel, *Shabab of Oman* was acquired by the Sultanate of Oman in 1979. *Shabab of Oman*, which means "youth of Oman," serves as a training ship for the royal navy of Oman and also trains young men from other Omani government bureaus. The sculptured figurehead on her bow is a replica of the fifteenth-century Omani mariner Ahmed bin Majed, who helped the Portuguese sailor Vasco da Gama explore Africa and India. The turban-clad Majed cuts a rakish figure, wearing a green sash and red "khunjar," a traditional dagger. The red coat-of-arms of the sultanate is recognizable on the sails of *Shabab of Oman* and consists of a khunjar superimposed on a pair of crossed scimitars.

Program type: Sail training vessel of the royal navy of Oman
Contact: Embassy of the Sultanate of Oman, 2535 Belmont Road, NW Washington, DC 20008 USA
Tel: 202-387-1980
Fax: 202-745-4933

SPECIFICATIONS

Flag: USA
Rig: Square topsail schooner, two-masted
Homeport: Vineyard Haven, Massachusetts
Normal cruising waters: Southern New England
Sparred length: 152'
LOA: 108'
LWL: 101'
Draft: 11'
Beam: 23'
Rig height: 94'
Freeboard: 3' (amidships)
Sail area: 7,000 square feet
Tons: 85 GRT

SHENANDOAH

While the *Shenandoah* is not a replica, the vessel's design bears a strong resemblance to that of the US Revenue Cutter *Joe Lane* of 1851. For her first 25 years, the rakish square topsail schooner was painted white, but she now wears the black and white checkerboard paint scheme of the 19th century Revenue Service. She is the only non-auxiliary power square-rigged vessel operating under the American Flag. Her hull form and rig, anchors, and all materials of construction adhere closely to mid-19th century practice. Every summer *Shenandoah* plies the waters of southern New England visiting the haunts of pirates and the homeports of whaling ships. *Shenandoah* runs 6-day sailing trips for kids ages 9-14 from late June through August, and day sails in early September. She is also available for private charter.

Who sails: School groups from elementary through college and individuals of all ages
Program type: Sail training for paying trainees ages 9-14; private charters and day sails are also available
Season: June to September
Coast Guard certification: Passenger Vessel (Subchapter T)
Crew: 9 **Trainees-passengers:** 35 day sails, 30 overnight
Contact: Captain Robert S. Douglas, Coastwise Packet Co., Inc., PO Box 429, Vineyard Haven, MA 02568 USA
Tel: 508-693-1699
Fax: 508-693-1881
Website: www.theblackdogtallships.com

Flag: USA
Rig: Sloop
Homeport: Newport, RI
Normal cruising waters:
Narragansett Bay, Rhode Island
Sound
LOA: 46'
LOD: 44'
LWL: 40'
Draft: 6' 6"
Beam: 11' 1"
Rig height: 62'
Freeboard: 4'
Sail area: 97 square feet
Tons: 11 GRT
Power: diesel
Hull: Aluminum

SIGHTSAILER

Designed by Yves-Marie Tanton and built out of aluminum by Intercoastal Ironworks in Bourg, Louisiana, *Sightsailer* is a large, very light daysailer. She was originally commissioned as *Bayou Eagle* and sailed on Lake Pontchartrain in New Orleans. *Sightsailer* is USCG inspected for 16 guests and offers public daysails, private and corporate charters from May through October in Newport, RI. With a very large, comfortable cockpit and generous sail area she offers exciting yet intimate sails through Newport Harbor and Narragansett Bay. *Sightsailing* also operates several smaller 6 pID boats including two O'Day 34's, *Starlight* and *Twilight*, and a Pearson Ensign, *Valentine*. Guests may purchase individual tickets or arrange private charters. For more information visit our website at www.sightsailing.com.

Who sails: Ages 6 to 90
Program type: Public day sails; private and corporate charters
Season: May through October
Built: 1992: Intracoastal Ironworks, New Orleans, LA
Coast Guard certification: Passenger Vessel (Subchapter T)
Crew: 2 **Trainees-passengers:** 16 day sails
Contact: Christine John Hirschler, President, Sightsailing, Inc. 22 greenough Place #2, Newport, RI 02840 USA
Tel: 401-849-3333 or 1-800-709-7245
Fax: 401-849-7715
E-mail: jhirschler@aol.com
Website: www.sightsailing.com

Flag: USA
Rig: Sloop
Homeport: Baltimore, Maryland
Normal cruising waters: Chesapeake Bay and the Delaware River
Sparred length: 76'
LOD: 50'
Draft: 3' 5"
Beam: 16'
Rig height: 68'
Freeboard: 2' 5"
Sail area: 1,767 square feet
Tons: 14 GRT
Power: 150 HP diesel

SIGSBEE

The skipjack *Sigsbee* was built in 1901 in Deale Island, Maryland and worked as an oyster dredge boat until the early 1990s. She was named after Charles D. Sigsbee, who was the Commanding Officer of the battleship *Maine.* The vessel was rebuilt by the Living Classrooms Foundation in 1994, and now sails Chesapeake Bay with students on board. While sailing on board the *Sigsbee*, students learn the history of skipjacks and the oyster industry, marine and nautical science, and gain an appreciation of Chesapeake Bay and the hard work of the watermen of a bygone era.

Who sails: Students and other organized groups, individuals, and families
Program type: Sail training with paying trainees; sea education in marine and nautical science, maritime history, and ecology for school groups from elementary through college
Season: March through September
Built: 1901: Deale Island, Maryland
Coast Guard certification: Passenger Vessel (Subchapter T)
Crew: 4 **Trainees-passengers:** 30 day sails, 15 overnight **Age:** 13+ **Dockside visitors:** 30
Contact: Christine Truett, Director of Education, Living Classrooms Foundation, 802 South Caroline Street, Baltimore, MD 21231-3311 USA
Tel: 410-685-0295
Fax: 410-752-8433
Website: www.livingclassrooms.org

SPECIFICATIONS

Flag: Canada
Rig: Three-masted schooner
Homeport: Halifax, Nova Scotia, Canada
Normal cruising waters: Halifax Harbour, Nova Scotia Coast
Sparred length: 130'
LOA: 115'
Draft: 9'
Beam: 24'
Rig height: 75'
Freeboard: 4'
Tons: 199 GRT
Power: 350 Cummins

SILVA

Silva was built at Karlstads Mekaniska, Verksta, Sweden as a three masted steel schooner. During the first 2 decades of her life, she was used in the Scandinavian fishing industry, with regular trips to Iceland. In the 1960s, *Silva* was refitted as a bulk freighter, having her sailing rig removed. *Silva* continued coastal trading until 1994 and remained in Sweden until the summer of 2001 when Canadian Sailing Expeditions bought her and delivered her, for the first time, to North America. She now offers sailing tours of Halifax Harbour. She runs educational programs for students, day trade for general public, and private and corporate charters. Canadian Sailing Expeditions is dedicated to providing opportunities for people of all ages to experience and explore our seacoast the traditional way.

Who sails: Groups and individuals of all ages
Program type: Sail training for paying trainees; passenger day sails; private charters
Season: April through October
Built: 1939: Verksta, Sweden, Karlstads Mekaniska
Certification: Transport Canada
Trainees-passengers: 150 day sails
Contact: Captain Doug Prothero, Owner/operator, Canadian Sailing Expeditions, PO Box 2613, Halifax, NS B3J 3N5 Canada
Tel: 902-429-1474
Fax: 902-429-1475
E-mail: doug@canadiansailingexpeditions.com
Website: www.canadiansailingexpeditions.com

Photo and text by Thad Koza

SPECIFICATIONS

Flag: Venezuela
Rig: Barque
Homeport: La Guaira, Venezuela
Normal cruising waters: Worlwide
Sparred length: 270'
Draft: 14' 6'''
Beam: 35'
Hull: Steel

SIMON BOLIVAR

Simon Bolivar was one of four barques built in Spain for Latin American countries. Similar in design and rigging, the four ships are nearly identical sister ships: *Gloria* from Columbia, *Guayas* from Ecuador, *Cuauhtemoc* from Mexico, and *Simon Bolivar*. All four are frequent visitors to the United States and at major tall ship gatherings. The 270-foot *Simon Bolivar* was completed in 1980 and named for the "great liberator" of northern South America. Bolivar (1783-1830) was instrumental in the independence of Columbia, Ecuador, Panama, Peru, and Venezuela. *Simon Bolivar* embodies the spirit of idealism and freedom of her namesake. Her figurehead is an allegorical depiction of Liberty and was designed by the Venezuelan artist Manuel Felipe Rincon.

Program type: Training vessel of the Venezuelan Navy
Contact: Embassy of the Bolivarian Republic of Venezuela, 1099 30th Street, NW Washington, DC 20007 USA
Tel: 202-342-2214
Fax: 202-342-6820

SPECIFICATIONS

Flag: UK
Rig: Brigantine
Homeport:
Auckland, New Zealand
Normal cruising waters: New
Zealand and South pacific plus
world wide voyage once every 4
years
Sparred Length: 145'
LOA: 145'
LOD: 105'
Draft: 11' 3"
Beam: 25' 6"
Rig height: 98'
Sail Area: 6,750 Square feet
Tons: 126 GRT
Power: B&W ALPHA Diesel,
143 hp
Hull: Danish Oak

SOREN LARSEN

Sail Training and square rig adventure for all ages. This oak hulled brigantine specializes in authentic tall ship voyaging to the remoter tropical islands of the South Pacific and short cruises in the idyllic home waters of the New Zealand coast. Join the ship as Voyage Crew for either a 5 or 10 day tropical island voyage, or the rare opportunity of an extended ocean passage. No previous experience is needed in either case – just the desire to experience the freedom of the seas aboard a traditional tall ship. Berths in the twin or 4 berth cabins are booked individually online. Fully surveyed under the British flag for world wide voyaging, this magnificently restored square rigger is also available for school groups, project charters, and location film work. Read the ship's Voyage Log of present and previous voyaging at the website – as well as the voyaging schedule and pricing.

Who sails: 17 to 75 (as long as fit and healthy)
Program type: Adventure Sail Training for all ages
Season: Year-round
Designer: Soren Larsen Ship Yard
Built: 1949: Soren Larsen and Sons, Nykobing Mors, Denmark
Crew: 13 **Trainees–passengers:** 22 overnight
Contact: Captain Anthony Davies, Squaresail Pacific, PO Box 310, Kumeu, Auckland, 1250 New Zealand
Tel: +64 9 411 8755
Fax: +64 9 411 8484
E-mail: escape@sorenlarsen.co.nz
Website: www.sorenlarsen.co.nz

SPECIFICATIONS

Flag: Norway
Rig: Full-rigged ship
Homeport: Kristiansand, Norway
LOA: 210'
LOD: 186'
LWL: 158'
Freeboard: 17'
Draft: 15'
Beam: 29'
Rig height: 112'
Sail area: 6,500 square feet
Tons: 499 GRT
Power: 560 HP engine
Hull: Steel

SØRLANDET

The *Sørlandet* was built as a schoolship for the merchant marine in 1927 in Kristiansand, Norway, and served this purpose up until 1974. She was named *Sorlandet* meaning "the Southland" after the Southern region of Norway of which Kristiansand is the capital. Thousands of young men have received their first seagoing experience onboard the *Sørlandet.* During the war the German occupation force took her under command and she was used as a recreation ship for German U-boat crew. Later during the war she was used as a prison camp for Russian prisoners of war. During one of the many air-raids she sunk in the Kirkenes Bay far up North in Norway with only her masts above water. She was later brought afloat and towed back to her homeport heavily damaged. In 1947 she was restored and once again able to welcome young cadets. In the early seventies the Government of Norway had different ideas on how to educate young seamen and the schoolship era in Norway came to an end. Lying idle until the late seventies the *Sorlandet* was again over-hauled and ready for new ventures. A new administrative organization was established and a new business concept worked out which offers young people of all ages from 15-80 a tall ship experience as paying trainees for short or longer trips. The *Sørlandet* was the first ship in the world to offer sail training for females.

Who sails: 15-80 year old trainees accepted.
Program type: Sail training ship, tall ship adventures
Season: May through September
Desiner: Hoivold Shipyard
Built: 1927: Hoivold Shipyard, Kristiansand, Norway
Crew: Up to 20 **Trainees-passengers:** 70
Contact: Leif Brestrup, Director, Stiftelsen Fullriggeren Sorlandet, Gravane 6, Kristiansand, N-4610 Norway
Tel: +47 38 02 98 90
Fax: +47 38 02 93 34

Flag: USA
Rig: Gaff schooner, three-masted
Homeport: Stamford, Connecticut
Normal cruising waters:
Long Island Sound
Sparred length: 80'
LOD: 65'
Draft: 3' (centerboards up),
8' (centerboards down)
Beam: 14'
Rig height: 60'
Freeboard: 3' 6"
Sail area: 1,510 square feet
Tons: 32 GRT
Power: Diesel
Hull: Steel

SOUNDWATERS

SoundWaters, Inc. is a non-profit education organization dedicated to protecting Long Island Sound and its watershed through education. Annually *SoundWaters* offers shipboard and land- based programs to 35,000 children and adults from Connecticut and New York. The schooner *SoundWaters* is the platform for a variety of programs includes seamanship, navigation, helmsmanship, and field exploration of marine ecosystems. *SoundWaters* crew includes environmental educators, biologists, naturalists, and a licensed captain. In addition, *SoundWaters*, Inc. operates the *SoundWaters* Community Center for Environmental Education, featuring educational exhibits and displays, classroom and community meeting space, a wet lab, and cutting-edge "green" construction. The organization also conducts many free outreach programs, which are offered through public schools and community centers.

Who sails: School groups from elementary through college; individuals and families
Program type: Sea education in marine science and ecology in cooperation with accredited institutions and other groups, and as informal, in-house programming
Season: April to November
Designer: William Ward
Built: 1986: Norfolk, Virginia, Marine Metals, Inc.
Coast Guard certification: Passenger Vessel (Subchapter T)
Crew: 3 - 5 instructors **Trainees-passengers:** 42 day sails, 15-20 overnight
Contact: SoundWaters, Inc. Cove Island Park, 1281 Cove Road, Stamford, CT 06902 USA
Tel: 203-323-1978
Fax: 203-967-8306
E-mail: connect@soundwaters.org
Website: www.soundwaters.org

SPECIFICATIONS

Flag: USA
Rig: Schooner
Homeport: Dana Point, California
Normal cruising waters: Southern California
Sparred length: 118'
LOD: 86'
LWL: 79'
Draft: 10'
Beam: 24'
Freeboard: 6'
Rig height: 100'
Sail area: 5,000 square feet
Power: HP diesel
Tons: 64 GRT
Hull: Wood

SPIRIT OF DANA POINT

A young colony, in a new land, dreamed of independence and built some of the fastest and best sailing ships in the world. These ships were the result of ingenuity, independence and a strong desire to accomplish something. It was Dennis Holland's life dream to build an accurate replica from the period when America fought for independence and world recognition. Armed with talent, determination, a little money and plans he purchased from the Smithsonian Institute, he laid the keel in his yard on May 2, 1970. Thirteen years later this fast privateer was launched and his vision became reality. Today at the Ocean Institute this dream continues as young students step aboard and back in time. During their voyages students relive the challenges and discoveries of early ocean exploration. Through a series of national award winning living history programs, the *Spirit of Dana Point* serves as an excellent platform for our youth to directly experience life at sea, as it has been for hundreds of years. She sails throughout Southern California for more than 150 days a year.

Who sails: School groups from elementary school through college; adult education groups; families and individuals of all ages
Program type: Sail training for volunteer crew or trainees; sea education in marine science, maritime history, and ecology based on informal in-house programming and in cooperation with other organizations; day sails and overnight passages; affiliated institutions include the Ocean Institute, other school education programs, and museums
Season: Year-round
Designer: Howard Chapelle
Built: 1983: Costa Mesa, California, Dennis Holland
Coast Guard certification: Passenger Vessel (Subchapter T)
Crew: 7 **Trainees-passengers:** 75 day sails, 30 overnight
Contact: Adam Himelson, Program Director, Ocean Institute, 24200 Dana Point Harbor Drive, Dana Point, CA 92612 USA
Tel: 949-496-2274 **Fax:** 949-496-4715
E-mail: ahimelson@ocean-institute.org **Website:** www.ocean-institute.org

Flag: USA
Rig: Square topsail ketch
Homeport: Cape Cod, MA
Normal cruising waters: Canada to the Caribbean
Sparred length: 103'
LOD: 65'
LWL: 62'
Draft: 6'
Beam: 22'
Rig height: 75'
Freeboard: 3'
Sail area: 4,200 square feet
Tons: 58 GRT
Power: Twin diesels
Hull: Wood

SPIRIT OF LARINDA

Sailing from the west coast of California, the *Spirit of Larinda* has arrived at Cape Cod, Massachusetts in order to continue the tradition and mission of the Schooner *Larinda*. Youth of all ages are provided the opportunities of sail training, cooperation and adventure. The *Spirit of Larinda* is a modified replica of an 18th century colonial coastal trading vessel. Modern safety features offer a secure sailing platform of ongoing sea education through history and actual hands on experiences. Special programs include our Sea Challenges for Challenged Youth. This is an individually crafted schedule that builds confidence and self esteem for challenged youth. Private charters for corporate groups, schools and special events are available. Day sails at various ports along the eastern seaboard allow all walks of life a sea experience with our unique tall ship. Step aboard and join us for a team building experience and expand your own life changing horizons.

Who sails: School groups from elementary through college and individuals of all ages
Program type: Sail training for volunteer and paying trainees; sea challenges for youth; sea education in marine science, maritime history and ecology in cooperation with organized groups and as informal in-house programming
Season: Year-round
Designer: Raymond R. Richards
Built: 1988: Lahaina, Maui, Hawaii, Lahaina Welding Co.
Coast Guard certification: Passenger Vessel (Subchapter T)
Crew: 8   **Trainees-passengers:** 47 day sails, 22 overnight
Contact: Captain Lawrence Mahan, President, Wolverine Motor Works Shipyard, LLC, 26 Redmond Avenue, North Reading, MA 01864 USA
Tel: 508-648-0797 or 508-428-8728
E-mail: spiritoflarinda@aol.com **Website:** www.spiritoflarinda.com

SPECIFICATIONS

Flag: USA
Rig: Gaff tops'l schooner, two-masted
Homeport: Boston, Massachusetts
Normal cruising waters: North Atlantic Ocean and Caribbean Sea, Canada to South America
Sparred length: 125'
LOA: 103'
LOD: 100'
LWL: 80'
Draft: 10' 6"
Beam: 24'
Rig height: 103'
Freeboard: 7'
Sail area: 7,000 square feet
Tons: 90 GRT
Power: 235 HP diesel
Hull: Wood

SPIRIT OF MASSACHUSETTS

Owned by the Ocean Classroom Foundation, the schooner *Spirit of Massachusetts* sails on programs of education under sail fro the youth of America. Programs range from 4 month semesters-at-sea to week-long programs with schools and youth groups. Trainees sail the ship and learn traditional seamanship skills under the Captain and crew, and they explore maritime subjects with the onboard academic staff. The Ocean Classroom program is a semester-at-sea for qualified high school students, fully accredited by Proctor Academy. The voyage covers more than 4,000 nautical miles, connecting South American shores to the Canadian Maritimes. Students live and work as sailors on a true voyage of discovery, while they study maritime history, maritime literature, marine science, applied mathematics, and navigation. Ocean Classroom is offered Fall, Spring, and Summer Terms. Other programs include SEAmester (a complete semester-at-sea for college credit), OceanBound (for high school and college students) and Summer Seafaring Camp (for teens age 13-16). The Ocean Classroom Foundation also owns and operates the schooners *Harvey Gamage* and *Westward*.

Who sails: Individuals and school groups from middle school through college; affiliated institutions include Proctor Academy, Long Island University, Center for Coastal Studies, Hurricane Island Outward Bound School and other schools
Program type: Traditional seamanship training combined with accredited academic studies in maritime subjects
Season: Year-round
Designer: Melbourne Smith and Andrew Davis
Built: 1984: Boston, MA, New England Historic Seaport
Coast Guard certification: Sailing School Vessel (Subchapter R), Passenger Vessel (Subchapter T)
Crew: 7 - 11 including instructors **Students-trainees:** 22 overnight
Contact: Bert Rogers, Director, Ocean Classroom Foundation, 23 Bay Street, Watch Hill, RI 02891 USA
Tel: 800-724-7245, 401-596-4582 **Fax:** 401-596-4583
E-mail: mail@oceanclassroom.org
Website: www.oceanclassroom.org

SPECIFICATIONS

Flag: USA
Rig: Schooner
Homeport: Charleston, South Carolina
Sparred length: 140'
LOD: 91'
LWL: 88'
Draft: 10'
Beam: 24'
Hull: Wood

SPIRIT OF SOUTH CAROLINA

The South Carolina Maritime Heritage Foundation, is undertaking to build a magnificent tall ship to be named the *Spirit of South Carolina*. She will belong to all the people of South Carolina. The *Spirit* will provide educational opportunities, while sailing, for the youth of our State. The *Spirit of South Carolina* will be a pilot schooner reminiscent of the circa 1870s pilot schooner *Frances Elizabeth*, which was originally built by the Samuel J. Pregnall & Bros. Shipyard on Charleston Harbor. Plans for the ship were found in the Smithsonian Institution ship plans collection. The *Spirit's* primary mission will focus on providing unique sail training and maritime educational opportunities for South Carolina youth. However, wherever she sails, the world over, *Spirit* will also be serving as South Carolina's floating 'Goodwill Ambassador'. The primary mission will be as sail training and classroom-at-sea vessel, offering a variety of academic programs through South Carolina and regional schools and colleges. Youth who sail aboard the *Spirit* will learn leadership, teamwork, the taking of responsibility, and environmental awareness. The ship may also be available for corporate educational and professional development programs for forward thinking organizations.

Trainees-passengers: 29
Contact: Brad Van Liew, Executive Director, South Carolina Maritime Heritage Foundation
PO Box 22405, Charleston, SC 29413 USA
Tel: 843-722-1030
E-mail: bvanliew@scmaritime.org
Website: www.scmaritime.org

SPECIFICATIONS

Flag: USA
Rig: Schooner
Homeport: Mobile, Alabama
Sparred length: 149'
LOA: 121'
LOD: 118'
LWL: 103'
Draft: 6' 6"
Beam: 19'
Rig height: 118'
Freeboard: 4'
Tons: 149 GRT
Power: Twin GM 671 diesels
Hull: Riveted steel

ST CHRISTOPHER

The *St. Christopher* is a classic three-masted schooner built in 1932 just as the age of sail was coming to a close. She was built in Delfzijl, Netherlands under Germanischer Lloyd Certification and designed to operate in some of the roughest sea conditions in the world, the North Sea. *St. Christopher* had unfortunately been allowed to slide into very poor condition and was then blown from her moorings by hurricane Georges into a salt marsh. St. Christopher Services Inc. a 501c3 nonprofit organization has acquired the vessel and recovery is underway. Plans for the *St. Christopher* include a complete rebuild to USCG Passenger carrying certification. This is being accomplished through volunteers and donations from individuals and businesses.
St. Christopher Services is an all-denominational Christian Service Organization. Our goals of   service are storm recovery, medical missions, training for economic recovery, and evangelism. Donations of time, materials and finances are always welcome and appreciated towards the restoration of this classic vessel for its mission.

Who sails: Groups and individuals of all ages
Program type: Christian missionary work/mercy ship
Built: 1932: Niestern Sander bv, Delfzijl, Netherlands
Crew: 6
Contact: Mr. Bryan Leveritt, St. Christopher Services LLC, 9275 Old Highway 43 South, Creola, AL 36525 USA
Tel: 251-442-0171 or 251-442-3247
Fax: 251-442-3247
E-mail: bryanleveritt@bellsouth.net
Website: www.stchristopherservices.org

SPECIFICATIONS

Flag: Canada
Rig: Brigantine
Homeport: Kingston, Ontario, Canada
Normal cruising waters: Lake Ontario and adjacent waters
Sparred length: 72'
LOA: 60'
LOD: 57'
LWL: 46'
Draft: 8' 6"
Beam: 15'
Rig height: 54'
Freeboard: 4' 6"
Sail area: 2,560 square feet
Tons: 34 GRT
Power: 165 HP diesel
Hull: Steel

ST LAWRENCE II

The *St Lawrence II* is a purpose built sail training vessel in operation since 1957, primarily on the Great Lakes. She was designed to be manageable by a young crew, yet complex enough with her brigantine rig to introduce teenagers to the challenge of square-rig sailing. The ship is owned and operated by Brigantine, Inc., a nonprofit charity staffed by local volunteers who share the conviction that the lessons of responsibility, self-reliance, and teamwork provided by sail training are especially applicable to teenagers. With 42 years of operation, Brigantine, Inc. is one of the pioneering sail training programs in North America. Cruises in this hands-on program range from six to ten days or more in length. *St. Lawrence II*'s crew complement of 28 is comprised of 18 new trainees, plus a crew of watch officers, petty officers, cook, and bosun, all aged 13 to 18. The captain is usually the only adult onboard. The ship's teenage officers are graduates of Brigantine, Inc.'s winter training program, involving lessons in seamanship, navigation, and ship's systems, as well as the ongoing maintenance of the ship. Every year the *St. Lawrence II* sails over 4,000 miles, spends more than 40 nights at sea, and introduces over 300 trainees to the rigors of life aboard a ship on the Great Lakes.

Who sails: School groups and individuals of all ages
Program type: Sail training with paying trainees
Season: April to November (sailing); October to March (winter program)
Designer: Francis McLachlan/Michael Eames
Built: 1953: Kingston, Ontario, Canada, Kingston Shipyards
Crew: 10   **Trainees-passengers:** 36 day sails, 18 overnight
Contact: Brigantine, Inc., 53 Young Street, Kingston, Ontario K7M 6G4, Canada
Tel: 613-544-5175
Fax: 613-544-5175
E-mail: briginc@kos.net
Website: www.brigantine.ca

STAD AMSTERDAM

Flag: The Netherlands
Rig: Full-rigged ship, 3-masted
Homeport: Amsterdam,
The Netherlands
Normal cruising waters: Worldwide
Sparred length: 250'
LOD: 199'
Beam: 34' 5"
Rig height: 152'
Sail area: 23,700 square feet
Tons: 723 GRT
Power: Caterpillar 1000 HP diesel
Hull: Welded steel

The Clipper *Stad Amsterdam* is absolutely unique: a modern 'extreme' clipper built on historic lines. The final design for the *Stad Amsterdam* combines the best characteristics of historic clippers with state of the art technology and the level of comfort expected in this day and age. Construction of the Clipper started in December 1997, in Amsterdam, The Netherlands. During the construction period she served as a training opportunity for unemployed youngsters to gain valuable working experience. The Clipper is designed to fulfill the requirements of luxury charters, day trips, harbor receptions, conferences and seminars. Owned by the city of Amsterdam and Randstad Group, the world's third largest employment agency, the Clipper provides opportunities for young people to gain work experience, while working alongside a professional crew. The Clipper *Stad Amsterdam* can be found in European waters in summer. In winter the ship sails the Caribbean with the possibility to visit the East Coast of the US or Canada.

Who sails: Groups and individuals of all ages
Program type: Charters (coastal and passage), public relations activities, STA Races, sail training, harbor parties, seminars, meetings
Designer: Gerard Dijkstra, Naval Architects and Marine Engineers, NBJA, Amsterdam
Built: Damen Oranjewerf, Amsterdam
Certification: Sailing Passenger Vessel
Crew: 25   **Trainees-passengers:** 120 day trips, 32-64 cruises
Contact: Cees Rosman, Hospitality Manager RCSA, Rederij Clipper Stad Amsterdam, P.O. Box 12600, 1100 AP Amsterdam The Netherlands
Tel: +31 (0)20 569 5839
Fax: +31 (0)20 569 1720
E-mail: mail@stadamsterdam.nl
Website: www.stadamsterdam.nl

SPECIFICATIONS

Flag: USA
Rig: Barque, three-masted
Homeport: San Diego, CA
Normal cruising waters: Coastal waters between San Diego, CA and northern Baja California, Mexico
Sparred length: 278'
LOD: 210'
LWL: 200'
Draft: 21' 6"
Beam: 35'
Freeboard: 15'
Rig height: 148'
Sail area: 18,000 square feet
Tons: 1,197 GRT
Hull: Iron

STAR OF INDIA

The *Star of India* is the world's oldest active ship. She was built at Ramsey shipyard on the Isle of Man and launched as the Euterpe in 1863. She began her working life as a cargo ship in the India trade and was nearly lost on her first two voyages, surviving a mutiny, collision, cyclone and the death of her captain. In 1871 she embarked on a quarter century of hauling emigrants to New Zealand. She circumnavigated the globe 21 times during this service. She was sold to American owners in 1898 and renamed the Star of India in 1906. By 1923 steam power had replaced sails on merchant ships and the *Star of India* was laid up in Oakland. A group of San Diegans purchased the ship and had her towed to San Diego in 1927. Depression and war delayed the beginning of her restoration until the late 1950s. In 1976, with her restoration complete, she sailed on San Diego bay for the first time in 50 years. The *Star of India* is now the pride of the Maritime Museum of San Diego's fleet of historic ships. She is maintained by a dedicated group of volunteers and skilled craftsman and sailed at least once a year.

Who sails: Selected volunteers, permanent crew, and invited passengers
Program type: Sail training for crew and apprentices; sea education in maritime history; dockside interpretations
Designer: Edward Arnold
Built: 1863: Ramsey, Isle of Man, UK, Gibson, McDonald & Arnold
Coast Guard certification: Museum Attraction Vessel
Contact: Jeff Loman, San Diego Maritime Museum, 1492 North Harbor Drive, San Diego, CA 92101 USA
Tel: 619-871-8836
E-mail: shipsoperations@sdmaritime.org
Website: www.sdmaritime.org

SPECIFICATIONS

Flag: United Kingdom
Rig: Brig
Homeport: Portsmouth, England
Normal cruising waters: UK, Europe, Mediterranean, Canaries, Azores and Caribbean
Sparred length: 195'
LOA: 159'
LOD: 159'
LWL: 133'
Draft: 15'
Beam: 33'
Rig height: 148'
Sail area: 12,503 square feet
Power: 2x MTU 330KW
Tons: 493 GRT

STAVROS S NIARCHOS

Stavros S Niarchos is one of the two purposely built sail training vessels owned by the Tall Ships Youth Trust. She is a 60 meter, steel hulled, square-rigged brig built in Appledore, Devon, and was launched in 2001. She is named after a very generous Greek benefactor. The Tall Ships Youth Trust, incorporating the Sail Training Association, is a registered charity founded in 1956 and is dedicated to the personal development of young people aged 16-25 through the crewing of tall ships. Every year over 2,000 people aged 16 to 75 from all over the world sail on either *Stavros S Niarchos* or her identical sister ship *Prince William*. *Stavros S Niarchos* operates all year round. In the summer months she frequents European and Mediterranean waters and during the winter she may head south for the Canaries, Azores and Caribbean. Youth voyages for 16-25 year olds last from 7-14 nights whereas 18+ voyages range from day sails to a 24 night Trans-Atlantic.

Who sails: Groups and individuals of all ages
Season: Year-round
Program type: Sail training for paying trainees
Designer: Burness, Corlett & Partners & Captain Mike Willoughby
Built: 2000: North Devon, United Kingdom, Appledore Shipbuilders
Crew: 6 pemanent, 13 volunteer   **Trainees-passengers:** 44 day sails, 48 overnight
Contact: Tall Ships Youth Trust, 2A The Hard, Portsmouth, Hampshire P01 3PT England
Tel: +44 (0) 23 9283 2055
Fax: +44 (0) 23 9281 5769
E-mail: tallships@tallships.org
Website: www.tallships.org

Flag: USA

Rig: Gaff schooner

Homeport: Penobscot Bay, Maine

Sparred length: 115'

LOD: 68'

LWL: 58'

Draft: 5' centerboard up, 14.6' centerboard down

Beam: 22.6'

Rig Height: 90'

Sail Area: 3,200 square feet

Tons: 41 GRT

Hull: Oak

STEPHEN TABER

The *Stephen Taber*, built in 1871, is the nation's oldest sailing vessel in continuous service and is designated a National Historic Landmark. She is one of a kind, and one of the last of the coasters that formed the backbone of American commerce a century ago. Built in an era when highly skilled shipwrights built fine vessels to be aesthetically beautiful as well as functional, she stands as a proud tribute to American craftsmanship. Today she is refitted to carry 22 guests in comfort.

Who sails: Groups and individuals of all ages

Program type: Three and six-day overnight sailing adventures; corporate team building; day sails

Season: May through October

Built: 1871, Glenwood Landing, Long Island

Crew: 5   **Trainees-passengers:** 49 day sails, 22 overnight

Coast Guard certification: Passenger Vessel (Subchapter T)

Contact: Capt. Noah Barnes, Captain/Owner, P.O. Box 1050, Rockland, Maine, 04841, USA

Tel: 800-999-7352

E-mail: info@stephentaber.com

Website: www.stephentaber.com

SULTANA

SPECIFICATIONS

Flag: USA
Rig: Square topsail schooner, two-masted
Homeport: Chestertown, Maryland
Normal cruising waters: Chesapeake Bay & Mid-Atlantic
Sparred length: 97'
LOD: 53'
LWL: 53'
Draft: 8'
Beam: 17'
Rig height: 72'
Freeboard: 5'
Tons: 50 GRT
Power: Single screw diesel
Hull: Wood

The Schooner *Sultana* Project is a non-profit, 501(c)(3) organization based in the historic port of Chestertown, Maryland. The *Sultana* Project provides unique, hands-on educational opportunities for children and adults that focus on the history and natural environment of the Chesapeake Bay and its watershed. The principal classroom for the *Sultana* Project is a full-sized reproduction of the 1767 schooner *Sultana* launched in March of 2001. *Sultana* is notable as one of the most thoroughly documented vessels from the time of the American Revolution. The schooner's original logbooks, crew lists, correspondence, and design drawings have all survived intact to the present day. Together these documents tell a vivid story of life along the coast of Revolutionary America - a story that has been incorporated into the schooner's educational programs. *Sultana's* educational programs are designed to compliment and support national, state and local curriculum goals - but just as importantly, they are meant to excite students about the process of learning. Again and again teachers have found that a day on *Sultana* can help to bring subjects like history, science, math and reading alive.

Who sails: School & adult groups as well as individuals of all ages
Program type: Under-sail educational experiences in environmental science and history, including both day trips and live-aboard programming
Season: April to November
Designer: Benford Design Group, St. Michael's, Maryland
Built: 2001: Millington, MD, Swain Boatbuilders, LLC
Coast Guard certification: Passenger Vessel (Subchapter T)
Crew: 5 **Trainees-passengers:** 32 day sails, 11 overnight
Contact: Drew McMullen, Executive Director, Sultana Projects Inc., PO. Box 524, Chestertown, MD 21620 USA
Tel: 410-778-5954
Fax: 410-778-4531
E-mail: dmcmullen@schoonersultana.com
Website: www.schoonersultana.com

SPECIFICATIONS

Flag: USA
Rig: Full-rigged shiphip
Homeport: San Diego, CA
Normal cruising waters: San Diego Bay
LOA: 179'
LOD: 135'
Draft: 13'
Beam: 30'
Rig Height: 130'
Sail Area: 13,000 square feet
Tons: 263 GRT
Hull: Wood

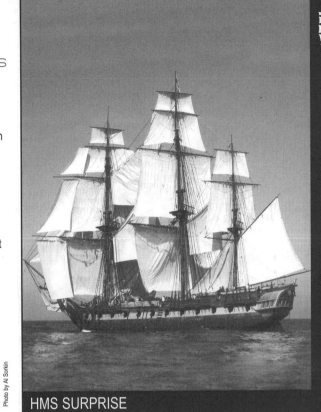

Photo by Al Sorkin

HMS SURPRISE

"HMS" *Surprise* is a 179' full rigged ship. Her designers and builders made painstaking efforts to recreate a 24 gun frigate of Great Britains' Nelson era Royal Navy. The result is a replica vessel unmatched in its authenticity and attention to detail. Originally christened "HMS" *Rose* when she was launched in 1970, she served as a sail training vessel operating out of several east coast ports for over 30 years. The ship underwent extensive modifications for the production of the film "Master and Commander: The Far Side of the World" in 2002. The Maritime Museum of San Diego purchased "HMS" *Surprise* from 20th Century Fox in October, 2004. Plans include restoring the ship to seaworthy condition, but she will probably not be ready to sail until 2006 at the earliest.

Who sails: Museum Vessel at this time
Program type: No programs as yet
Designer: Admiralty
Built: 1970: John Fitzhugh Millar, Lunenburg, Nova Scotia
Contact: San Diego Maritime Museum, 1492 N. Harbor Drive, San Diego CA 92101 USA
Tel: 619-234-9153
Fax: 619-234-8345
E-mail: info@sdmaritime.org
Website: www.sdmaritime.org

SUSAN CONSTANT

SUSAN CONSTANT

SPECIFICATIONS

Flag: USA
Rig: Barque, three-masted (lateen mizzen)
Homeport: Jamestown Settlement, Virginia
Normal cruising waters: Chesapeake Bay
Sparred length: 116'
LOA: 96'
LOD: 83'
LWL: 77'
Draft: 11' 6"
Beam: 24' 10'
Rig height: 95'
Freeboard: 11'
Sail area: 3,902 square feet
Tons: 180 GRT
Power: Twin diesels
Hull: Wood

Susan Constant is a full-scale re-creation of the flagship of a small fleet that brought America's first permanent English colonists to Virginia in 1607. Together with the smaller *Godspeed* and *Discovery*, *Susan Constant* is on exhibit at Jamestown Settlement, a living history museum of 17th-century Virginia, and hosts nearly a half-million visitors every year. Jamestown Settlement is administered by the Jamestown Yorktown Foundation, an agency of the Commonwealth of Virginia. Built on the museum grounds and commissioned in 1991, *Susan Constant* replaced a vessel built for the 1957 Jamestown Festival commemorating the 350th anniversary of the colony's founding. While no plans or renderings of the original *Susan Constant*, *Godspeed*, and *Discovery* have ever been located, the replicas are based on the documented tonnages of the 17th century ships, and *Susan Constant's* design incorporates research information that emerged after the first replicas were built. With a crew of staff and volunteers, *Susan Constant* and *Godspeed* periodically sail to other ports in the Chesapeake Bay region to participate in commemorative and community events and host educational programs. A volunteer sail training program is offered to individuals of all ages.

Who sails: Crew consisting of Jamestown Settlement staff and volunteers
Program type: Sail training for crew and apprentices; dockside interpretation
Designer: Stanley Potter
Built: 1991: Jamestown Settlement, VA, Allen C. Rawl
Crew: 25
Contact: Eric Speth, Maritime Program Manager, Jamestown Settlement, PO Box 1607, Williamsburg, VA 23187 USA
Tel: 757-229-1607
Fax: 757-253-7350
Website: www.historyisfun.org

SPECIFICATIONS

Flag: USA
Rig: Staysail Schooner
Homeport: Seattle, WA
Normal cruising waters: Puget Sound and Canadian Waters
Sparred length: 63'
LOD: 55'
LWL: 45'
Draft: 6'8"
Beam: 14'3"
Rig height: 64'
Freeboard: 36'"
Tons: 32 GRT
Power: 4-53 Detroit Diesel
Hull: Teak

SUVA

Drayton Harbor Maritime (DHM) is a private, nonprofit, 501(c)(3) organization whose mission is to preserve, restore, and interpret the past and present maritime, marine, and estuarine heritage of Drayton Harbor, Washington and its associated waters. Thanks to Bill Brandt, DHM now operates the classic sailing vessel, *Suva*, a 63' Ted Geary schooner providing sail training, environmental education and selective charter in U.S. and Canadian waters. *Suva* was built in 1925 for Frank J. Pratt, of Pratt & Whitney Aircraft engines. DHM, with grant funding and the assistance of the Trillium Corporation, is restoring the former Alaska Packers Association (APA) cannery wharf complex at Tongue Point, Semiahmoo, which in its heyday, was the home of the APA-Star Fleet, which included *Star of India* and *Balclutha*. DHM concurrently operates the Semiahmoo Park Maritime Museum and the historic 1944 pedestrian ferry, *Plover*, built to transport workers to the bygone APA cannery on Semiahmoo Spit, providing visitors with a voyage back in time.

Who sails: All Ages
Program type: Sail training, environmental education, selective charters
Season: Year round
Designer: L.E. Geary
Built: 1925: Hong Kong
Coast Guard certification: in process
Crew: 3 **Trainees-passengers:** 6
Contact: Captain Richard Sturgill, Founding Director, Drayton Harbor Maritime, 1218 4th Street
 Blaine, Washington 98230   USA
Tel: 360-295-3507
E-mail: o_and_a@hotmail.com
Website: www.draytonharbormaritime.org

SWIFT OF IPSWICH

Homeport: Los Angeles, California
Flag: USA
Normal cruising waters: Coastal California and offshore islands
Rig: Square topsail schooner, two-masted
Sparred length: 90'
LOA: 70'
LOD: 66'
LWL: 62'
Draft: 10'
Beam: 18'
Rig height: 74'
Freeboard: 5'
Sail area: 5,166 square feet
Tons: 46 GRT
Power: Diesel
Hull: Wood

The Los Angeles Maritime Institute operates the square topsail schooner *Swift of Ipswich* in the TopSail Youth Program, alongside the twin brigantines, *Irving Johnson* and *Exy Johnson*, providing character building sail training adventures for youth. As LAMI's original vessel, *Swift of Ipswich* is a learning environment that nurtures the development of knowledge, skills and attitudes that are necessary for the education of today's youth, but difficult to teach in a traditional class-room. About two-thirds the size of one of LAMI's twin brigantines, *Swift* is especially well suited for working with younger youth and is a special favorite of youth-of-all-ages. Built to the lines of an historic Revolutionary War privateer, *Swift of Ipswich* was once the personal yacht of actor James Cagney and has been known as a floating landmark, mostly serving youth, in Southern California for over 60 years. She is currently undergoing restoration and continues to welcome special support. The LAMI family takes pleasure in welcoming visiting tall ships and other 'educationally significant' ships to San Pedro.

Who sails: Referred youth-at-risk and groups catering to students and adults
Program type: Educational sailing adventures for "at-risk" youth and other youth or adult groups
Season: Year-round
Designer: Howard I. Chappelle
Built: 1938: Ipswich, MA, William A. Robinson
Coast Guard certfication: Passenger Vessel (Subchapter T)
Crew: 6 **Trainees-passengers:** 49 day sails, 31 overnight - Age: 12+
Contact: Captain Jim Gladson, Los Angeles Maritime Institute, Berth 84, Foot of Sixth Street, San Pedro, CA 90731 USA
Tel: 310-833-6055
Fax: 310-548-2055
Website: www.tollway.com/swift/

SPECIFICATIONS

Flag: USA
Rig: Gaff schooner, two-masted
Homeport: Marion, Massachusetts
Normal cruising waters: Coastal New England (summer), offshore Atlantic Ocean (school year)
Sparred length: 115'
LOA: 92' 10"
LOD: 84' 6"
LWL: 78' 8"
Draft: 10' 4"
Beam: 21' 8"
Rig height: 95'
Sail area: 3,540 square feet
Tons: 100 GRT
Power: 295 HP diesel
Hull: Iron

TABOR BOY

Tabor Boy has been engaged in sail training as a seagoing classroom for Tabor Academy students since 1954. Offshore voyaging and oceanographic studies go together in the curriculum, with cruises to destinations as distant as Mexico and Panama adding adventure to the experience. Many Tabor Academy graduates go on to the US Merchant Marine, Naval, or Coast Guard academies. The schooner also offers seven summer orientation voyages for newly enrolled freshmen and sophomore students. During this time, trainees are fully involved in sail handling while studying Gulf of Maine marine wildlife and ecology. Winter programs feature sailing and snorkeling in the US and British Virgin Islands to observe and study coral reef ecosystems.

Who sails: Enrolled students at Tabor Academy
Program type: Seamanship and oceanography for high school students
Built: 1914: Amsterdam, The Netherlands, Scheepswerven & Machinefabrik
Coast Guard certification: Sailing School Vessel (Subchapter R)
Crew: 6   **Trainees-passengers:** 23 - Age: 14-18
Contact: Captain James F. Geil, Master, Tabor Boy, Tabor Academy, 66 Spring Street, Marion, MA 02738-1599 USA
Tel: 508-748-2000
Fax: 508-748-0353
E-mail: jgeil@taboracademy.org
Website: www.taboracademy.org

SPECIFICATIONS

Flag: USA

Rig: Square topsail/marconi rigged staysail schooner

Homeport: La Paz Harbor, La Paz, Mexico

Normal cruising waters: Sea of Cortez

LOA: 97'

LOD: 72'

Draft: 8'

Beam: 18'

Rig height: 68'

Freeboard: 9' fore, 5' aft

Tons: 115 GRT

Power: Diesel

Hull: Wood

TALOFA

This great ship's name in Polynesian means "QUEEN OF THE SEAS". Two brothers, Charles and Chester Carter, built her to fly between the islands of the South Pacific looking for the treasure of a sunken ship run aground somewhere near the Solomon Islands. Filled with copper ingots that were headed for the Allied Munitions factories, Charley and Chester witnessed seeing the sunken ship while serving on a military ship during World War I. A dream was born. They would build a ship to retrieve their fortune. She would be stout, strong, and heavy, nearly 115 tons, and she would become the "strongest, toughest private sailboat constructed in the 20th Century in America – possibly in the world" according to Winn Joseph Bagley, son of a master wooden ship constructor in whose boatyard the *Talofa* would be built. Sadly, the Carter brother's visions were never to become reality and although ship building began in January of 1928, they never finished her. Today the *Talofa* provides adventure cruises for guests in the beautiful Sea of Cortez. Owners Cactus and Betsy Bryan sail their guests to the magnificent, unspoiled, uninhabited islands off La Paz where they drop anchor each day in a beautiful, calm cove.

Who sails: All ages

Progam type: Adventure sailing

Contact: Baja Schooner Cruises, Betsy Bryan

Tel: 805-216-6494

E-mail: info@bajaschoonercruises.com

Website: www.bajaschoonercruises.com

Flag: India
Rig: Barque, three-masted
Homeport: Kochi, India
Normal cruising waters:
Worldwide
Sparred length: 177'
Draft: 15'
Beam: 28'
Sail area: 10,392 square feet
Power: Twin 320 HP diesels
Hull: Steel

TARANGINI

Tarangini is a three-masted barque designed by the world famous sail ship designer Mr. Colin Mudie and was built by Goa Shipyard Limited, Goa, India. The name *Tarangini* comes from the Hindi word, "TARANG" which means waves. Besides being an ideal platform for basic seamanship, *Tarangini* provides character building and sail training capsule for officer cadets of the First Training Squadron and officers/sailors of Indian Navy. *Tarangini* provides an ideal setting for first hand experience of the natural elements to the cadets embarking on a Naval career. The training imparted onboard *Tarangini* includes general points and terms used in sailing, parts of sails and rigging, setting and furling of sails, watch-keeping under sails, safety while under sails and sail maneuvers such as tacking, veering and boxhauling. It further includes Navigation, ROR (COLREGS), Astro Navigation and other professional subjects. In addition the trainees undertake various activities such as manning the masts, mast drills, and tug of war. INS *Tarangini* fosters the old fashioned and time-tested virtues of courage, camaraderie, and endurance. She instills among the trainees the indefinable "sea sense", apart from qualities of humanity and prudence, which are inseparable from safe and successful seafaring.

Who sails: Officer cadets of the First Training Squadron and officers of the Indian Navy
Program: Sail training and seamanship for cadets and officers of the Indian Navy
Season: Year-round
Design: Colin Mudie
Built: 1997: Goa, India, Goa Shipyard Limited
Crew: 37 **Trainees:** 30
Contact: CDR S Shaukat Ali, C/O Fleet Mail Office, Kochi, India

TENACIOUS

SPECIFICATIONS

Flag: United Kingdom
Rig: Barque, three-masted
Homeport: Southampton, United Kingdom
Normal cruising waters: United Kingdom (summer) Canary Islands and Southern Europe (winter)
Sparred length: 213' 3"
LOA: 177' 3"
LOD: 163' 6"
LWL: 151' 3"
Draft: 14' 9"
Beam: 34' 9"
Rig height: 129' 9"
Freeboard: 7' 3"
Sail area: 12,956 square feet
Power: Twin 400 HP
Hull: Wood/epoxy

The 213-foot, three-masted barque *Tenacious* is the Jubilee Sailing Trust's (JST) new, second ship. She is the largest wooden tall ship of her kind to be built in Great Britain this century. JST promotes the integration of able-bodied and disabled people though the mediums of tall ship sailing and building. Such has been the suc-cess of the JST's first ship, *Lord Nelson*, that JST decided to build *Tenacious*. Bringing the ethos of integration ashore, the JST has developed the concept of Shorewatch, weeklong ship-building holidays. Professional ship-wrights and mixed-ability volunteers have worked side-by-side as part of this amazing project. Like the *Lord Nelson*, *Tenacious* enables all members of her crew to sail together on equal terms. Features include signs in Braille, power-assisted hydraulic steering, and points throughout the ship that enable Wheelchairs to be secured during rough weather. Voyages are open to anyone between 16 -70+ and no previous experience is required. The crew of 40 is split 50/50 between able bodied and physically disabled people, with eight wheel-chair users. There is a permanent crew of 10, including a medical purser and cook.

Who sails: Physically disabled and able-bodied people, aged 16 to 70+
Program type: Sail training for paying trainees; integration of physically disabled and able-bodied people through the medium of tall ship sailing
Season: Year-round
Designer: Tony Castro, Ltd.
Built: 1996-2000: Woolston, Southampton, United Kingdom
Crew: 8   **Trainees-passengers:** 40
Contact: Mrs. Lindsey Neve, Jubilee Sailing Trust Jubilee Yard, Hazel Road, Woolston, Southampton, Hampshire, S019 7GB United Kingdom
Tel: 44-23-8044-9108
Fax: 44-23-8044-9145
E-mail: jst@jst.org.uk
Website: www.jst.org.uk

SPECIFICATIONS

Flag: USA
Rig: Square topsail schooner, 3-masted
Homeport: Long Beach, California
Normal cruising waters: Channel Islands and beyond
Sparred length: 156'
LOD: 123'
LWL: 101'
Draft: 13' 6"
Beam: 31'
Rig height: 110'
Freeboard: 6'
Sail area: 8,500 square feet
Tons: 229 GRT
Power: 575 HP Deutz diesel
Hull: Steel

TOLE MOUR

Tole Mour is a 156-foot three-masted square topsail schooner owned and operated by the non-profit organization Guided Discoveries. With her incredibly seaworthy construction, fifteen sails, hands-on science equipment, professional crew dedicated to teaching, and close proximity to Southern California's biologically rich Channel Islands, she is the ultimate platform for sail training and marine science education. *Tole Mour* was purchased in 2001 to carry out the work of the Catalina Island Marine Institute (CIMI). CIMI Tall Ship Expeditions, founded in 1998, is a Guided Discoveries program that is dedicated to "taking young people to sea in order to build character and minds." CIMI Tall ship Expeditions offers live- aboard voyages during the school year, summer, and winter, that focus on sail training and marine science education and range from 2 to 21 days in length. *Tole Mour* accommodates groups of up to 36 and ages 10 to adult. She sails the waters of Southern California's eight off-shore islands and beyond. Her name *Tole Mour* means gift of life and health - and was bestowed upon her by the school children of the Marshall Islands where she was originally commissioned as a health care support ship.

Who sails: School groups 4th grade through college; educational adult groups; individuals
Program type: Live-aboard educational voyages focusing on sail training and marine science
Designer: Ewbank, Brooke, and Associates
Built: 1988: Whidbey Island, WA, Nichols Brothers
Coast Guard certification: Sailing School Vessel (Subchapter R)
Crew: 13 **Trainees-passengers:** 53 day sails, 36 overnight
Contact: CIMI Tall Ship Expeditions, PO Box 1360, Claremont, CA 91711 USA
Tel: 1-800-645-1423
Fax: 909-625-7305
Website: www.guideddiscoveries.org or www.tolemour.org

SPECIFICATIONS

Flag: USA
Rig: Gaff schooner
Homeport: Newport, Rhode Island
Sparred length: 93'
LOA: 70'
LOD: 70'
LWL: 58'
Draft: 8' 5"
Beam: 18' 6"
Rig height: 85'
Freeboard: 4' 5"
Sail area: 4,200 square feet
Tons: 70 GRT
Power: Diesel
Hull: Wood/epoxy

TREE OF LIFE

The schooner *Tree of Life*, launched in 1991, was built in Nova Scotia, Canada and Jacksonville, Florida. Her owners and a crew of four plus two trainees sailed out of Newport Harbor October 2002 on a six-year circumnavigation. Sailing to Bermuda, St. Martin thru the Caribbean to Grenada and west to Venezuela, Colombia, the San Blas Islands, Panama, Ecuador, Galapagos, Easter Island, Pitcairn Island, the Gambier Islands, and Tahiti. In 2003, *Tree of Life* spends five months in Auckland, New Zealand via Bora Bora, the Southern Cooks and Fiji for the America's Cup challenge. Permanent crew includes Captain, First Mate-Engineer, Bosun, Chef and two trainees. The owners are on board for the duration of the voyage. *Tree of Life* was chosen as one of the top ten yachts in North America by Sail magazine (1993), and in 1997 won the Bay of Islands Race. She is the 1995 and 2000 winner in her class at the Antigua Classic Yacht Race Week. The *Tree of Life* also won first place, "Best Schooner in Fleet" at the 2001 Newport Classic Yacht Race and Festival.

Who sails: Adult individuals and families
Program type: Sail training for volunteer and paying trainees; sea education in marine science and maritime history
Designer: Ted Brewer
Built: 1991: Covey Island, Canada
Crew: 4   **Trainees-passengers:** 6
Contact: Sheri and John Laramee, Owners, 447 Bellevue Avenue, Newport, RI 02840 USA
Tel: 401-847-0444 or 401-732-6464
E-mail: JohnGL@aol.com
Website: www.schoonertreeoflife.com

SPECIFICATIONS

Flag: Canada
Rig: Topsail schooner
Homeport: Halifax, Nova Scotia
Normal cruising waters: Great Lakes, Atlantic, Caribbean
Sparred length: 118'
LOD: 90'
LWL: 83'
Draft: 10'
Beam: 22'
Rig height: 90'
Freeboard: 3' 6"
Sail area: 9,688 square feet
Tons: 98 GRT
Power: 350 HP diesels
Hull: Steel

UNICORN

Originally built in 1947, the *Unicorn's* hull was crafted from the metals of captured German U-boats salvaged after World War II. The Dutch-built fishing vessel trawled the North Atlantic's fishing grounds for 32 years. When her fishing days were over, she was acquired by a Dutch skipper and his wife, Pieter and Agnes Kaptein of Hoorn in the Netherlands. By 1979 she had been converted into a sailing ship and renamed *Eenhorn* or "one horn", Dutch for *Unicorn*. In 1986, under new American owners, *Eenhorn* crossed the Atlantic to the United States and her name was anglicized to *Unicorn*. In 1999, the vessel was acquired by its current owners, Dawn and Jay Santamaria of Hunterdon County, New Jersey. Together with their 4 daughters and professional crew they continue to promote the preservation of traditional maritime life and provide leadership development opportunities to executives, adults and families through sail training programs at sea. The square topsail, gaff rigged schooner has just undergone a complete interior refit and safety and equipment upgrades, making her one of the most beautiful, yet traditional, tall ships in the fleet.

Who sails: Individuals of all ages
Program type: Sail training for groups and individual; nautical curriculum, waterfront festival, and film work
Built: 1947: Alphen, The Netherlands, Gouwsluis
Crew: 8 **Trainees-passengers:** 50 daysails, 25 overnight
Contact: Dawn and Jay Santamaria, 2 Gravel Hill Road, Asbury, New Jersey 08802 USA
Tel: 908-713-1808
E-Mail: dawn@tallshipunicorn.com
Website: www.tallshipsunicorn.com or www.beampines.com or www.canadiansailingexpeditions.com

URANIA

Photo & Copy by Thad Koza

URANIA

SPECIFICATIONS

Flag: Netherlands
Rig: Ketch
Homeport: Den Helder, Netherlands
LOA: 78'
Draft: 9' 10"
Beam: 18'
Hull: Steel

Urania is the flagship of the Royal Netherlands Naval College. Every executive officer who has graduated from the naval college over the past forty years trained on the *Urania*. Generally she sails with three officers, two petty officers, and twelve cadets. She is a very active ship and has thrice been the recipient of the prestigious Cutty Sark Trophy, which is awarded annually to a ship that best demonstrates the spirit of sail training. Her original wishbone rig was modified to her present Bermudian ketch rig in the late 1950s.

Program type: Training vessel of the Royal Netherlands Naval College
Built: 1928
Crew: 5 **Trainees-passengers:** 12
Contact: Royal Netherlands Embassy, 4200 Linnean Avenue, NW, Washington, DC 20008 USA
Tel: 202-244-5300
Fax: 202-362-3430

Flag: USA
Rig: Cutter
Homeport: San Francisco, California
Normal cruising waters: San Francisco Bay and tributaries
Sparred length: 30'
LOA: 30'
LOD: 30'
LWL: 28'
Draft: 4' 6"
Beam: 8'
Rig height: 35'
Freeboard: 2'
Sail area: 600 square feet
Tons: 8 GRT
Hull: Wood

VIKING

Viking is a sailing whaleboat, an open boat designed to be launched from a larger ship while at sea, and was built at Puget Sound Naval Shipyard in 1939 for use in the Navy's fleet sailing program. As the US prepared for war, the Navy stripped its ships and whaleboats were sent ashore. The sailing program was never reinstated, and surplus Navy whaleboats found their way to Sea Scout units around the country, offering thousands of youth the opportunity to learn sailing, seamanship, and teamwork on the water. Of those boats, only a handful remain. The Sea Scout Ship *Viking* has been serving the youth of the Bay Area for over 60 years, offering programs that teach sailing, seamanship, and leadership to young women aged 14-21. Her sister ship, *Corsair*, offers similar programs for young men. The two ships participate in many joint activities. In addition to the annual two-week summer cruise in the Sacramento Delta, the Sea Scouts organize day sails, races, weekend outings, dances, and regattas. New members are always welcomed, both young and adult.

Who sails: High school students and individuals; affiliated institutions include Sea Scouting, Boy Scouts of America, San Francisco Bay Area Council
Program type: Sail training for female trainees, aged 14-21; sea education in marine science and maritime history in cooperation with other groups
Designer: US Navy
Built: 1939: US Navy, Puget Sound Naval Shipyard
Coast Guard certification: Uninspected Vessel
Crew: 6-18
Contact: Nick Tarlson, Skipper Sea Scout Ship Viking, 220 Sansome Street, Ste. 900, San Francisco, CA 94104 USA
Tel: 415-956-5700
Fax: 415-982-2528
E-mail: seascouts@dictyon.com
Website: www.tbw.net/~chriss/scouts

SPECIFICATIONS

Flag: USA
Rig: Gaff topsail knockabout schooner, two-masted
Homeport: Norfolk, Virginia
Normal cruising waters: Worldwide
Sparred length: 126'
LOA: 121' 10"
LOD: 114'
LWL: 84'
Draft: 12' 3"
Beam: 24"
Rig height: 112'
Freeboard: 6' 6"
Sail area: 6,385 square feet
Tons: 97 GRT
Power: 205 HP diesels
Hull: Wood

VIRGINIA

The last pure sail pilot schooner serving the Chesapeake Bay, the 118-foot *Virginia* served the Virginia Pilot Association from 1917 to 1926. Fast and seaworthy, *Virginia* remained in service long into an age where power vessels become the preferred platform for pilot station ships. The *Virginia* Maritime Heritage Foundation in construction partnership with TriCoastal Marine Inc., is building a recreation of the schooner on Norfolk's historic waterfront. Piolet Schooner *Virginia* will be sailing the eastern seaboard of the US in 2005, with a scheduled voyage to Europe in 2006. In 2007 the vessel will participate in the 2007 Jamestown 400th anniversary celebrations. The Foundation, working closely with the public and private sector, will create an international schedule to serve the economic needs of the Commonwealth. Educational programming will be built into the schedule taking full advantage of *Virginia's* geographical locations to create stimulating educational requirements. While in transit, on board college and adult education curriculums will be provided to those accompanying the professional crew.

Who sails: Students from elementary through college including adult programs
Program type: Sail training for volunteer crew and trainees; sea education in marine science, maritime history, and ecology in cooperation with accredited institutions; dockside interpretation during port visits
Season: Year-round
Designer: Tri-Coastal Marine, Inc.
Built: 2004: Norfolk, VA, Tri-Coastal Marine, Inc.
Coast Guard certification: Sailing School Vessel (Subchapter R), Passenger Vessel (Subchapter T)
Crew: 12 **Trainees-passengers:** 35 day sails, 12 overnight
Contact: Captain Robert C. Glover III, Executive Director, Virginia Maritime Heritage Foundation, 5000 World Trade Center, Norfolk, VA 23510 USA
Tel: 757-627-7400 **Fax:** 757-627-8300
E-mail: execdir@schoonervirginia.org
Web site: www.schoonervirginia.org

SPECIFICATIONS

lag: USA
Rig: Full-rigged ship
Homeport: New York, New York
Sparred length: 325'
LOD: 263'
Draft: 11' (min.), 22' (max.)
Beam: 40'
Rig height: 167'
Sail area: 31,495 square feet
Tons: 2,170 GRT
Hull: Iron

WAVERTREE

Wavertree was built in Southampton, England in 1885. She was first employed to carry jute for use in making rope and burlap bags, voyaging between India and Scotland. Within two years, she entered the tramp trade, taking cargoes anywhere in the world. After 25 years, she limped into the Falkland Islands in 1911, having been almost dismasted in a gale off Cape Horn. Rather than rerigging her, her owners sold her for use as a floating warehouse at Punta Arenas, Chile. *Wavertree* was converted into a sand barge at Buenos Aires, Argentina in 1947, and was acquired there by the South Street Seaport Museum in 1968 for eventual restoration to her appearance as a sailing vessel. By the time *Wavertree* was built, she was nearly obsolete, being replaced by ocean crossing steam ships. At the same time, iron-long the choice of ship builders in iron producing countries such as England-was giving way to steel. *Wavertree* was one of the last large sailing ships built of wrought iron, and today is the largest afloat.

Program type: Sea education in marine science, maritime history, and ecology in cooperation with accredited schools and other groups; other education programs focused toward restoration
Built: 1885: Southampton, England, Oswald Mordaunt & Co.
Contact: South Street Seaport Museum, 207 Front Street, New York, NY 10038 USA
Tel: 212-748-8681
Fax: 212-748-8610
Website: www.southstseaport.org

SPECIFICATIONS

Flag: USA
Rig: Square topsail sloop
Homeport: Traverse City, Michigan
Normal cruising waters: Upper Great Lakes
Sparred length: 90'
LOA: 56'
LWL: 49'
Draft: 8'
Beam: 16'
Rig height: 96'
Freeboard: 6'
Power: Diesel

WELCOME

The *Welcome* is a 55-foot sloop, a replica of the original Welcome built in 1775 at Fort Michimackinac during the Revolutionary War, which later became a British military vessel. The current *Welcome* is under construction at the Heritage Harbor in Traverse City, Michigan. The Mackinac Island State Park Commission built the Welcome for the 200th anniversary of Independence Day. The vessel sailed the Great Lakes for a number of years before serving as a dockside museum in Mackinac City. In December of 1992 the Maritime Heritage Alliance (MHA), a nonprofit organization located in Traverse City, MI, was awarded the vessel for reconstruction. Volunteers of the MHA, having built the schooner *Madeline*, are using the traditional boat building skills to restore this magnificent vessel.

Who sails: Families and adults of all ages
Program type: Sail training for volunteer crew and trainees; sea education in maritime history; overnight passages; dockside interpretation
Season: June – October
Designer: Ted McCutcheon
Built: 1976: Mackinaw City, MI, State of Michigan
Coast Guard certification: Moored Attraction Vessel
Crew: 5
Contact: Maritime Heritage Alliance, 322 Sixth, Traverse City, MI 49684 USA
Tel: 231-946-2647
Fax: 231-946-6750
E-mail: mhatc@bignetnorth.net

SPECIFICATIONS

Flag: USA
Rig: Staysail schooner, two-masted
Homeport: Islesboro, Maine
Normal cruising waters: North Atlantic Ocean and Caribbean Sea, Canada to South America
Sparred length: 125'
LWL: 82'
Draft: 12'
Beam: 22'
Rig height: 105'
Sail area: 7,000 square feet
Tons: 138 GRT
Power: 500 HP Diesel
Hull: Steel

WESTWARD

Owned by the Ocean Classroom Foundation, the schooner *Westward* sails on programs of education under sail for the youth of America. Programs range from 4 month semesters-at-sea to week-long programs with schools and youth groups. Trainees sail the ship and learn traditional seamanship skills under the captain and crew, and they explore maritime subjects with the onboard academic staff. The Ocean Classroom Foundation program is a semester-at-sea for qualified high school students, fully accredited by Proctor Academy. The voyage covers more than 4,000 nautical miles, connecting South American shores to the Canadian Maritimes. Students live and work as sailors on a true voyage of discovery, while they study maritime history, maritime literature, marine science, applied mathematics, and navigation. Ocean Classroom is offered Fall, Spring, and Summer terms. Other programs include SEAmester (a complete semester-at-sea for college credit), OceanBound (for high school and college student), and Summer Seafaring Camp (for teens age 13 – 16). The Ocean Classroom Foundation also owns and operates the schooners *Harvey Gamage* and *Spirit of Massachusetts*.

Who Sails: Individuals and school groups from middle school through college; affiliated institutions include Proctor Academy, Long Island University, Center for Coastal Studies, Hurricane Island Outward Bound School, and other schools
Program type: Traditional seamanship training combined with accredited academic studies in maritime subjects
Season: Year round
Designer: Eldridge McInnis
Built: 1961: Lemwerder, Germany, Abeking & Rasmussen
Coast Guard Certification: Sailing School Vessel (Subchapter R)
Crew: 11 including instructors **Trainees-passengers:** 24 overnight
Contact: Bert Rogers, Director, Ocean Classroom Foundation, Inc., 23 Bay Street, Watch Hill, RI 02891 USA
Tel: 800-724-7245 or 401-596-4582 **Fax:** 401-596-4583
E-mail: mail@oceanclassroom.org **Website:** www.oceanclassroom.org

SPECIFICATIONS

Flag: USA
Rig: Gaff topsail schooner, two-masted
Homeport: Miami, Florida
Normal cruising waters: Biscayne Bay, Florida Keys, and Bahamas
Sparred length: 70'
LOA: 60'
LOD: 56'
LWL: 49'
Draft: 6'
Beam: 14'
Rig height: 64'
Freeboard: 6'
Sail area: 2,100 square feet
Tons: 24 GRT
Power: 150 diesel
Hull: Wood

WILLIAM H. ALBURY

In an era when the Atlantic crossing is measured in hours rather than weeks and most people's occupations anchor them to a desk, counter, or workbench, Sea Exploring offers a learning-by-doing environment. Lessons of character building and teamwork apply to all facets of one's life. The Sea Explorer program requires that each trainee exerts and extends him or herself physically, morally, and mentally to perform duties which contribute to the ship. The reward, over and above the experience of a world of beauty and challenge, is the satisfaction and self assurance that contributes to self-dis-cipline. The *William H. Albury's* Sea Explorer Program offers lessons in ecology and international cooperation, as well as history, science, literature, and art. Subject to the dictates of nature, the Sea Explorer program is adventuresome while also a developer of character and a molder of lives. The *William H. Albury* is now in its 30th year of sailing under the command of Captain Joe Maggio and was co-winner of the 1999 ASTA Sail Training Program of the Year Award.

Who sails: School and other groups and individuals; Affiliated institutions include Boy Scouts and schools in Dade County, Broward County and Abaco, Bahamas
Program type: Sail training with crew, apprentices, and paying trainees; sea education in maritime history and ecology in cooperation with accredited schools and colleges and other groups; passenger day sails and overnight passages
Built: 1964: Man o' War Cay, Abaco, Bahamas, William H. Albury
Coast Guard certification: Uninspected Vessel
Crew: 3 **Trainees-passengers:** 30 day sails, 14 overnight
Contact: Captain Joseph A. Maggio, Marine Superintendent Inter-Island Schooner, 3145 Virginia St., Coconut Grove, FL 33133 USA
Tel: 305-442-9697 **Fax:** 305-442-0119
E-mail: heritage2@mindspring.com
Website: www.heritageschooner.com

SPECIFICATIONS

Flag: USA
Rig: Gaff schooner, two-masted
Homeport: Maine
Sparred length: 75'
LOA: 75'
LOD: 65'
LWL: 50'
Draft: 8' 6"
Beam: 15'
Rig height: 80'
Sail area: 2,200 square feet
Tons: 43 GRT
Hull: Wood
Power: Cummings B210 diesel

WILLIAM H. THORNDIKE

The *William H. Thorndike* sails the coast of Maine in the summer. She has received several awards, including the "Most Photogenic" at the 1994 Antigua Wooden Boat Regatta. Formerly the schooner *Tyrone*, the *William H. Thorndike* is the fourth ship to be named for Dr. William H. Thorndike of Boston. Voyages feature traditional sailing with a spirit of lighthearted competition and camaraderie.

Who sails: Individuals and families
Season: Year-round
Program type: Sail training and seamanship for trainees of all ages
Designer: Sam Crocker
Built: 1939: Sims Brothers
Coast Guard certification: Uninspected Vessel
Crew: 2 **Trainees-passengers:** 4
Contact: Townsend D. Thorndike, 222 Whiteface Intervale Road, North Sandwich, NH 03259 USA
Tel: 603-284-7174
Fax: 603-284-9258
E-mail: tdtfarm@worldpath.net

Flag: USA
Rig: Gaff topsail schooner, 4-masted
Homeport: Chicago, Illinois
Normal cruising waters: Great Lakes, Eastern Seaboard, and Caribbean
Sparred Length: 148'
LOA: 109'
LOD: 109'
LWL: 95'
Draft: 8' 6"
Beam: 25'
Rig height: 85'
Freeboard: 8'
Sail area: 4800 square feet
Power: 300 HP diesel
Hull: Steel

WINDY AND WINDY II

Built as modern interpretations of the last days of commercial sail, the *Windy and the Windy II* are true to func-tion while using modern materials and safety features. In 1996, *Windy* was the first four-masted commercial sailing vessel built since 1921, and *Windy II* was completed in 2001. They have many features not found on older tall ships like hot water showers, private bunks, great cabin, furling topsails, as well as bowthruster, shoal draft, and wing keel. Although sister ships, *Windy* is rigged as a schooner and *Windy II* as a barquentine with three square sails. With their divided and easily managed multi-sail designs, there are ample oppor-tunities for persons of all walks of life to participate in the sailing experience. During the summer at Navy Pier, Chicago, both vessels offer hands on sailing experiences to the public as well as private charters for corporations, weddings, team building, and private parties.

Who sails: 5th grade and up, adults and seniors of all ages
Season: Spring and Fall
Designer: R. Marthai
Built: 1996/2001: Detyens Shipyard/Southern Windjammer, Ltd.
Coast Guard certification: Passenger Vessels (Subchapter T)
Trainees-passengers: 150 day sails, 26 overnight
Contact: In season: Captain Bob Marthai, Windy of Chicago, Ltd., 600 E. Grand Avenue, Navy Pier, Chicago, IL 60611 USA, Off Season: 2044 Wappoo Hall Road, Charleston, SC 29412 USA
Tel: 843-762-1342 or 312-595-5472
Website: www.tallshipwindy.com

SPECIFICATIONS

Flag: USA
Rig: Staysail schooner
Homeport: Annapolis, Maryland
Normal cruising waters:
Chesapeake Bay
Sparred length: 74'
LOA: 61'
LOD: 61'
LWL: 51'
Draft: 7'
Beam: 16'
Rig height: 65'
Freeboard: 5'
Sail area: 1,800 square feet
Tons: 25 GRT
Power: 100 HP diesel

WOODWIND and WOODWIND II

The Schooner *Woodwind* and her sister ship the *Woodwind II* are identical 74-foot wooden schooners that sail out of Annapolis, Maryland and can accommodate up to 48 passengers each. These staysail-rigged schooners do a variety of different activities based out of the Annapolis Marriott Waterfront Hotel. The *Woodwind's* offer 2-hour public cruises that depart up to four times daily from downtown Annapolis and sail into the Chesapeake Bay. These schooners also offer private charters for special events, family gatherings and corporate events. One of our specialties is our team building program where the clients Match Race both schooners and really learn what it is like to work as a team to get around the race course (hopefully first). *Woodwind* has four staterooms where couples can stay aboard on Friday & Saturday nights including a sunset sail, accommodations, and breakfast in the morning. In mid-October, there are four cabins available to cruise the Chesapeake for five days on a one-way cruise from Norfolk, Virginia to Annapolis, Maryland. All meals, instruction, accommodations, sailing lore and plenty of lighthouse history are included on this 130-mile journey.

Who sails: School groups from elementary through college, individuals of all ages
Program type: Sail training for paying trainees; informal sea education; team building (including match racing); passenger day sails and group charters; special sailing packages available
Season: April through November
Designer: John Scarano, Scarano Boat Builders
Built: 1993: Albany, NY, Scarano Boat Builders
Coast Guard certification: Passenger Vessel (Subchapter T)
Crew: 10 **Trainees-passengers:** 49 day sails, 8 overnight
Contact: Jennifer Brest, Captain and Director of Marketing Running Free, Inc., 1930 A Lincoln Drive, Annapolis, MD 21401 USA
Tel: 410-263-8619 **Fax:** 410-280-6952
E-mail: woodwind@pipeline.com
Website: www.schoonerwoodwind.com

SPECIFICATIONS

Flag: USA
Rig: Gaff
Homeport: St. Petersburg, FL
Normal cruising waters:
Sparred length: 78'
LOD: 62' 6"
LWL: 50'
Draft: 6'
Beam: 17' 6"
Rig height: 64'
Sail area: 2,500 square feet
Tons: 44 GRT
Power: Ford Lehman 120
Hull: Steel

YANKEE

Yankee, the 78-foot gaff rigged sailing schooner, is designed by Merrit Walter as a traditional topsail tall ship. She has prowled the waters from Cape May, to Key West, the last 20 years. A participant and top finisher for ten years in the Great Chesapeake Schooner Race. During the past two years *Yankee* has been working with the Boy Scouts of America in the High Sea Adventure program bringing to life the adventure. Coast Guard Certified for 49 passengers, she will carry your charter group safely as you participate in the rewarding lifestyle of a tall ship at sea. Today the vessel is available for your group to host a unique custom tailored program. Become a part of the crew and lend a hand as you experience the ship on way to your cruising destination. Professionally captained by Master Richard Moore, his twenty-five years in the Florida Keys, a Gulf of Mexico and Caribbean islands will navigate your group to a reward which will become a life memory.

Who sails: All Aboard
Program type: Custom Educational
Season: Year round
Designer: Merrit Walter
Built: 1993: Norfolk, VA, Norfolk Yards
Coast Guard certification: Passenger Vessel (Subchapter T)
Crew: 3 **Trainees-passengers:** 46 day sails, 22 overnight
Contact: John Ullrich, Owner, Yankee Charter, 10204 Alden Rd., Alden, IL 60033 USA
Tel: 815-648-4683
Fax: 815-648-4683
E-mail: jullrich@stans.com

SPECIFICATIONS

Flag: Australia
Rig: Brigantine
Homeport: Sydney, Australia
Sparred length: 144' 6"
Draft: 13'
Beam: 25' 6"
Hull: Steel

Photo & Copy by Thad Koza

YOUNG ENDEAVOUR

Given by the United Kingdom to the government and people of Australia in celebration of that country's bicentenary, *Young Endeavour* serves as Australia's national sail training vessel. She was dedicated with the words of Prime Minister Robert Hawke "This ship – *Young Endeavour* – bears a name imperishably linked with Captain Cook's great voyage of discovery. And the name itself expresses a great deal of our aspirations for our country." For a land surrounded by the sea, this brigantine is a reminder of the country's maritime heritage. *Young Endeavour's* arrival in Sydney also heralded the start of a new era of sail training in Australia. *Young Endeavour* sails with a permanent crew of nine from the Royal Australian Navy and hosts a coeducational crew of twenty-four young people. Each year *Young Endeavor* provides hundreds of youngsters with the opportunity to participate in one of twenty ten-day voyages off the Australian coast.

Program type: Sail Training Vessel
Built: 1987
Crew: 9 **Trainees-passengers:** 24
Contact: Embassy of Australia, 1601 Massachusetts Avenue, NW, Washington, DC 20036 USA
Tel: 202-797-3000
Fax: 202-797-3168

Photo & Text by Thad Koza

ZENOBE GRAMME

SPECIFICATIONS

Flag: Belgium
Rig: Bermuda ketch
Homeport: Zeebruge, Belgium
Sparred length: 93'
Draft: 8' 6"
Beam: 22' 6"
Rig height: 105'
Hull: Wood

Serving first as a coastal survey ship, *Zenobe Gramme* is now a training ship for the Belgian Navy. She is a frequent participant in sail training races and gatherings and is easily recognizable when she set her spinnaker which displays the Belgian royal coat-of-arms. *Zenobe Gramme* is named for the Belgian inventor who perfected the technology for alternating-current motors and generators in the 1860s and 1870s.

Program type: Training vessel of the Belgian Navy
Built: 1961
Contact: Embassy of Belgium, 3330 Garfield Street, NW, Washington, DC 20008 USA
Tel: 202-333-6900
Fax: 202-333-3079

SPECIFICATIONS

Flag: USA
Rig: Gaff schooner, two-masted
Homeport: Seattle, Washington
Normal cruising waters: Puget Sound, San Juan Islands, Canadian Gulf Islands
Sparred length: 160'
LOA: 127'
LOD: 127'
LWL: 101'
Draft: 16'
Beam: 26'
Rig height: 101'
Freeboard: 5'
Sail area: 7,000 square feet
Tons: 147 GRT
Power: Diesel
Hull: Wood

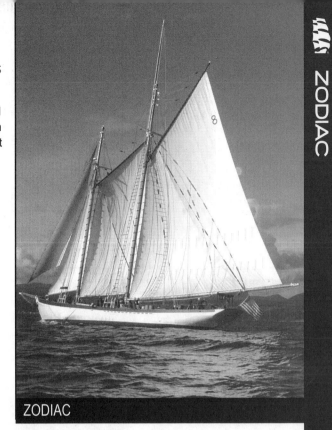

ZODIAC

Designed to reflect the highest achievement of naval architecture under working sail, *Zodiac* was fundamentally a yacht. Built in 1924 for the Johnson & Johnson Pharmaceutical Company, she raced the Atlantic from Sandy Hook, New Jersey to Spain in 1928. The crash of 1929 forced her sale to the San Francisco Pilots Association in 1931. Renamed *California*, she served forty years off the Golden Gate as the largest schooner ever operated by the Bar Pilots. She was bought in 1975 by a group of young craftsmen experienced in wooden boat restoration and was renamed *Zodiac*. In 1982 she was placed on the National Register of Historic Places. Today she sails Puget Sound, the San Juan Islands, and the Canadian Gulf Coast. *Zodiac's* spaciousness and amenities make her the ideal boat for sail training and education programs enjoyed by a wide range of people. In early spring and late fall *Zodiac* hosts Elderhostel sessions, offering courses on sailing, navigation, Northwest Native American culture, legends of the Pig War Island, and geology and natural resources of the San Juan Islands. Summer sessions are open to sailing enthusiasts sixteen years and older.

Who sails: High school through college age students; families, groups, and adults of all ages
Program type: Sail training for trainees sixteen and older; learning by standing watches on the helm, on sailing stations, and in the chart house
Season: March to November
Designer: William Hand, Jr.
Built: 1924: East Boothbay, ME, Hodgdon Brothers
Coast Guard certification: Passenger Vessel (Subchapter T)
Crew: 8 **Trainees-passengers:** 49 day sails, 24 overnight
Contact: June Mehrer, Vice President, Vessel Zodiac Corporation, PO Box 322, Snohomish, WA 98291-0322 USA
Tel: 425-483-4088 or 206-325-6122 **Fax:** 360-563-2469
E-mail: june@schoonerzodiac.com
Website: www.schoonerzodiac.com

Newest Members of the Fleet

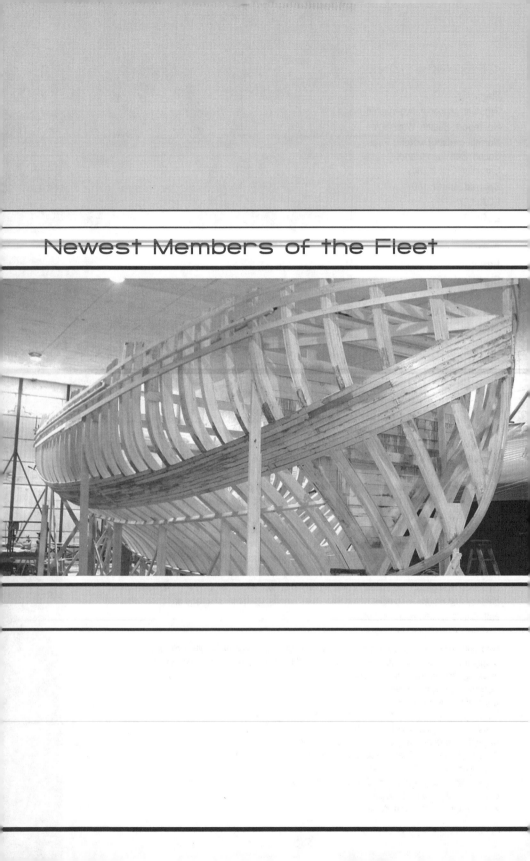

SPECIFICATIONS

Flag: USA
Rig: Gaff ketch
Homeport:
Coupeville, Washington
Sparred length: 52'
LOA: 40'
LOD: 40'
LWL: 33' 4"
Draft: 6' 6"
Beam: 13' 6"
Rig height: 55'
Sail area: 1,100 square feet
Freeboard: 3' 6"
Tons: 19 GRT
Power: 225 HP diesel
Hull: Teak

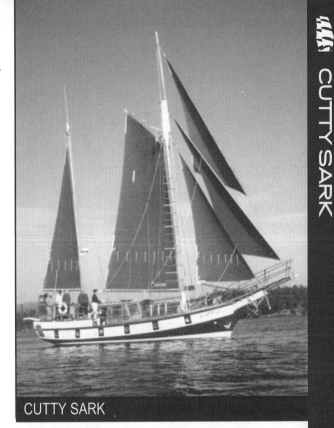

CUTTY SARK

Cutty Sark sails the waters of the State of Washington and operates as a commercial charter sailing ship from the historic Captain Whidbey Inn on the shores of Penn Cove, Whidbey Island, as well as offering volunteer educational opportunities for local school districts and scout troops. Charterers are encouraged, though not required, to lend a hand at running the ship. School groups however, stand watch, navigate the ship, and sing sea chanteys as they raise the sails while learning the history, ecology, and lore of the San Juan Islands. Programs can be designed for groups of any type, from gourmet country Inn cruises, small business retreats, overnight excursions for middle school, high school, and college students, to day sails for elementary school students.

Who sails: School groups from elementary through college; families and individuals of all ages
Program type: Sail training for volunteer or paying trainees; sea education in marine science, maritime history, ecology, and other subjects in cooperation with organized groups.
Designer: Hugh Angleman/Charlie Davies
Built: 1960: Hong Kong, American Marine
Normal cruising waters: Whidbey Island and San Juan Islands, Washington
Contact: Captain John Colby Stone, Æolian Ventures, Ltd., 2072 West Captain Whidbey Inn Road, Coupeville, WA 98239   USA
Tel: 800-366-4097 or 360-678-4097
Fax: 360-678-4110
E-mail: captjohn@whidbey.net
Website: www.captainwhidbey.com/cutty.htm

LOIS McCLURE

SPECIFICATIONS

Flag: USA
Rig: Schooner
Homeport: Burlington, Vermont

The *Lois McClure* is a full-size replica of an 1862-class canal schooner modeled after two historic shipwrecks located within 1/2 of a mile of the construction site. The primary mission of the Burlington Schooner Project is to provide a living vehicle to stimulate student interest in the history and archaeology of Burlington, Lake Champlain and the nation. The Lake Champlain Maritime Museum's Philadelphia II Project demonstrated the public's fascination with boat building projects where, upon seeing a boat being built, young and old alike were stimulated to want to know its history. The Burlington Schooner Project has already produced the same effect. The boat building phase of the project had a life of its own and provided extraordinary opportunities for educational programming and student participation. The launching ceremony was the culmination of this chapter and galvanized great community interest. The schooner *Lois McClure* quickly became a fixture on the Burlington waterfront, drawing local people and visitors alike. Now as the boat tours Lake Champlain, the *McClure* continues its mission to connect the region to this extraordinary history.

Contact: Lake Champlain Maritime Museum, 4472 Basin Harbor Rd., Vergennes, VT 05491 USA
Tel: 802-475-2022
Fax: 802-475-2953
E-mail: info@lcmm.org
Website: www.lcmm.org

PATHFINDER

SPECIFICATIONS

Flag: Canada
Rig: Brigantine
Homeport: Toronto, Ontario, Canada
Normal cruising waters: Great Lakes
Sparred length: 72'
LOA: 60'
LOD: 58'
LWL: 45'
Draft: 8'
Beam: 15' 3"
Rig height: 54'
Freeboard: 4'
Sail area: 2,600 square feet
Tons: 31.63 GRT
Power: 150 HP diesel
Hull: Steel

Tall Ship Adventures conducts sail training on board *Pathfinder*, a square--rigged ship designed specifically for youth sail training on the Great Lakes. Since 1964 over 15,000 young people have lived and worked aboard *Pathfinder* and her sister ship, *Playfair*. Youth between the ages of 14 and 18 become the working crew on one or two week adventures, making 24-hour passages from ports all over the Great Lakes. The program is delivered by youth officers between the ages of 15 and 18, trained and qualified during Tall Ship Adventures' Winter Training Programs. The captain and first mate are the only adults on board. Every year each ship sails over 4,000 miles, spends over 40 nights at sea, and introduces 300 trainees to the tall ship experience. *Pathfinder* is owned and operated by Toronto Brigantine, Inc., a registered charity.

Who sails: In July and August, youth programs for ages 14-18; in May, June, and September, school groups from middle school through college, and interested adult groups
Program type: Sail training for paying trainees, including seamanship and leadership training based on informal, in-house programming; shoreside winter program; dockside interpretation. Affiliated institutions include the Canadian Sail Training Association and the Ontario Camping Association
Designer: Francis A. Maclachian
Built: 1963: Kingston, Ontario, Canada, Kingston Shipyards
Crew: 10 **Trainees-passengers:** 25 day sails, 18 overnight
Contact: Toronto Brigantine, Inc., 370 Queen's Quay West, Ste. 203 Toronto, Ontario, M5V 3J3, Canada
Tel: 416-596-7117 **Fax:** 416-596-9119
E-mail: mail@tallshipadventures.on.ca
Website: www.tallshipadventures.on.ca

PATHFINDER

PETER PUGET

SPECIFICATIONS

Flag: USA
Rig: Standing lug
Homeport: Los Angeles, California
Normal cruising waters:
Los Angeles and Long Beach
Harbors, Alamitos Bay, Newport
Harbor, Mission Bay and
San Diego Bay
Sparred length: 20'
LOA: 20'
LOD: 19' 3"
LWL: 20'
Draft: 13"
Beam: 6' 8"
Rig height: 17'
Freeboard: 18"
Sail area: 153 square feet
Hull: Wood

The *Peter Puget* is named after the trusted lieutenant of Captain Vancouver who led several small boat expeditions in the waters that now bear his name, Puget Sound. Long boats like the *Peter Puget* were the tools for exploring the waters of Puget Sound, the San Juan Islands, and the islands of the inner waters of Vancouver Island. The *Peter Puget* is a reproduction of the type of ship's boat common in the 1790s when Vancouver and Puget explored the Pacific Northwest looking for the Northwest Passage. He (the boat's name is Peter after all) is powered by six oars and a two masted standing lug rig. In the waters of Southern California he will join the program of the Pacific Maritime Institute offering Christian sail training adventures to urban youth. Often there are too few youth to man the tall ships *Swift of Ipswich* and *Bill of Rights* which the Institute charter from the L. A. Maritime Institute. The *Peter Puget* provides an up close experience with the bays, estuar-ies, and yacht/working harbors of the Southern California region.

Who sails: Middle school through college groups and individuals, adult groups for team building
Program type: Character building sail training adventures for volunteer crew and paying trainees, using the adventure of exploring bays and harbors to open trainees to the adven-ture of Christian living and teamwork, marine science and ecology, seaport eco-nomics and maritime history; day long sails, day camp experiences, dockside interpretation
Coast Guard certification: Six-passenger, uninspected
Crew: 2 **Trainees-passengers:** 4 – 6 day sails
Contact: Mark R. Klopfenstein, President, Pacific Maritime Institute, PO box 1883, Garden Grove, CA USA 92840-1883
Tel: 714-813-7707 **Fax:** 714-539-2221
E-mail: markklop@pacbell.net
Website: www.pacificmaritime.org

SPECIFICATIONS

Flag: Canada
Rig: Brigantine
Homeport: Toronto, Ontario, Canada
Normal cruising waters: Great Lakes
Sparred length: 72'
LOA: 60'
LOD: 58'
LWL: 45'
Draft: 7' 6"
Beam: 16'
Rig height: 54'
Freeboard: 4'
Sail area: 2,600 square feet
Tons: 33 GRT
Power: 110 HP diesel
Hull: Steel

PLAYFAIR

Tall Ship Adventures conducts sail training on board *Playfair*, a square rigged ship designed specifically for youth sail training on the Great Lakes. Since 1964 over 15,000 young people have lived and worked aboard *Playfair* and her sister ship, *Pathfinder*. Youth between the ages of 14 and 18 become the working crew on one or two week adventures, making 24-hour passages from ports all over the Great Lakes. The program is delivered by youth officers between the ages of 15 and 18. Our youth officers are trained and qualified during Tall Ship Adventures' Winter Training Programs. The captain and first mate are the only adults on board. Every year each ship sails over 4,000 miles, spends over 40 nights at sea, and introduces 300 trainees to the tall ship experience. *Playfair* is owned and operated by Toronto Brigantine, Inc., a registered charity.

Who sails: In July and August, youth programs for ages 14-18; in May, June, and September, school groups from middle school through college, and interested adult groups
Program type: Sail training for paying trainees, including seamanship and leadership training based on in-house programming; shoreside winter program; dockside interpretation. Affiliated institutions include the Canadian Sail Training Association and the Ontario Camping Association
Designer: Francis A. Maclachian
Built: 1973: Kingston, Ontario, Canada, Canada Dredge and Dock Co.
Crew: 10 **Trainees - passengers:** 25 day sails, 18 overnight
Contact: Toronto Brigantine, Inc., 370 Queen's Quay West, Ste. 203, Toronto, Ontario, M5V 3J3, Canada
Tel: 416-596-7117 **Fax:** 416-596-9119
E-mail: mail@tallshipadventures.on.ca **Website:** www.tallshipadventures.on.ca

SPECIFICATIONS

Flag: USA
Rig: Gaff schooner
Homeport: Chicago , IL
Normal cruising waters: Great Lakes
Sparred length: 77'
LOA: 57'
LOD: 54'
LWL: 49'
Draft: 6' 6"
Beam: 17' 6"
Rig height: 73'
Freeboard: 4' 6"
Sail area: 2,100 square feet
Tons: 41 GRT
Power: 125 HP diesel
Hull: Wood

RED WITCH

The flagship of the Ohio Bicentennial, *Red Witch* is typical of the schooners that once plied Lake Michigan and the Great Lakes. She was built in the tradition of the schooners which were the workhorses of America's 19th century transportation system. Designed by John G. Alden, the *Red Witch* has a hull of cyprus on oak, wooden blocks, and a gaff rig. Although traditional in appearance, the schooner was purpose-built for charter and day cruise service. She has full amenities for up to 49 passengers. *Red Witch* calls Chicago and the southern end of Lake Michigan as home. She has sailed as far as Hawaii and worked in San Diego before coming to the Great Lakes. As Ohio's Bicentennial flagship, she is representing the state on goodwill cruises to Michigan, Indiana, Wisconsin, and Illinois as well as Ontario, Canada during 2003. In addition to walk-on and group charters, the *Red Witch* offers dockside interpretation, sea chanty festivals and freshwater whale watching (none seen yet, but still trying). Sail training programs for disadvantaged and at-risk youth are being developed. *Red Witch* is a popular attraction vessel with waterfront restaurants around the Great Lakes

Who sails: Corporate outings, School groups from elementary school through college; individuals and families
Program type: Sail charters; Sail training for volunteer or paying trainees; sea education in marine science and maritime history in cooperation with accredited institutions and organized groups; passenger day sails
Season: May through October
Designer: John Alden
Built: 1986: Bayou La Batre, Alabama, Nathaniel Zirlott
Coast Guard certification: Passenger Vessel (Subchapter T)
Crew: 4 **Trainees-passengers:** 49
Contact: Captain Bruce Randall, Lakeshore Sail Charters, (mail only address) 30 N. Michigan Ave, #1316, Chicago, IL 60602 USA
Tel: 708-769-4220 **Fax:** 312-782-1205
E-mail: schooner@redwitch.com
Website: www.redwitch.com or www.lakeshoresail.com

Affiliate Members

ActionQuest Programs

ActionQuest worldwide summer adventure programs offer teenagers the excitement of yachting while living aboard, developing new friendships through teamwork, and acquiring valuable, lifelong leadership skills. Shipmates gain internationally-recognized certifications in sailing and scuba diving with marine science, water skiing, wake boarding and windsurfing during their three weeks on board. Most shipmates arrive with no previous experience, yet the first time they set sail from the dock, it will be a shipmate who takes the helm under the guidance of licensed sailing masters. Programs operate in the Caribbean, Mediterranean, Galapagos, Australia and the South Pacific. Attracting over 450 teens from 37 states and 18 countries, ActionQuest creates an environment in which teens can discover the extraordinary in their lives and expand both geographical and personal horizons. ActionQuest also offers 80- , 40- and 20-day college-level Sea-mester programs (www.seamester.com) and community service-learning programs for teenagers (www.lifeworks-international.com).

ActionQuest Programs
James Stoll, Director
PO Box 5517, Sarasota, FL 34277 USA
Tel: 941-924-6789 or 800-317-6789
Fax: 941-924-6075
E-mail: info@actionquest.com
Website: www.actionquest.com

American Schooner Association

Founded in 1972 at Mystic Seaport, the American Schooner Association promotes and encourages the preservation, traditions and enjoyment of schooners and other traditionally rigged vessels. These goals are pursued by providing a record of these vessels, past and present, by supporting organizations that sponsor events for traditional vessels and through its newsletter Wing & Wing. Membership is open to schooner owners and others with an interest in schooners. An annual meeting is held every February at Mystic Seaport. ASA works with many maritime museums and sail training organizations such as ASTA and coordinates members' participation in regattas and tall ship events. A keen rivalry with the Nova Scotia Schooner Association has existed for years and ASA has arranged schooner rendezvous with that group in Gloucester, MA. ASA recently established its first regional Chapter and is seeking to form chapters across the country.

American Schooner Association
Peter Thompson, Commodore
PO Box 484, Mystic, CT 06355 USA
E-mail: Commodore@AMSchooner.org
Website: www.amschooner.org

Block Island Maritime Funding Inc.

Block Island Maritime Funding is a non-profit organization whose purpose is the creation and financial support of marine science programs for New England children in grades K through 12. "Marine Science" encompasses the disciplines of marine biology, marine ecosystems, fisheries science and the development of traditional marine skills such as navigation, sailing and boat building. Maritime Funding, working with other non-profit organizations, specializes in programs for children from varied socio-economic backgrounds in New England and without regard to race, creed or religion. A special emphasis is placed on disadvantaged children from inner city locations.

We are actively supporting the following organizations:

• American Sail Training Association
• Rhode Island Red Cross
• Atlantic Challenge
• The Community School
• Maine Island Trail Association
• Piers Park Sailing Center
• The Paul Cuffee School
• The Fulton Project
• Sail Block Island
• Schooner Sound Learning

Our funding is primarily derived from our boat donation program. To learn more about donating your boat, please visit our website.

Block Island Maritime Funding Inc.
Administrative Office, 12 Bowen's Wharf, Newport, RI 02840
Tel: 401.842.0752
Fax: 401.842.0251
E-mail: info@blockislandmaritime.com
Website: www.blockislandmaritime.com

Girl Scouts of the USA

Girl Scouts sail into the future, in boats small to tall! Whether learning from sailing around a pond or around the world, girls say the "best part's the fun!" A sailing ship is a superb "camp of the sea," where girls can focus on goals like teamwork and leadership through environmental action, international friendship, maritime heritage, arts, technology, science, careers, etc. Indeed sail training is a great way to "just add water" to Girl Scout handbooks, badges, interest projects and the progression of activities for every age level. Starting with basic safety for the youngest Daisy Girl Scouts through sailing adventures for teenage Senior Girl Scouts, Girl Scouts and volunteer leaders in over 300 local Girl Scout councils are always eager for more local, national and international opportunities for fun and learning under sail!

Still on course with sailing adventures, we're involving more girls in port and underway in TALL SHIPS CHALLENGES every year, planning a Girl Scout Mariner reunion with the Los Angeles Maritime Institute's twin brigantines, *Irving Johnson* and *Exy Johnson* (named in honor of *Yankee* pioneers who voyaged with thousands of Mariner Girl Scouts) and other exciting opportunities under sail! On the bow wave of 'Girl Scouting,

315

Where Girls Grow Strong!' (For Tall Ship and GS Mariner links, contact Nancy Richardson at nancy@sailtraining.org or 310-833-6055.)

Kathleen Cullinan, Camping Consultant
Girl Scouts of the USA
420 Fifth Avenue - 15th Floor, New York, NY 10018-2798 USA
Tel: 212-852-8553
Fax: 212-852-6515
E-mail: kcullinan@girlscouts.org
Website: www.girlscouts.org

Golden Gate Tall Ships Society

The Golden Gate Tall Ship Society (GGTSS) is a California nonprofit organization dedicated to educating people in nautical skills and supporting the preservation and operation of traditional sailing vessels, particularly tall ships.
Goals and strategies include:

• Provide opportunities for sail training experiences for young people.
• Provide sailing and shipboard education for members.
• Support shore-side education.
• Support tall ship visiting San Francisco Bay.

Golden Gate Tall Ships Society (formerly Sausalito Tall Ships Society) provides scholarships for young people aboard tall ships, including high school students in San Francisco.

Golden Gate Tall Ship Society
PO Box 926, Sausalito, CA 94966 USA
Tel: 415-332-6999
E-mail: info@ggtss.org
Website: www.ggtss.org

The Gundalow Company

The Gundalow Company is a non-profit organization founded in 2002 with a mission to preserve the gundalow *Captain Edward H. Adams* in order to serve as a platform for maritime, historical, social, and environmental education on and about the waters of the Piscataqua Region. The *Captain Edward H. Adams* was built in 1982 as a replica of the type of 18th century cargo vessel – known locally as a gundalow - that carried salt-marsh hay, bricks, timber, and raw materials between Portsmouth Harbor and the towns on seven rivers that define the Piscataqua Region. The gundalow design evolved over time as an adaptation to the extremely strong currents in the Piscataqua River, very shallow water, and the need for a barge with a capacity to hold up to 50 tons of bulk cargo. The earliest gundalows were simple flat-bottomed barges that moved with the tides and currents. By the mid-19th century the design had evolved to include a leeboard, long sweeps or oars, and a lateen rig that could be lowered to the deck when the vessels passed under bridges. Today, the *Captain Edward H. Adams* visits several ports in the

Piscataqua Region each season providing hands-on educational programs, collaborative community events, and interpreted tours to over 15,000 people.

Gundalow Company
Molly Bolster
PO Box 425, Portsmouth, NH 03801 USA
Tel: 603-433-9505
Fax: 603-433-6403
E-mail: info@gundalow.org
Website: www.gundalow.org

Herreshoff Marine Museum

The Herreshoff Marine Museum bordering Narragansett Bay is arguably Rhode Island's most important maritime historical site. From 1863 to 1945, the Herreshoff Manufacturing Company produced the world's finest yachts, the first United States Navy torpedo boats, and a record eight consecutive successful defenders of the America's Cup. Rhode Island's oldest boat *Sprite* (also the oldest catboat in the US) and *Reliance*, the largest America's Cup boat ever built and featured on the Rhode Island State Quarter, were Herreshoff designs.

The America's Cup Hall of Fame brings alive the history of the America's Cup, tracing advances made in the design, construction and sailing in cup competition, while providing permanent recognition to those who demonstrated outstanding performance and sportsmanship.

Museum activities include presentation of an extensive collection, educational programs for adults and youth, a boat restoration program, research and scholarship, outreach programs and community events.

Herreshoff Marine Museum
Teri Souto
One Burnside Street, PO Box 450, Bristol, RI 02809 USA
Tel: 401-253-5000
E-mail: t.souto@herreshoff.org
Web site: www.hereshoff.org

Inland Seas School of Expeditionary Learning

The Inland Seas School of Expeditionary Learning is the major program initiative of Learn the Seas ~ America, Inc. Learn the Seas ~ America, Inc. (LSA) a not-for-profit organization, has been established to serve as a dynamic educational community for the academic and character development of adolescent youth through marine education activities. The organization brings together two of the greatest and most important resources – youth and the planet's oceans and seas.

The core of LSA is its charter high school, the Inland Seas School of Expeditionary Learning. The "base camp" of the school will be located in Milwaukee, Wisconsin, with learning expeditions planned on the Great Lakes, oceans, and coasts. The school's educational philosophy is guided by the ten design principles and five core practices of Expeditionary Learning Outward Bound. Equal emphasis is given to intellectual and character development. An ethic of service, compassion, and healthy life styles are purposefully practiced. The curriculum will draw extensively from the school's "wilderness classroom" – the Great Lakes and the oceans. Fieldwork, voyages, internships, service projects, and physical training will be combined with internet-based coursework. Fieldwork and projects will range from intensive shore-based core studies to voyages on an offshore school vessel. Marine and maritime topics are the organizing thread of the curriculum. Inland Seas School students will earn a high school diploma and be prepared to advance to college, employment, and further service. The school is being developed currently, with a schedule to open in September 2005 with 40-50 freshmen and sophomores. The enrollment plan will cap at 180-200 students in grades 9-12.

William J. Nimke, Planning Phase Contact
8368 N. Grandview Drive, Brown Deer, WI 53223
Tel: 414-362-9930
E-mail: bnimke13@hotmail.com
Website: www.dpi.state.wi.us/dpi/dfm/sms/inlandse.html

Landing School of Boatbuilding and Design

Established in 1978 and located in Kennebunkport, Maine, The Landing School of Boatbuilding and Design is a non-profit post-secondary career school dedicated to providing the highest quality vocational education in boatbuilding, yacht design, and marine systems technology available. The School was created to provide a gateway to the marine industry for students seeking career opportunities in the marine trades focusing on both recreational and commercial watercraft in both power and sail. The Landing School's ability to reinforce and preserve traditional skills and knowledge while advancing the art and science of boat design, construction, outfitting and repair through the integration of modern techniques and contemporary materials is recognized and valued throughout the marine industry. Our School has earned an international reputation for program quality, and, as an educational institution, is considered by many in the marine industry to be unequaled. The graduates and hundreds of alumni of the School are highly sought after for their craftsmanship, productivity, work ethic, and passion for their chosen careers in, on, and around boats.

Landing School of Boatbuilding and Design
Post Office Box 1490, Kennebunkport, Maine 04046 USA
Tel: 207-985-7976
Fax: 207-985-7942
E-mail: landingschool@cybertours.com
Website: www.landingschool.org

Museum of Yachting

Through a variety of exhibits, the Museum explores the many ways yachting demonstrates human achievement in the arts, in technology, in design, and as a cultural phenomenon. Visitors from around the world marvel at the "Single-Handed Sailors' Hall of Fame", the America's Cup Gallery and the Museum's collection of classic boats, including the Museum's flagship, two-time America's Cup winner Courageous- US12-26. Scholars, marine historians and members have access to a library collection of treasures dating back 300 years. The Museum also presents spectacular special events, including the largest Classic Yacht Regatta on the East Coast.

Overall, the Museum of Yachting creates opportunities for people of all ages to experience elements of yachting culture, demonstrating the possibilities for personal satisfaction, growth, and achievement that are defined by the yachting tradition. The Museum of Yachting is open to the public daily from mid-May through October 31.

Museum of Yachting
SallyAnne Santos, Creative Director
Fort Adams State Park, Newport, RI 02840 USA
Tel: 401-847-1018
Fax: 401-847-8320
E-mail: sallyanne@moy.org
Website: www.museumofyachting.org

National Maritime Historical Society

The National Maritime Historical Society is an educational organization dedicated to promoting greater awareness and appreciation of America's seafaring heritage. The Society advances seafaring knowledge through its quarterly magazine Sea History as well as through its other publications and through programs with schools, museums and universities.

We are currently pursuing "Young America Defends the Hudson," a program commemorating the 225th Revolution and the pivotal role played by the [Royal Navy and American forces to take and defend the waterway that could have divided the colonies.

The Society is also active in historic ship preservation, publication and occasional research projects. It is funded by a large and active membership, which all who cherish the seafaring heritage are invited to join.

In 2001, NMHS initiated "Passage Making," a campaign to build a sound financial future for the Society so that its members, trustees and staff can continue to advance the causes we serve: Communication, the Maritime Education Initiative, and Historic Ship Preservation, In pursuit of this goal, our new mission statement is:
"To preserve and perpetuate the maritime history of the United States and to invite all Americans to share in the challenging heritage of seafaring."

National Maritime Historical Society
5 John Walsh Boulevard, PO Box 68, Peekskill, NY 10566 USA
Tel: 914-737-7878
Fax: 914-737-7816
E-mail: nmhs@seahistory.org
Website: www.seahistory.org

Ocean Voyages, Inc.

Ocean Voyages was founded 23 years ago to provide participatory educational sailing programs throughout the world. Programs are open to sailing enthusiasts of all ages. Most programs run from one to four weeks in length. Ocean Voyages works with educators and institutions to design customized programs for youth participation for "youth of all ages." Ocean Voyages also has extensive experience in scientific research projects and documentary and feature films.

Ocean Voyages works toward preserving our maritime heritage and sailing arts, and providing opportunities for people to gain sailing education and seafaring experience.

Coastal and inter-island programs are available in addition to offshore passage-making and around-the-world voyaging opportunities. Program areas include: Hawaii, California, the Pacific Northwest, Galapagos Islands, Aegean Sea, Caribbean, French Polynesia, and New Zealand, as well as Pacific and Atlantic Ocean crossings.

Ocean Voyages
1709 Bridgeway, Sausalito, CA 94965 USA
Tel: 415-332-4681 or 800-299-4444
Fax: 415-332-7460
E-mail: sail@oceanvoyages.com
Website: www.oceanvoyages.com

Ocean Youth Trust

The Ocean Youth Trust is a co-operative activity between 6 registered charities, each providing Sail Training and personal development for young people between the ages of 12 – 25: OYT-Scotland, OYT Northeast, OYT East, OYT South, OYT Northwest and OYT N. Ireland.   Each organization sails in a different overlapping area but pursues the same aims and objectives. A wide range of other voyages such as the Tall Ships Races are also undertaken.

OYT- EAST
Mr. Barry Johnson
102 Ewe Lamb Lane
Bramcote, Nottingham   United Kingdom NG9 3JW
Website: www.oyc.org.uk

Oswego Maritime Foundation

Chartered in 1980, OMF is a non-profit volunteer organization dedicated to public service through maritime-related education, recreation, and research. The basic purposes of the foundation are to:
• Encourage, sponsor, and coordinate a variety of maritime-related programs
  and activities.
• Promote increased knowledge of, and respect for, skills regarding appropriate utilization
  of maritime resources.
• Work with other established organizations devoted to meaningful maritime activities.

Through the work of dedicated volunteers the foundation has grown and broadened its community service programs, and has become affiliated with the National Safe Boating Council, American Sail Training Association, and the U.S. Sailing Community Sailing Council. The foundation's organizational structure and programs have served as models for other communities throughout the country. In 1992, the Oswego Maritime Foundation was cited by the National Community Sailing Council as conducting one of the two best seasonal instructional boating programs in the U.S.

The Foundation office, library, and classroom facilities are open year-round.

Oswego Maritime Foundation
Roy C. McCrobie Civic Center, 41 Lake Street in Oswego, NY 13126 USA
Tel: 315-342-5753
E-mail: OMF@oswegomaritime.org
Website: www.oswegomaritime.org

The Port Alberni Maritime Heritage Society

The Society is a non-profit community based organization incorporated in 1984 with a mandate to aid in the preservation and exhibition of the maritime history and heritage of Port Alberni, and the west coast of Vancouver Island. The Society advises the Alberni Valley Museum on the development of maritime projects and collections. It also has membership in the Vancouver Maritime Museum, and the World Ship Society (Vancouver Chapter).

Two significant Port Alberni harbor front heritage attractions have recently been completed by the society. They are; THE MARITIME DISCOVERY CENTRE, and the restoration of the Canada Coast Guard historic BAMFIELD LIFEBOAT.

The DISCOVERY CENTRE is open daily during the summer months, and features a changing exhibit each year. Children's special events and "hands on" learning experiences are offered from time to time. MEMBERSHIP: $10.00 Canadian Annually.

Port Alberni Maritime Heritage Society
PO Box 330, Port Alberni, BC V9Y 7M8 Canada
E-mail: PA_Maritime_Heritage_Society@hotmail.com

Mr. Ken Hutcheson, President
PO Box 336, Port Alberni, BC V9T 7M8 Canada

Rose Island Lighthouse Foundation

A mile offshore from Newport, RI lies The Little Lighthouse That Could – Beyond the reach of the city's services and utilities, the restored, operating lighthouse is directly dependent on nature for rainwater and wind-powered electricity. The lighthouse is listed in the National Register and abuts a 17-acre protected wildlife refuge.

Home to historic keepers and their families for over a hundred years, today the restored Rose Island Lighthouse is maintained by vacationing keepers who stay for a night or a week at a time, complete with chores. Families are particularly welcome.

Island For Sale - You can help preserve Rose Island by purchasing 100% guaranteed UNbuildable square-foot lots. This fundraiser is for those who want the privilege of boasting, "I own waterfront property in Newport," while getting a tax deduction in the process. Create a legacy. Have fun. Make a difference. Lots make great gifts for any occasion! Order on-line at www.RoseIsland.org.

Rose Island Lighthouse Foundation
Charlotte Johnson, Executive Director
P.O. Box 1419, Newport, RI   02840 USA
Tel: 401-847-4242
Fax: 401-847-7262
E-mail: Charlotte@roseisland.org
Website: www.roseisland.org

Sail America

Sail America was founded in 1990 by members of the US sailing industry who wanted to play a very active role in growing sailing as a sport, an industry, and a way of life. Its over 600 members represent every segment of the industry from manufacturers to sailing schools, charter companies to publications. It is the only nonprofit industry association exclusively working to promote the growth of the sailing industry.

Sail America's mission statement is: "To promote the growth of the sailing industry." To achieve this they have developed programs and events which will significantly increase participation in sailing. Sail Expo® St. Petersburg, Atlantic Sail Expo®, Pacific Sail Expo®, Strictly Sail® Chicago, and Strictly Sail® Miami not only boost sales for the businesses involved, but serve to educate sailors and non-sailors. Special events and over 300 seminars – a compilation of the best technical, safety, and entertainment presentations offered to the sailing public – take place during the Sail Expo® and Strictly Sail® events.

Scot West, Executive Director
850 Aquidneck Avenue, Unit B-4, Middletown, RI 02842-7201 USA
Tel: 401-841-0900
Fax: 401-847-2044
E-mail: scotw@sailamerica.com
Website: www.sailamerica.com

Sail Martha's Vineyard, Inc.

To All Who See these Presents Greetings! Sail Martha's Vineyard welcomes all tall ships, sail trainers, maritime educators, and seafarers to our "place most pleasant" * (*Concorde log entry 22 May 1602, Gabriel Archer) Sail Martha's Vineyard is a 501(c)(3) non-profit organization dedicated to celebrating and perpetuating the maritime heritage of Martha's Vineyard. A major effort toward fulfilling that mission is to welcome historic and educational vessels to Martha's Vineyard and assist them in all ways possible. This includes a full spectrum of possibilities, from setting up island tours and cross educational opportunities (focusing on the distinct geography and ecology of Martha's Vineyard) to arranging chandlery and personal services. Sail Martha's Vineyard also serves as the focal point for maritime activities and organizations on the island, and as such is happy to provide information and services (as available) to transient vessels and other visitors. Sail Martha's Vineyard's core program focus is teaching individual sailing, boating, water safety and maritime skills to ensure that our traditional bond to the sea always remains stout. Feel free to contact for more information, assistance or potential opportunities.

Tom Rancich, Executive Director
PO Box 1998, Vineyard Haven, MA 02568-1998 USA
Tel: 508-696-7644
E-mail: sail_mv@verizon.net
Website: www.sailmv.com

Sail Newport, Inc

Sail Newport is a non-profit organization dedicated to offering public access to the sport of sailing. To accomplish its mission, we offer educational programs and foster one-design racing in Narragansett Bay. As Rhode Island's Public Sailing Center, the organization endeavors to make it easy and affordable to learn and enjoy the sport of sailing at any age, with its youngest students starting at age seven. Sail Newport also offers a rental fleet of J/22s and Rhodes 19s for use seven days a week during the sailing season.

The broad array of educational programs for youth and adults include novice, intermediate, and advanced levels of instruction. In addition, Sail Newport custom designs sailing programs for schools, colleges, community groups, municipal organizations, youth groups, and disabled organizations. The organization is especially proud of its Scholarship Program which provides financial aid to eligible community families.

Sail Newport has also earned a reputation for excellence in regatta management and is recognized as the leader in hosting world-class sailing competitions and premiere racing events in New England. Each year, we host a number of renowned national and international events with ample shoreside facilities serving regularly as race headquarters. Some of these events have included Sail Newport's own annual Newport Regatta" , now in its eighteenth year, the Rolex International Women's Keelboat Championship, the Laser World Championship, Etchelis North Americans, Junior Olympic Festivals, the 1998 Hartford World Disabled Championship, the 1998 J/24 North Americans, and the 2000 J/24 World Championship.

Sail Newport, Inc.
60 Fort Adams Drive, Newport, RI 02840 USA
Tel: 401-846-1983
E-mail: kimh@sailnewport.org
Website: www.sailnewport.org

Sail San Francisco

Sail San Francisco is a non-profit organization founded to foster international friendships and good will in the San Francisco Bay area. The organization hosts events such as international tall ship gatherings and supports local youth focused tall ship sailing programs which are designed to enhance leadership skills, self-esteem and experience with intercultural exchanges. Special emphasis is placed on community outreach during international tall ship visits. Sail San Francisco strives to offer a variety of free events and ensure that these events are accessible to disabled individuals. Exchanges between local and foreign tall ship crews and under-served residents and students of the Bay Area who share the same language is also a priority.

Sail San Francisco
Alison Healy, Executive Director
2801 Leavenworth Street, San Francisco, CA 94137 USA
Tel: 415-447-9822
Fax: 401-447-7320
E-mail: info@sailsanfrancisco.org
Website: www.sailsanfrancisco.org

Salish Sea Expeditions

Salish Sea Expeditions is located on Bainbridge Island in Washington state and offers 3-5 day trips with 5th-12th grade students from all over the Puget Sound region and beyond. Salish uses inquiry-based science to help students explore the Puget Sound right near their own community. They combine science instruction with hands-on sail training, giving students the opportunity to raise the sails, chart their position, complete the logbook, and take the helm. On longer trips, the students often have the opportunity to "take over the boat" and employ the knowledge that they have collected over the week. Developing and maintaining partnerships with local schools and organizations, Salish Sea Expeditions provides an opportunity for students to engage in real world scientific research using state of the art oceanographic research equipment and data collection strategies. Primarily using the vessel *Carlyn*, Salish Sea Expeditions reaches hundreds of students annually.

Salish Sea Expeditions
Lori Mitchell, Education Director
647 Horizon View Place, Bainbridge Island, Washington 98110 USA
Tel: 206-780-7848
Fax: 206-780-9005
E-mail: info@salish.org
Website: www.salish.org

Seattle Area Sea Scouts / Yankee Clipper

A familiar sight on Puget Sound, the gaff headed ketch *Yankee Clipper* has been training young men and women in the ways of the sea since 1950. Based in West Seattle at the mouth of the Duwamish River, she carries on a Sea Scout program that began 75 years ago. Crew members are of high school age and meet weekly to learn basic seafaring skills, then put into practice what they have learned, while cruising local and distant waters.

The *Yankee Clipper* has participated in each of the previous ASTA Tall Ships® events held in the Northwest and her crew is preparing her for the 2005 season. They have recently made a new set of dacron sails and are overhauling the masts and renewing the ship's standing rigging.

Over the years the ship and crew have taken part in many historical reenactments and civic celebrations, including pioneer landings, Indian canoe events and various water festivals. Each fall they conduct Ecology and History Tours for the public on the lower reaches of the Duwamish, emphasizing water quality, pollution, shoreside industries and protection of fish and wildlife.

Members learn about water safety and during the summer have opportunity to handle several types of small sailing dinghies. Confidence is gained by experience and many find lifetime careers and a love and respect for the sea.

Yankee Clipper is Coast Guard certified for 30 passengers (12 trainees overnight) and is 44' on deck, 11' beam and 5' draft. Her engine is a 100 hp diesel and she carries 1000 sq ft of sail.

John E. Kelly,
5271 45th Ave. S.W., Seattle, WA 98136 USA
Tel: 206-932-0971

Gordon Wickward
941 Davis Place S., Seattle WA 98144 USA
Tel: 206-323-4278

The Sound School Regional Aquaculture Center is a unique public high school offering students a blend of the academic and practical education necessary to succeed in today's ever-changing world. The Sound School enrolls students from New Haven and ten surrounding towns creating a community of diversity that develops students' social and intellectual skills. Our mission is to help students become full participants in the global, multi-cultural society of the twenty-first century by involving them in a broad based high school experience that focuses on aquaculture, marine trades and sciences. We encourage all students to develop sophisticated qualitative problem solving and critical thinking skills in order to apply scientific and ecological principles to everyday life. In this way, we believe that we will prepare Sound School graduates for employment in society as well as for the pursuit of additional opportunities at the post-secondary level.

Mr. Edward Flanagan
17 Sea Street, New Haven, CT 06519 USA
Tel: 203-946-7106
Fax: 203-946-6103
E-mail: Edward.flanagan@new-haven.k12.ct.us
Website: www.soundschool.com

Tall Ship Education Academy/Tall Ship Semester for Girls

TSEA combines an exciting curriculum with the challenges of living at sea and learning to sail. Our students have sailed within San Francisco Bay, along the coast of Baja, and through the Caribbean while developing life skills and engaging in studies that earn them high school credit. TSEA is a special project of the Department of Recreation and Leisure Studies and the College of Health and Human Services at San Francisco State University.

Our cornerstone program, the Tall Ship Semester for Girls is an innovative high school program that combines a strong academic curriculum with experiential learning. The semester breaks into three six week phases: first, students attend academic classes in our classroom on the San Francisco State University campus. Second, students sail aboard a traditionally rigged sailing vessel and visit foreign countries and third, students participate in internships in San Francisco businesses.

In addition to the semester program, we offer other sail training experiences for youth of all ages. For current offerings, please visit our website.

Tall Ship Education Academy
c/o RLS Dept, 1600 Holloway Ave
San Francisco, CA 94132-4161
Phone: 415.405.3703
Fax: 415.338.0543
Email: info@tallshipsemester.org
Web: www.tallshipsemester.org

The Thunder Bay National Marine Sanctuary and Underwater Preserve (NMS/UP) encompasses 448 square miles of northwest Lake Huron, off the northeast coast of Michigan's Lower Peninsula. The landward boundary of the sanctuary/preserve is marked by the northern and southern limits of Alpena County, and extends east from the lakeshore to longitude 83 degrees west. The largest city in the vicinity is Alpena.

NOAA's National Marine Sanctuary Program focuses on protecting our nation's marine resources - both natural and cultural. Before NOAA can designate a National Marine Sanctuary, the proposed sanctuary must be shown to contain resources of "special national significance" because of their conservation, recreational, ecological, historical, research, educational, or aesthetic qualities. The Thunder Bay National Marine Sanctuary and Underwater Preserve contains a collection of shipwrecks that are believed to be of special national significance. The addition of Thunder Bay to the NMS family enhances NOAA's national program for the management of underwater cultural resources in a number of ways. Lake Huron's cold, fresh waters have created a remarkable state of shipwreck preservation that is unmatched by the other sanctuaries' saltwater environments. Thunder Bay's collection of shipwrecks represents the diversity of vessels that navigated the Great Lakes in the 19th and 20th centuries. These sunken ships reflect transitions in vessel architecture and construction while conveying stories of Great Lakes transportation and commerce. A study completed in 1996 indicates that this collection qualifies for National Historic Landmark status, making Thunder Bay an appropriate candidate for National Marine Sanctuary designation.

Ms Kathy Green
145 Water Street, Alpena, MI 49707 USA
Tel: 989-356-8805
Fax: 989-354-0144
E-mail: Kathy.green@noaa.gov
Website: www.thunderbay.noaa.gov

Ventura County Maritime Museum

Located on Fisherman's Wharf at the corner of Channel Islands Boulevard and Victoria Avenue in Oxnard, California, the Ventura County Maritime Museum is the focal point of Channel Islands Harbor's entertainment center, and where maritime history comes alive. The Museum is dedicated to the interpretation of world maritime history, and is acknowledged as housing the finest collection of marine art and ship models on the Pacific Coast. The art collection spans four centuries of marine painters, beginning with the 17th century Dutch and Flemish masters and ending with the work of contemporary artists such as John Stobart and David Thimgan. An international parade of models of historic ships make up a "Genealogy Of Sail" presentation representing nearly 5,000 years of sailing history. Temporary exhibits featuring both local and internationally recognized artists, as well as timely subjects of maritime interest, assure that there is always something new to appeal to and attract repeat as well as first-time visitors. The museum also has an active elementary education program targeted to grades 4 – 7, featuring California, American, and ancient maritime history. The museum combines its programs with the Channel Islands Marine Floating Lab, which offers an oceanography program, to provide students with a rich, rewarding field trip to Channel Islands Harbor.

These programs touch about 4500 students each year. The museum is open seven day a week; hours are 11 – 5. Suggested donation is $3.00 for adults, $1.00 for children under 12. Group tours, special activities for school groups, and social events can be arranged.

Ventura County Maritime Museum
2731 S. Victoria Avenue, Oxnard, CA 93035 USA
Tel: 805-984-6260
Fax: 805-984-5970
E-mail: VCMM@aol.com

Williams-Mystic Maritime Studies Program

The Maritime Studies Program of Williams College and Mystic Seaport offers undergraduates an exciting interdisciplinary curriculum of ocean and coastal studies. Four Williams College courses are offered in the semester-long program at Mystic Seaport, in Mystic, Connecticut: Maritime History, Literature of the Sea, Environmental Policy, and either Marine Ecology or Oceanography. Students earn a full semester's credit and transcript from Williams College. Throughout the semester, students sail on a tall ship, travel the Pacific Coast, and journey to the Mississippi Delta on three extended, hands-on field seminars. Students live in historic, cooperative houses at Mystic Seaport, the nation's largest maritime museum, where they learn traditional maritime skills, and have full access to world-class maritime collections, museum experts, and diverse coastal habitats. College sophomores, juniors, and seniors may participate and all majors are welcome. Financial aid is available. Interested students should contact:

Williams-Mystic
Tel: 860-572-5359
Email: admissions@williamsmystic.org
Website: www.williamsmystic.org

WoodenBoat School

The WoodenBoat School is located on a 64-acre waterfront campus in Brooklin, Maine. Founded in 1981, the school's twin focus is on wooden boat building and seamanship taught by experienced professionals in the marine industry. Sailing courses are taught by experienced, licensed instructors on cutters, Friendship sloops, ketches, and more than 20 assorted small craft ranging from sailing prams to Herreshoff 12-1/2's. Instruction in related crafts such as lofting, marine mechanics, marine survey, painting and varnishing, marine photography, navigation, and marine art is also offered.

Accommodations are available at the school. Courses are also offered at various off-site locations around the country.

Rich Hilsinger, Director
WoodenBoat School
PO Box 78, Brooklin, ME 04616 USA
Tel: 207-359-4651
Fax: 207-359-8920
Website: www.thewoodenboatschool.com

The Working Waterfront Maritime Museum

The Working Waterfront Maritime Museum (WWMM) is a project under the auspices of the Commencement Bay Maritime Association (CBMA) a 501(c)3 charitable organization since March of 1997.

The Museum was incorporated in 1996 to carry on the work begun in the early 1990s by Life on the Sound founders Phyllis Harrison and Mike Vlahovich to create community space to celebrate art, culture, crafts and skills of Puget Sound. The Museum is presently located in the northern one-third of the Puget Sound Freight Warehouse (PSFW) building on Dock Street along Tacoma's Thea Foss Waterway. Our home is a century-old wheat transfer facility that is one of two remaining wooden warehouses originally built as a "mile long" complex around 1900. These warehouses were built to accommodate cargo carrying, square-rigged ships that frequented the port during the early years of Tacoma's history. These wharves hosted many beautiful sailing vessels, as well as steam- and diesel-powered cargo traders well into the twentieth century. The PSFW was last commercially active in the 1970s. The building is owned by the City of Tacoma.

The WWMM is an active participant in Tacoma's annual Maritime Fest, held each September and the annual Classic Boat and Car Show, held on the last weekend in June. The Museum also helps arrange visits to Tacoma by the historic tugboat Arthur Foss, the steamship Virginia V and Argosy excursion cruises. We have a cooperative relationship with the Grays Harbor Historical Seaport Association, *Lady Washington's* parent organization, hosting her visits to the Port of Tacoma.

Working Waterfront Museum
Tom Cashman, Executive Director
705 Dock Street , Tacoma, WA. 98402 USA
Tel: 253-272-2750
Website: www.wwfrontmuseum.org

The Yorktown Waterfront

A 21,000 square-foot retail/restaurant destination, located on approximately seven acres of scenic waterfront property in historic Yorktown, Riverwalk Landing will consist of eight new buildings, a renovated freight shed building, two public piers, and a parking terrace. The project is being developed by York County to revitalize the waterfront and augment the tourism experience in Yorktown and the Historic Triangle. Authentic Colonial architecture is being designed utilizing materials like ballast stone, slate, brick and clapboard. Green space will provide a venue for art shows, wine tasting and musical performances. The construction of a 395 foot pier in length and 20 feet wide will accommodate tall ships, government vessels, and regional passenger cruise ships. The pier will have more than 1,000 feet of dock frontage and electrical, water and telephone and sewer pumpout hookups all provided pierside. Another pier will allow pleasure boaters to dock near the retail complex. Work will be completed by Spring 2005. Visit our website to follow the progress at www.riverwalklanding.com.

The Yorktown Foundation is a non-profit organization dedicated to preserve and perpetuate the special historic character of Yorktown (site of the last major battle of the American Revolutionary War in 1781).

Kristi Olsen
York County Tourism and Events
P.O. Box 532, Yorktown, VA 23690-0532 USA
Tel: 757-890-3525
E-mail: olsen@yorkcounty.gov
Website: www.yorkcounty.gov/tourism

Youth Adventure, Inc.

Youth Adventure, Inc. is the oldest nonprofit sailing organization in the Pacific Northwest. Founded in 1959, Youth Adventures purchased the 1913 schooner *Adventuress* and began to offer a sail training program for "youth of all ages." This limited program became more active in the 60s when stewardship of the historic schooner was assumed by Ernestine "Erni" Bennett. For the next 25 years, Erni and a dedicated group of volunteers operated sail training programs aboard the venerable ship for thousands of youth, adults, and seniors - in Girl and Boy Scout, school, environmental education, elderhostel and other groups. In 1991, Youth Adventures passed ownership and stewardship of the *Adventuress* to Sound Experience, a nonprofit environmental education and sail training organization. Since then, Youth Adventure has continued to help fund regional sail training and sea education programs, youth scholarships, and related activities.

In recognition of her commitment to sail training, Erni Bennett was presented the ASTA Lifetime Achievement Award in 1998. Know to many as "Mrs. B," Erni passed away at the age of 83 in August 2001. However, her sail training legacy will continue on through the newly established Ernestine Bennett/American Sail Training Association Scholarship program as will her enduring example of supporting sailing-based, lifelong learning opportunities for "youth of all ages."

Ms Sandy Bennett
707 Esquimalt Road, Apt 539, Victoria, British Columbia, Canada V9A 3L7
Tel: 250-384-4086 or 250-812-7231
E-mail: snowmaidengirl@yahoo.com

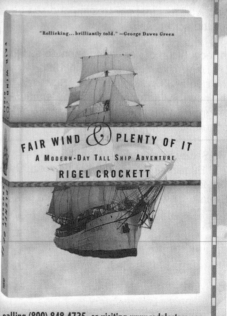

Business Partners

AMIST Concession

Mr. and Mrs. Ken and Betty Stenger
PO Box 93, Ovid, MI 48866 USA
Tel: 989-834-2490
E-mail: amistbetty@yahoo.com

Bay Queen Cruises

The Bay Queen was named for the nineteenth century vessel, '"BAY QUEEN," which operated between Providence and Newport from 1865 until it was dismantled in Providence, May 5, 1906. Today, Four Bay Queens and our newest vessel the "Vista Jubilee" have carried well over a million people to relax and enjoy the spectacular views of our pristine Narragansett Bay and Newport.

We have maintained a local workforce throughout the years. For some it has provided a summer job out of high school and through college. Others have been with us ten or fifteen years. A few of us have even been here for over twenty years! The most satisfying accomplishment we see is the development of our young people. Many of our employees come to us at 16-18 years of age, some for their first jobs. We watch them change in size, maturity, responsibility and attitude. Many of our kids have gone on to be Captains, marine insurance specialists, state representatives, various types of engineers, a seminary student and at least one doctor. Some have even found their husbands or wives here!

We have provided the setting for over 1000 wedding receptions, many corporate/customer parties, birthdays, anniversaries, school trips, fund-raisers, senior proms, and nature cruises (our new seal watch cruises).

Come join us for a "Day on the Beach" on a one-day vacation! You can enjoy a murder mystery cruise, a variety of comedy night cruises, or you can dance the night away with one of our talented entertainers or disc jockeys. Or, perhaps just sit back for a relaxing cruise on the cool and sparkling waters of Narragansett Bay. The Vista Jubilee is handicapped accessible, and now our office and ticket windows are also. So, come and be a part of our history!

Bay Queen Cruises, Inc.
461 Water Street, Gate #4, P.O. Box 368, Warren, RI 02885-0368 USA
Tel: 401-245-1350 or 800-439-1350
Fax: 401-245-6630
E-mail: info@bayqueen.com
Website: www.bayqueen.com

Bellingham Bell Company

Using the centuries old lost wax method to create classic personalized bronze bells, we cast each bell individually with your logo, name, or personal design. Your design is cast in raised letter format to proudly proclaim your vessel's heritage in the traditional style of the historic tall ship era. Choose from three sizes measured across the bottom of the bell: 6" (usually a desk mount or front door bell), 8" as required by the USCG for vessels up to 19.9 meters (65 ft.) and our flagship Classic 12" for all vessels over 19.9 meters.

Visit our website at www.bellinghambell.com and see for yourself what hundreds of discerning vessel owners already know. Bellingham Bells are the finest bronze bells available on the market today.

Bellingham Bell Co.
Tel: 360-671-0404
Website: www.bellinghambell.com

Boothbay Harbor Shipyard

Marine Railway Service Since 1840, Samples Shipyard in Boothbay Harbor, Maine, has recently changed hands. The new general manager is David Stimson who has 30+ years experience designing, building and restoring wooden vessels. Former owner Chris Braga has stayed as operations manager, and Joe Jackimovicz, yard foreman since 1978, will also remain. Samples has a long history of wooden boat work. Recent projects include major restoration work on *Bounty*, the tug *Luna*, and the schooner *Roseway*. Current projects include restoration of the 100 year old Herreshoff New York Thirty *Alera*, a new centerboard schooner designed by David Stimson and repair work on the *Concordia* yawl *Donegal*. The 700-ton railway can haul vessels up to 200', and our skilled labor is available for new building, restoration and repairs in steel and wood. We take pride in doing top-quality work quickly and efficiently.

Boothbay Harbor Shipyard
dba Samples Shipyard
P.O. Box 462 Boothbay Harbor, Maine 04538
Tel: 207 633-3171
Fax: 207-633-3824
E-mail: samples@gwi.net
Website: www.bbhshipyard.com

Channel Islands Harbor Department

The Channel Islands Harbor, owned by the County of Ventura, is located 60 miles north of Los Angeles, halfway between Los Angeles and Santa Barbara. The harbor is best known for it's year round events and gateway to a wilderness playground, the Channel Islands National Park. Called the "gateway" to the Channel Islands because of its proximity, the harbor is the perfect location from which to take day or extended trips. Located in a picturesque setting, the harbor is home to nine full-service marinas with more than 2,600 boat slips, three nautically themed shopping centers, yacht clubs, more than a dozen restaurants with spectacular views, a year round water taxi , a weekly Farmers' Market, a waterfront hotel and a variety of shops and services. The harbor is home to one of the country's finest maritime collections housed at the Ventura County Maritime Museum located at Fisherman's Wharf. The museum is a cultural center dedicated to the interpretation of maritime history through interactive exhibits and educational outreach. Outdoor adventure activities include boating, sportfishing, kayaking, scuba diving and whale watching. Beautiful parks are scattered throughout the harbor, miles of sandy beaches and special events year round as well as regular visits by historic tall ships.

The Channel Islands hosts several annual events including Celebration of the Whales, Fireworks by the Sea, Concerts by the Sea, Ventura County Boat Show, Ventura Vintage Rods Harbor Run, Channel Islands Harbor Seafood Festival and Parade of Lights. The Channel Islands Harbor was proud to become a host port for the

ASTA TALL SHIPS CHALLENGE® Race Series in 2005.

Visitor Information: The Channel Islands Harbor Visitors Center is located at 3810 West Channel Islands Blvd., Suite E   Tel: 805-985-4852.

Michele Gilmour, Marketing Director
Channel Islands Harbor Department
3900 Pelican Way, Oxnard, CA 93035 USA
Tel: 805-382-3013
Fax: 805-382-3015
E-mail: Michele.Gilmour@ventura.org
Website: www.channelislandsharbor.org

Charleston Maritime Center, Charleston, South Carolina

Located on the peninsula's edge of the historic district, The Charleston Maritime Center makes a perfect stop for all types of visiting vessels. It is nestled in the center of Charleston's protected harbor and is approximately 3.5 miles from the open sea. Access is direct and immediate from the sea to the dock. No bridges are located from the mouth of the harbor to the docks. While on land, you are in close proximity to the new public library, historic tours and attractions, food and equipment provisioning.

The Charleston Maritime Center has hosted several tall ships to date, including the *Spirit of Massachusetts*, *Liberty Clipper*, *Windy*, *Voyager*, *Bill of Rights*, *Bounty* and the HM Bark *Endeavour*. The Center also hosted Tall Ships 2000® Charleston and the 2004 TALL SHIPS CHALLENGE® Atlantic Coast fleet.

The Center is Charleston's premier and only waterfront facility created for the community's use and enjoyment through many varieties of maritime related activities. The good currents and swift winds are especially conducive to races. With plenty of room to dock your boats, you can cruise to the finish line and literally step off your vessel to accept the winning trophy. Showers and free parking are also on-site, so make the most of a good day on the water. Should you prefer a little sightseeing or nightlife, the Charleston Maritime Center is just a few short blocks from the historic district.

Charleston Maritime Center
Mr. Victor Smith, Manager
10 Wharfside Street, Charleston, SC 29401 USA
Tel: 843-853-362
Fax: 843-577-6675
E-mail: smithvi@ci.charleston.sc.us

City of New London, Connecticut

New London's new, $20 million waterfront park offers a half mile promenade and five piers to visiting vessels and tourists from around the world. This deep water port welcomes tall ships and luxury cruise lines as a destination port for travel up and down the Eastern Seaboard. Floating docks for transient boaters are available to the public, and kayakers and cancers can launch from a car-top boat ramp. The City Pier Plaza has a fiber-optic lighted stage area to entertain thousands for events year round. SeaPony Express offers cruises and charters in the river and Long Island Sound. Customs House Pier can accommodate large and small vessels and nearby mooring fields welcome visiting sailors. A dinghy dock allows access to the waterfront park and downtown New London. New London and Southeastern Connecticut have everything visitors look for when planning travel experiences. Visit the best in the arts, family attractions, quiet beaches, the world's largest casinos and Yankee heritage, all in a bustling New England port.

City of New London, Connecticut
Richard M. Brown, City Manager
181 State Street, New London, CT 06320 USA
Tel: 860-447-5201
Fax: 860-447-7971

City of Sarnia, Ontario, Canada

Sarnia hugs the St.Clair River, and shores of the one of the world's largest freshwater lakes, Lake Huron. It is one of the busiest recreational boating and shipping regions of the Great Lakes. Here, the landmark twin Blue Water Bridges join Ontario with Port Huron, Michigan, just an hour north of Detroit.

For thousands of years, natives have inhabited the area. The first European settlers arrived early in the 19th century. They named their community "The Rapids" for the fast-flowing St. Clair River. In 1836, The Rapids was renamed Port Sarnia, but in 1856 it was given a final new name, which was Sarnia.

Sarnia marks the northern starting point of the St. Clair Parkway, one of three parkway systems in the province. The city boasts approximately 20 kilometers (12 miles) of waterfront and is home to over 73,000 residents. One of the features of the Sarnia Bay district is Centennial Park, home to the annual Christmas-themed Celebration of Lights and a variety of summer festivals. The Sarnia Highland Games have been held in Centennial Park for two decades. Dow People Place, located within the park, is an outdoor entertainment stage featuring regular summer concerts. Beside Sarnia Bay Marina is a 100 foot wide model of the Great Lakes. The ample outdoor park settings create an ideal environment for waterfront picnics and location to view the busy river activity. Annually more than 5,000 freighters pass by Sarnia, traveling up and down the St. Clair River. Two cruise boats run regular excursions from Sarnia and Point Edward out onto Lake Huron.

The area enjoys a moderate climate, rarely receiving significant snowfalls, but often just enough to put glimmer on the ground for the lights festival. Summers are hot but a cool breeze off the lake or a dip in its refreshing waters makes Sarnia a perfect vacation spot.

City of Sarnia, Ontario
Henk Vanden Ende
946 Toro Street, Sarnia, Ont, N7V 3N9 Canada
Tel: 519-333-6344
E-mail: henkv@ebtech.net

Columbia Trading Company

Columbia Trading Company offers used, out-of-print, rare and selected new nautical books to readers and collectors of maritime and naval history, yachting and cruising, shipbuilding and design, ship modeling, navigation and seamanship, diving, ocean liners, warships, the merchant marine and nautical fiction.

Our downtown Hyannis, Cape Cod, shop also displays the full spectrum of ship models, artwork, artifacts and distinctive gifts listed here -- and more besides.

We are always interested in purchasing good books and book collections.

Columbia Trading Company
One Barnstable Road, Hyannis, MA 02601 USA
Tel: 508-778-2929
Fax: 508.778-2922
E-mail: info@columbiatrading.com
Website: www.columbiatrading.com

District of Squamish, British Columbia, Canada

Squamish is "The Outdoor Recreation Capital of Canada™". This region has an abundance of world-class outdoor recreational opportunities set within truly spectacular scenery.

There are well over 25 activities available in the region including world famous rock climbing, wind/kite surfing, mountain biking and eagle watching. In addition there is hiking, river rafting, kayaking, sailing and boating, fishing, diving, golf, snowmobiling, bird watching, horseback riding and more - as well as five provincial parks surrounding the area.

The Squamish area also has great historical and geological attractions such as the West Coast Heritage Railway Park, B.C. Museum of Mining in Britannia Beach, Shannon Falls and the Stawamus Chief – a large granite monolith famous for rock climbing.

Community events include the Mountain Bike Festival in June - with the gruelling 67 km Test of Metal mountain bike race, the Bob MacIntosh Triathlon in July, the Squamish Days Loggers Sports with the international logging competitions in August, and Squamish was the site of the Canadian Men's National and Women's World Windsurfing Championships in 2003. There are many more arts, cultural, sports and entertainment events throughout the year.

Whether it is your first time or you are back for more we hope you enjoy Squamish, The Outdoor Recreation Capital of Canada™.

Mayor Ian Sutherland
PO Box 310, Squamish, British Columbia V0N 3G0 Canada
Tel: 604-892-5217
Fax: 604-892-1083

Eastern Salt Co.

Eastern Salt is a family-owned business operating on Boston Harbor in the City of Chelsea. We are Massachusetts' leading importer of road salt, and are able to accommodate all sizes and types of vessels, from tall ships to tankers. Located in a designated port area, our facility is a five-acre site with a low-water depth of 40 feet.

The City of Chelsea has always played an important role in the maritime history of Massachusetts, and we at Eastern believe in continuing to connect the citizens of Chelsea with her working ports.

To celebrate the relationship of community to ocean, Eastern Salt welcomes tall ships to our dock each summer for community groups, schools, and neighbors to tour.

Eastern Salt Co.
Paul Lamb
37 Marginal Street, Chelsea, Massachusetts USA
Tel: 617-884-5201

Fairwinds Schooner Cove Resort and Marina

Located 15nm northwest of Nanaimo on Vancouver Island (49deg 17.28'n -- 124deg 7.9'w) Fairwinds boasts many activities: 18 hole championship golf course, hotel/pub overlooking our 350 berth marina, approx 1300 acres of brilliant trails to hike & bike using our rental bikes, paddle to the many small islands using Seadog's rental kayaks, tennis and outdoor heated pool & hot tub. We hosted *Europa* en route to the Steveston Tallship Festival in 2002 -- Over 3000 people in one day, to date our biggest event. We would like to host mini tall ship festivals in the future and could handle 6 to 8 vessels 50 to 120ft, With advanced notice revenue sharing activities could be arranged. Complimentary moorage will be offered to any tall ship that calls ahead of time. We look forward to seeing some of your majestic ladies gracing our docks soon.

Fairwinds Schooner Cove Resort and Marina
Wayne Newport, Marina Manager
3521 Dolphin Drive, Nanoose Bay, British Columbia V9P 9J7 CANADA
Tel: 250-468-5364
E-mail: wnewport@fairwinds.ca
Website: www.fairwinds.ca

Great Lakes Marketing Group

Great Lakes Marketing Group works to bring ships to ports and ports to ships. Our goal is to provide ships with a constant audience, while helping the community to develop long-term waterfront programs. These opportunities may include student, community and environmental education programs, waterfront festival development, grants and sponsorship recruitment. Through strategic marketing and communications, and as liaison between ships and ports, Great Lakes Marketing Group integrates mutually successful port visits.

Great Lakes Marketing Group

Ship Appearances for both
ships and ports
Festival Production
Special Events, Tour Coordination

C: 847-274-2475

E: PattiLock@greatlakesmg.com

Since 1998, Great Lakes Marketing Group has coordinated the Great Lakes tours of the U.S. Brig *Niagara* (2002, 2004), and the H.M.S. *Bounty* (2004), produced U.S. Cellular Kenosha Days of Discovery, Kenosha, Wisconsin (2003, 2004), developed Navy Pier's AT&T Wireless Tall Ships® Chicago (1998, 2000) and associate-produced/handled ship recruitment for the Huntington Cleveland Harborfest 2001, 2003 and ship recruitment for Ohio's Bicentennial celebration for 10 Lake Erie ports.

Patti Lock
Marketing Strategist for Ports & Ships
Great Lakes Marketing Group
Tel: 847-274-2475
E-mail: pattilock@aol.com

Hampton Event Makers

Hampton EventMakers is a non-profit corporation dedicated to the production of premiere festivals and events in Downtown Hampton, VIrginia. Hampton EventMakers annually produces and manages over 50 days of events and festivals presenting themes that concentrate on a wide range of cultural flavors and what makes the city of Hampton unique.

Mr. John Charles Sandhofer
756 Settlers Landing Road, Hampton, VA 23669 USA
Tel: 757-727-1540
Fax: 757-727-1225
E-mail: john@downtownhampton.com
Website: www.hamptoneventmakers.com

Jordan Harrison Insurance Brokers

Founded in 1995, Jordan Harrison Insurance Brokers are independent insurance brokers specializing commercial and marine insurance coverages. Our emphasis is on all facets of marine insurance; such as, Hull, Protection & Indemnity (P&I), Marine Liabilities, and Ocean Cargo Insurance coverages. Marine insurance coverages, by nature lend themselves to international insurance and their related exposures thus our interest is not only to the Hull and P&I insurances that a vessel owner would have but also the related shoreside exposures that need to be addressed when vessel visit Ports of Call. As a result, we also lend ourselves to marine liability programs that are designed to incorporate all liability exposures under one program if possible. Private or corporate members of ASTA can be assure that we have the capability of handling not only the marine insurance programs for their vessels but also the non-marine exposures that they will have including Directors & Officers liabilities that are typical of non-profit organizations. In addition, our expertise extends to exposures that you may have as a Charterer of vessel for your event or excursion as well as the events surrounding the promotion of your tall ships program.

All of the employees associated with Jordan Harrison Insurance Brokers either come from the national insurance underwriting background or also national broker background as well. We feel that we give all of our customers international expertise and capabilities with local service. Please do not hesitate to contact us.

Jeffrey Dickow or Serene Dong
Jordan Harrison Insurance Brokers
Tel: 415-398-5911
Fax: 415-398-6157
Website: www.jordanharrison.com

Nathanial S. Wilson, Sailmaker,Inc.

Mr. Nat Wilson
Lincoln St., PO Box 71 East Boothbay, ME 04544 USA
Tel: 207-633-5071
E-mail: nswsails@gwi.net

Nauticus - The National Maritime Center

NAUTICUS, The National Maritime Center is located on the downtown waterfront in Norfolk, Virginia. Home to the Battleship Wisconsin, Nauticus is an exciting 120,000 square-foot science and technology center exploring the power of the sea.

Nauticus features hands-on exhibits including computer and video interactives, films on a giant screen, exotic aquaria, interactive theaters, touch pools, shark touching, national-caliber traveling exhibits, and much more!

Berthed adjacent to Nauticus, the Battleship Wisconsin is one of the largest and last battleships ever built by the U.S. Navy. Explore its deck through a self-guided or audio tour that will take visitors back in time to experience this majestic ship that earned five battle stars during World War II. The Battleship Wisconsin remains an asset of the U.S. Navy and its daily operations are managed by The Hampton Roads Naval Museum, located within Nauticus.

The Hampton Roads Naval Museum introduces you to more than two centuries of naval history as seen through the eyes of the sailor in and around the great harbor of Hampton Roads. Your tour begins with the Revolutionary War's Battle off the Capes in 1781 and continues through the present day.

Nauticus, The National Maritime Center is an exciting interactive science and technology center that explores the naval, economic, and nautical power of the sea!

One Waterside Drive, Norfolk, VA 23510
Tel: 757- 664-1000 or 800-664-1080
Fax: 757-623-1287
Website: www.nauticus.org

Norfolk Festevents, Ltd.

Founded in 1977, Norfolk Festevents originated as an all volunteer organization dedicated to producing an annual waterfront and maritime festival - Norfolk Harborfest. Since then, Norfolk Festevents has evolved into a major East Coast event production company, producing over 80 waterfront events, festivals and concerts annually, as well as serves as the managing agency for the City of Norfolk for tall ship visits and related maritime projects.

Norfolk Festevents, Ltd
Karen Scherberger, Executive Director
120 W. Main Street, Norfolk, VA 23510
Tel: 757 441-2345
Fax: 757 441-5198
E-mail: scherbergerk@festevents.org

Piscataqua Maritime Commission

This Portsmouth based organization is dedicated to bringing tall ships to Portsmouth Harbor. Volunteers assist in fundraising efforts and when the ships are in Portsmouth, they act as guides, manage crowd control and staff the headquarters tent on the site.

Piscataqua Maritime Commission
PO Box 164
Portsmouth, New Hampshire 03801

Port Townsend Foundry

Port Townsend Foundry is a custom and production nonferrous foundry. We are able to produce a wide range of products using only the best materials available today. Since 1983, we have built our reputation on hard work and customer satisfaction. Although the road has not always been paved in gold or smooth as one would hope, we have managed to flourish with the ongoing support of customers and employees.

We are not affiliated with any other companies and don't supply any offshore products. We are proud to use the words made in The USA.

Our main product line is marine hardware for sail, power and commercial vessels of all sizes. Castings are produced in silicon (everdure), manganese, aluminum-bronze, white bronze and aluminum alloys. Items range from deck hardware, mast fittings to rudder pintles and gudgeons. We are sure you will like the number of things to choose from.

Our next line is public oriented products. These are the things you see on city streets or your neighborhood parks etc.

Our Custom line might be the most exciting to those who need something a little different than off-the-shelf parts. Engine components, antique replacements, one-offs, research and development. What can we cast for you?

Pete and Cathy Langley.
11 Crutcher Road, Port Townsend WA 98368 USA
Tel: 360-385-6425
Fax: 360-385-1947
E-mail: ptf@olypen.com
Website: www.porttownsendfoundry.com

Rite in the Rain

"Rite in the Rain" is a truly amazing paper created specifically for writing field notes in all weather conditions. From the torrential downpours in the Pacific Northwest to the blistering heat and humidity of a Florida summer day, "Rite in the Rain" sheds water, so users can continue to write on it, even in a downpour. Using a pencil or an all-weather pen, "Rite in the Rain" ensures that your notes survive the rigors of the field. Our recyclable paper is made with environmentally friendly materials, giving you peace of mind as you use our products. For over 80 years the J. L. Darling Corporation has been producing all-weather writing products for a variety of outdoor professionals worldwide.

Rite in the Rain
Bradley Jensen, Marketing & Graphics Assistant
J. L. Darling Corporation
Tel: 253-922-5000
Fax: 253-922-5300
E-mail: Brad@RiteintheRain.com

Sail Classics

The Sail Classics Collection is a continuing work. We started with six America's Cup yachts from *America* (1851) to the classic J-boat *Endeavour*. since that time, our collection has expanded to many American designed boats such as the Herreshoff 12 1/2, our new Beetle Cat and many more. Our sailboat models are all hand-made with plank on bulkhead construction. Our lacquer finish on each boat is hand rubbed to a glossy mirror-like finish. Each boat comes with easy assembly instructions and a wooden stand to display it on.

If you are interested in seeing our product in person, we sell only at boat shows and selected gift shops around the country.

Our commitment to our products and our customers is the goal we strive for. Our products are hand-crafted by people from around the world. Their creation is to inspire and create a place where we can all relax, and continue to "Dream of Sailing".

Sail Classics, Inc.
PO Box 747, Lakebay, WA 98349 USA
Tel: : 253-884-2267 or 800-652-3757
Fax: 253-884-7858
email: sales@sailclassics.com
Website: www.sailclassics.com

Sailing Ship Adventures

Sailing Ship Adventures is a specialty travel service that represents sailing ship owners and operators, including some of the sailing world's best-kept secrets. We book voyages for our customers on a wide variety of sailing ships ranging from the largest full rigged tall ship in the world (The *Royal Clipper*, at over 400 feet in length) to smaller vessels (ranging from 60 to 100 feet in length), as well as aboard crewed chartered yachts.

Unlike your local travel agent we do not represent just a few ships and tour providers, but a wide variety of ships in many different destination areas. We have researched tall ships and sailing ship vacations the world over. Our extensive knowledge of sailing ships and the resulting roster of vessels in our fleet means that, no matter where you would like to spend your next vacation or what you would like to do there, we can find the perfect voyage for you.

Our fleet is comprised of more than 100 full-rigged tall ships, brigantines, barkentines, schooners, and smaller vessels. This range of ships, from the most luxurious to the more spartan, offers you the widest range of choice available.

SAIL AWAY ON YOUR OWN TALL SHIP ADVENTURE!

Call Toll-Free: 1-877-882-4395

Or go to:
www.SailingShipAdventures.com
888 Worcester Road, Suite 260
Wellesley, MA 02482

Our ships sail to destinations through the world, ranging from popular itineraries in the Caribbean and Mediterranean Seas, to ocean crossings, to exotic areas such as the fjords of Patagonia, the Andaman Sea, and the Queen Charlotte Islands. Sailing to these destinations offers opportunities to experience exotic locations in an up-close and intimate way that is not possible on traditional cruises. Smaller vessels are able to stop at smaller, out-of-the-way ports of call not accessible to large cruise liners.

Climb aboard one of these majestic sailing ships and set sail to exotic locations

Dexter Donham
Tel: 781-237-4395 or toll free 877-882-4395
E-mail: ddonham@sailingshipadventures.com
Website: www.sailingshipadventures.com

SeaVancouver

A celebration of West Coast-style maritime fun, the new Sea Vancouver festival will be held July 6 -10, 2005. Visit Vancouver's shores this summer for music, comedy, sports, food, arts, culture, casino nights, fireworks and the best time you'll have all year!

The Sea Vancouver TALL SHIPS CHALLENGE® 2005 will anchor in Vancouver's harbors this year and will be back in 2008 and 2011.

The Sea Vancouver TALL SHIPS CHALLENGE® 2005 is expected to attract 500,000 visitors to the water's edge this year. To herald the ships' arrival, thousands will line the shores to welcome the fleet as it sails into the city during the Parade of Sail on July 7, 2005. Majestic vessels will navigate their way from ports around the world, including Russia, Mexico, New Zealand, the United States and Canada. Prime viewing spots include English Bay, False Creek, Kitsilano Beach and Jericho Beach.

The Sea Vancouver Festival Society was founded to create a brand new signature festival for Vancouver. Our goals are to celebrate Vancouver's connection to the sea and share our beautiful city with the people who live here and visit each year.

Tel: 604-779-7007
Website: www.seavancouver.ca
Email: info@fgenius.com

Societe du Vieux-Port de Montreal (Old Port of Montreal Corporation, Inc.)

Since May 1992, the Old Port of Montreal has been offering Montrealers, yachting tourists, and tall ships a quality marina The Port d'Escale. Located in the Jacques Cartier Basin, the Port d'Escale is equipped with a full range of up-to-date facilities to accommodate sailboats over 200 feet, docking on floating docks. Tucked into the heart of the Old Port, a few steps away from downtown Montreal, this secure facility provides a quiet haven for tall ships mooring there. Because of its varied activities and its unique atmosphere, the Old Port is an important site for recreation and tourism in Montreal. Set a heading for the Port d'Escale, and discover Montreal in style.

Sylvain A. Deschamps, Harbourmaster
333 de la Commune Street West, Montreal, Quebec H2Y 2E2 Canada
Tel: 514-283-5414
Fax: 514-283-8423
E-mail: deschamps@oldportofmontrealcorporation.com
Website: www.oldportofmontreal.com

Village of Greenport, New York

Located in the beautiful, deep and superbly protected waters of the Gardiners/Peconic Bay system of eastern Long Island, Greenport Harbor has been a uniquely appealing destination for mariners since the dawn of American history. Modern-day Greenport remains true to this heritage. A seaborn visitor arriving today steps off the boat, and back in time, to enjoy an authentic working seaport where a car is unnecessary. Deep water dockage for large and small vessels is available at a municipally owned marina in the heart of a downtown waterfront listed on the National Register of Historic Places. Stores, galleries, and services including those catering to mariners, such as welding, hauling, carpentry and marine hardware, even a hospital, are but steps away. A waterfront park has been developed upland of the marina which boasts a vintage carousel, an outdoor amphitheater and boardwalk. Additional board-walk will soon connect the marina to a transportation center where bus, rail, and ferry connections are available to Shelter Island, New York City, and destinations throughout Long Island.

Greenport is keenly interested in visits by tall ships and sail training vessels and will make special arrangements to host traditional sailing vessels, their crews and trainees.

Mayor David E. Kapell
236 Third Street, Greenport, NY 11944 USA
Tel: 631-477-3000
Fax: 631-477-2488

Village of Ontonagen, Michigan

Surrounded by beautiful Lake Superior and the Ontonagon River, the Village of Ontonagon is perched along the most northern coastline of Michigan's Upper Peninsula. Ontonagon's marine heritage showcases an historic lighthouse, recently purchased from the Army Corps of Engineers by the Ontonagon County Historical Society. We also have a 38 slip marina with a riverfront boardwalk and recreation area owned by the Village, a privately owned 600 foot concrete dock along the east shoreline of the Ontonagon River, and a gravel dock along the west shoreline of the Ontonagon River owned by the Ontonagon County EDC. Ontonagon boasts a Township park right on the shores of Lake Superior, with plenty of camp sites available, and beautiful sunsets guaranteed every summer evening. Ontonagon is located a mere 15 miles away from one of our State treasures; the Porcupine Mountains Wilderness State Park. The "Porkies" have 60,000 acres of some of the last true wilderness, with miles of hiking, beautiful vistas, camp sites and rustic cabins available for rent.

Penny Osier, Village Manager
315 Quartz St., Ontonagon, MI 49953
Tel: 906-884-2305
E-mail: ontmgr@up.net

Wild Rice Adventure Consulting, Training and Facilitation

Wild Rice Adventure Consulting, Training and Facilitation works with sail training and other experiential education programs in a variety of ways. Captain Richard "Rusty" Rice, founder of Wild Rice Adventure, uses his 17 years of adventure education experience to help sail training organizations in developing and implementing experiential education programs to train their staff and crews in experiential education philosophy, theory, and facilitation skills. Additionally, Wild Rice Adventure provides onsite first aid and CPR certification oriented to the program environment (ie: marine, wilderness, cold weather, tropical.) Wild Rice Adventure offers individual consultations to those who wish to gain facilitation and outdoor leadership skills, or to pursue a career in the outdoor experiential education and sail training fields.

Captain Richard E. Rice, Jr. WEMT
Wild Rice Adventure, Consulting and Facilitation
1004 Commecial Avenue, PMB-301
Anacortes, WA 98221 USA
Tel: 360-770-7075
E-mail: captrustyrice@aol.com

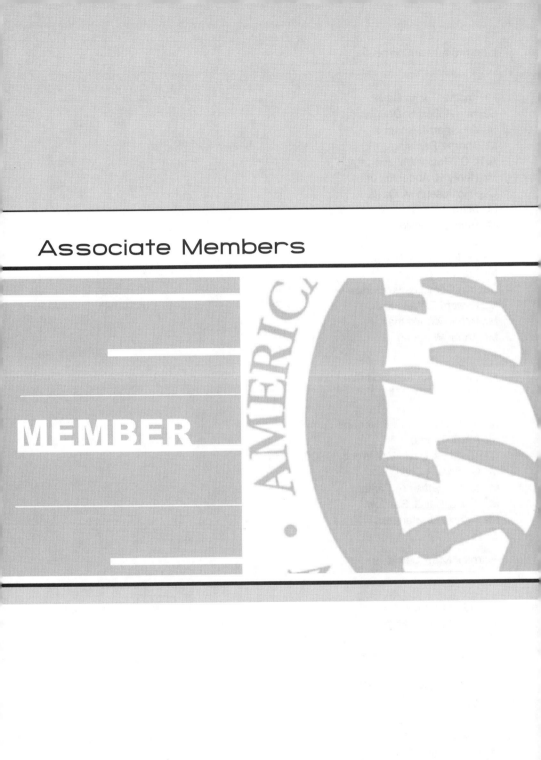

Lifetime Members

Mr. and Mrs. John Benson
Captain Robert S. Douglas
Mr. Jonathan T. Isham
Mr. Thor H. Ramsing
A. R. G. 'Robin' Wallace
Mr. Henry H. Anderson Jr.
Captain Joseph M. Davis
Mr. Murray Davis
Mr. Ronald V. Gallo
Mr. John M. Hopkins
RADM Michael A. Martin
Mr. Frederic S. Sater
Captain Cornelius Vanderstar
Mr. Edward B. Watson Jr.
Mr. Robert W. Wrathall
Mr. Arthur W. Young

Supporting Members

Mr. & Mrs. Steven H. Baker and Family
Ms Alix T. Thorne
CAPT & Mrs. David V. V. Wood, USCG (Ret.)
Mr. Gregory P. Child
Mr. & Mrs. Jeffrey N. Parker
Mr. & Mrs. Hal G. Barstow
Ms Patricia Dzintarnieks

Family Members

Mr. Arthur Birney
Mr. & Mrs. James Hutton
Mr. Robert Wheeler
Dr. & Mrs. Marshall Cushman
Mr. Stanley Martin and Family
Mr. & Mrs. Derek Klett
Mr. & Mrs. Daniel A. Mello
Mr. Joseph A. Ribaudo
Mr. & Mrs. Robert Waugh
Mr. & Mrs. Robert A. Smith
Dr. & Mrs. Cameron Hinman
Mr. Slavek Michalowski
Mr. Alexander M. Agnew

(Family continued)

CAPT Peter C. Wylie, USN (Ret.)
Captain Ed Burns Esq.
Captain & Mrs. Robert D. Rustchak
Mr. & Mrs. Rochester M. Johnson
Mr. & Mrs. Steve Moulton
CAPT & Mrs. Ivan T. Luke, USCG
Mr. & Mrs. Robert P. Hofmann
Mr. Richard Haggblad
Mr. & Mrs. E. MacGregor Strauss
Mr. Robert Petree
    & Mrs. Roxanne Delaney

Individual Members

Mr. Dexter Hoag
Captain and Mrs. Arthur M. Kimberly
Mr. John Osgood
Mr. John D. McShane
Mr. Kevin DeVries
Mr. Raymond A. Stache
Mr. Jeremy Kessenich
Mr. Thomas E. Dasson
Ms Deirdre O'Regan
Mr. Graham D. Briggs
Mr. Sym Colovos
Mr. George W. Crowninshield
Mr. Christopher Kluck
Mr. Roy H. Kruse
Captain Ian McIntyre
Captain Jan Miles
Mr. Robert Miorelli
Mrs. Donna Prieur
Mr. Robert J. Surprenant
Mr. Matthew Twomey
Mr. & Mrs. Eli Weinberg
Captain John C. Wigglesworth
Captain Stephen Connett
Dr. Michael S. Carlson
Ms Terese Ayre
Mr. John F. Boyle MD
Captain Gregory Gooch
Mr. Jim Heldberg
Mr. H. Jochen Hoffman
Captain Brian S. McNamara

347

Mr. James R. Neal
CAPT John T. O'Brien, USN (Ret.)
Mr. Daniel Powers
Captain High Samuel
Ms Joan Sharp
CAPT Harold J. Sutphen, USN (Ret.)
Greg F. White
Mr. Alan C. Johnson
Captain Thomas Baker II
Mr. Harvey Brillat
Mr. Jesse Schaffer
Ms Emily Evans
Mr. Thomas E Baker II
Ms Claudia Bankert
Mr. David H. Blomberg
Ms Irene Bodnaruk
Captain Robert Brittain
Ms Nicole Colasacco
Mr. Joe Ewing
Ms Aurora Fleming
Mr. Iver C. Franzen
Mr. George C. Hering III
M. Hickman
CDR Robert A. Johnson, USN (Ret.)
Ms Andrea Marcille
Kent Matsuoka
Mr. Dennis C. Mayhew
Mr. Darren O'Brien
Mr. J. Richard Pfund
Mr. Fritz Senftleber
CAPT Eric Shaw, USCG
Ms. Karla M. Smith
Mr. Ivan Stoner
Mr. Steve Tompkins
Mr. William Colby
Captain William F. Young
Dr. Sally H. Lunt
Mr. Tim Miller
Mr. Horton R. Shaw
Mr. Stephen K. Galpin
Mr. Lou Linden
Ms Mo Newman
Ms J. Catherine Roberts
Mr. Mark Rosenstein
Mr. Thompson Tully
Mr. Alan Creaser

Mr. Matt Johnson

Mr. Kevin Dykema

Mr. Paul C. Nicholson Jr.

Ms Lynn Ann Oschmann

Mr. David Schenk

Mr. Douglas T. Fischer

Mr. Doran E. Smout

Ms Sally Somsel

Mr. Paul H. Sheehan

Mr. Richard C. 'Chad' Loebs Jr.

Ms Sharon Hirsch

CAPT Elizabeth G. Wylie, USN (Ret.)

Dr. David R. Damon

Mrs. Deirdre Sykes

Mr. Donald F. Teal

Mr. Shane Walden

Mr. Charles Nelson

Ms Margaret Fenton

Mr. Edward V. Pietka

Ms Christine Cleary

Mr. & Mrs. Terashima

Mr. Nicholas Alley

Mr. Thomas D. Blanchard Jr.

Mr. Peter W. Evans

Ms Susan Trudeau

Mr. Paul E. Vardeman

Ms Dawn Fizzard

Mr. Michael L. Bachler

Ms Anna Soens

Mr. Fred LeBlanc Jr.

Captain Erik Berliner

Ms Jeanie Poole

Captain Richard Shannon, USCG (Ret.)

Mr. Howard Slotnick

Mr. Ron Casey

Mr. Ethan Gallogly

Captain Jim Wehan

RADM Tim Jenkins

Mr. & Mrs. George I. Rockwood Jr.

Ms Lia Dudine

Mr. Bart Dunbar

Mr. Ray O. Sisk

Dr. Peter Equi

Mr. Donald L. Nock

Mr. Richard T. Harris

Ms Erin Klein

(Individual continued)

Mr. William M. Gruber
Mr. Peter L. Crew
Mr. John C. Laible
Ms Jesse Leah Nankin
Captain Kenneth Greff
Mr. James W. Hiney
Mr. Robert P. Johnson
Mr. Richard Miller
Captain Randall S. Peffer
Mr. Richard 'Rusty' E. Rice
Mr. Henry Coppola
Ms Blythe Daly
Mr. David E. Fleenor
Mr. Georgeson Agbolosu
Mr. Emmanuel Cloutier
Mr. James E. Hilyard
Mr. Adrian McCullough
Ms Kae Paterson
Mr. Carl J. Schweizer
Mr. James E. Spurr
Mr. William Rudek

Junior Members

Mr. Austin Glenn
Ms Liz Tabor
Ms Madeline R. Baird
Ms Sara Martin
Ms Arielle Knuttel
Mr. Kai Lorenz
Ms Hannah Garrett
Mr. Brian Kliesen
Mr. Roger Wingfield

Sail Training International

Sail Training International is a registered Charity (not for profit organization). Its purpose is the education and development of young people of all nationalities, religions and social backgrounds through sail training worldwide. The Founding Members of Sail Training International are the national/representative sail training organizations of Australia, Belgium, Bermuda, Canada, Denmark, Finland, France, Germany, Ireland, Italy, Latvia, Netherlands, Norway, Poland, Portugal, Russia, Spain, Sweden, UK and USA.

Sail Training International

Sail Training International conducts a number of activities to promote and raise funds to support its charitable purpose. It organizes and manages The Tall Ships' Races and other events, an annual conference and seminars. It produces a range of publications, including a membership magazine Tall Ships and Sail Training International.   The Member national organizations of Sail Training International also organize and manage a wide range of events.

Sail Training International also plans a number of new initiatives to support the development and promotion of sail training internationally. The most recent of these (April 2004) is the creation of the Sail Training International Class 'A' Tall Ships Forum which is focused on the needs and interests of operators of the world's big square-rigged sail training ships.

Sail Training International Limited and Sail Training International Events Limited
Registered Office: 5 Mumby Road, Gosport, Hampshire PO12 1AA, UK
Tel +44 (0)23 9258 6367 Fax +44 (0)23 9258 4661
website: www.sailtraininginternational.org
Email: office@sailtraininginternational.org

Member Organizations

UNITED STATES
American Sail Training Association www.sailtraining.org
Founded in 1973, the organization represents the interests in the US of 300 member sail training vessels from more than 20 countries. There are also 100 affiliate members including museums, schools and universities, and close to 500 individual members who support the organization's mission. ASTA raises funds and administers several scholarship programs as well as a professional development grant program to support the continuing education of professional sail trainers and marine educators.

AUSTRALIA
Australian Sail Training Association www.sailtrainingaustralia.com
Founded in 1996, AUSTA represents the interests of 16 sail training organizations and tall ship operators in Australia and New Zealand. Its purpose is to promote the development of sail training with an emphasis on adventure training for young people at sea under sail in Australia and elsewhere. AUSTA also plays a key role in the development (for sail training vessel operators) of safety-related codes of conduct and on-board management systems, trainee and professional crew training programs and other related programs.

BELGIUM
Restored, owns and operates the T/S *Williwaw* and promotes sail training for young people on many other Belgian vessels.

BERMUDA
Sail Training Association Bermuda john.wadson@stabermuda@logic.bm
Formed in 2001 following the success of the Tall Ships 2000 transatlantic race, STA Bermuda promotes and helps to fund the participation of young Bermudians in sail training programs internationally. It is also working with The Bermuda Sloop Foundation to support the construction of its own unique Bermudian sloop for sail training.

CANADA
Canadian Sail Training Association www.sailtraining.ca
Founded in 1984, its membership now includes the owner/operators of 18 vessels ranging in size from a six-meter open sloop to an 80-metre barquentine and providing sail training programs as diverse in scope as the vessels themselves. A key priority for the organization now is to ensure a regulatory environment that is consistent with the goals and activities of sail training operators and their programs.

DENMARK
Danish Sail Training Association www.dsta.dk
Founded in 1996, DSTA represents the interests of 30 members in Denmark, the Faroe Islands and Greenland, including ten sail training vessels (ranging in size from an 18 metre ketch to two Class 'A' full rigged ships) and five ports. The organization operates a grant scheme to assist trainees taking part in The Tall Ships' Races.

FINLAND
Sail Training Association Finland www.staf.fi
STA Finland member sail training vessels have taken more than 12,500 young people to sea since the organization's foundation in 1973. These young trainees have also formed their own organization (The Sail Trainees of Finland Association) which provides opportunities for continuing contact between the trainees and also helps to promote sail training in Finland.

FRANCE
Sail Training Association France – Amis des Grands Voiliers
www.amisdesgrandsvoiliers.org
Founded in 1990, STA France represents the interests of 35 vessels and promotes sail

training for young people through exhibitions at various maritime festivals and other events. Through its quarterly publication "Grands Voiliers Infos" and its monthly newsletter, it helps potential young trainees find opportunities to go to sea on sail training vessels around the world.

GERMANY
Sail Training Association Germany www.sta-g.de
Founded in 1984 as a not-for-profit organization, STAG's main purpose is the education, development and support of young people of all nationalities through sail training. Its members include 50 sail training vessels and over 5,000 individual members. The organization operates a bursary programs for sail training vessels and individual trainees.

IRELAND
Coiste an Asgard www.irishsailtraining.com
Formed in 1968, Coiste an Asgard operates the state owned Class A sail training vessel *Asgard II* and promotes offshore sail training for young people generally in the Republic of Ireland. Coiste an Asgard provides the communications link for offshore sail training interests in Ireland with Sail Training International pending the development of a national sail training organization (as defined by Sail Training International).

ITALY
Sail Training Association Italy www.sta-italia.it
Founded in 1976 by a partnership of the Italian Navy and the Yacht Club Italiano, its charter is to develop and promote sea training for young people as a means to furthering their personal development and education. Through the co-operation of the Navy and many owner/operators of other vessels, STA Italy offers a variety of sail training opportunities to young people, including berths at no charge or highly subsidized. The organization also operates an international trainee exchange program which is currently expanding.

LATVIA
Sail Training Association Latvia www.sta-latvia.lv
Founded in 2002 by 23 sail training enthusiasts in Latvia, the organiztion also has three members who own/operate vessels, two yacht clubs and three maritime companies. STA Latvia's principal goals are to develop sail training for young people in Lativa by encouraging other vessel owners to participate in sail training activities and events, and through an international trainee exchange program.

NETHERLANDS
Sail Training Association Netherlands
Founded in 1985, STAN's goals are to encourage and develop sail training off-shore for young people in the Netherlands. In pursuit of this, STAN organizes maritime events and races for sail training Tall Ships in the Netherlands.

NORWAY
Norwegian Sail Training Association www.nsta.no
Founded in 1999, NSTA has four membership categories: sail training vessels, past and

prospective host ports for The Tall Ships' Races, individuals and organizations supporting NSTA ideals, and corporate entities. The organization promotes sail training for young people and international friendship through sail training.

POLAND
Sail Training Association Poland www.pogoria.pl
Established in 1993, STA Poland has more than 100 individual (voting) members and is co-owner and sole operator of the Class 'A' *Pogoria*. Supporting (non-voting) members include the Maritime Academy of Gdynia (*Dar Mlodziezy*), the Polish Navy (ORP *Iskra*) the Polish Scouts Union Sea Training Centre (*Zawisza Czarny*) and the Polish Yachting Association (*Kapitan Glowacki*).

PORTUGAL
Portuguese Sail Training Association www.aporvela.pt
Aporvela – Portuguese STA was founded in 1980 as a registered charity. It has three categories of membership and owns three sail training vessels including the Caravel Vera Cruz. The organization's main objectives are to promote off-shore sail training mainly for young people.

RUSSIA
Admiral Makarov State Maritime Academy
This institution represents the interests of sail training in Russia and operates the 100-meter sail training ship *Mir*. The Academy provides the communications link for all sail training activities in Russia with Sail Training International, pending the development of a national sail training organization (as defined by Sail Training International).

SPAIN
Sail Training Association Espana www.sta-espana.org
Created in 2003, STA Espana' membership includes all sail training vessels in Spain, the Spanish Navy and a number of ports.

SWEDEN
Sail Training Association Sweden www.stas.nu
STA Sweden was founded in 1998, initially to support the Tall Ships' Races. Today its members include a number of Swedish ports, the Swedish Navy and some 60 vessels engaged wholly or occasionally in sail training activities.

UNITED KINGDOM
Association of Sea Training Organizations www.asto.org.uk
Founded in 1972, ASTO represents the interests of 25 sail training organizations and five associate members: 50 sail training vessels ranging in size from a ten-meter sloop to a 65-metre barque. The organization grants bursary funding towards the costs of more than 70,000 berth days for young and disabled trainees each year.

Programs and Services

ASTA's Annual Conference on Sail Training and Tall Ships

ASTA's Annual Conference on Sail Training and Tall Ships gathers ships' masters, public officials, port representatives, marine suppliers, naval architects, program administrators, festival managers, preservationists, environmentalists, crewmembers, and educators. Topics concerning vessel operations, regulatory issues, management, educational programming, and safety at sea are addressed each year, as are sessions on media relations, marketing, funding, communications, and port event organization. Held annually during the first week in November, the ASTA Conference on Sail Training and Tall Ships is both fun and informative and offers oceans of networking opportunities.

At the 2005 American Sail Training Association Conference on Sail Training and Tall Ships, to be held in Bay City, Michigan on November 3 and 4, 2005, we plan to explore partnerships, both private and public and how they build the future of sail training and tall ships. We hope to challenge presenters and participants to explore how partnerships can meet both the needs of communities and ASTA member organizations.

ASTA's Biennial Safety Under Sail Forum

Initiated in 1992, the Safety Under Sail Forum expands the international dialogue among professional mariners by presenting case studies of actual incidents at sea, discussing emerging technologies, and sharing "best practices" so as to constantly insure a high

level of safety and professionalism in the sail training industry. Professionals engaged in sail training, sea education, vessel operations, and tall ship events from throughout the world participate in this annual symposium. Topics covered have included preparing for heavy weather, hypothermia, technology and forecasting, survival gear and much more. The American Sail Training Association hosts the Safety Forum during odd-numbered years, in conjunction with the Annual Conference on Sail Training and Ships. In 2005, the Safety Under Sail Forum will take place in Bay City, Michigan on Saturday, November 5, following the 33rd Annual Conference on Sail Training and Tall Ships.

ASTA's Biennial Education Under Sail Forum

The ASTA Education Under Sail Forum made its grand premiere in Chicago in 2000. The first of what has now become a program-focused complement to the International Safety Forums biennial series. The Education Under Sail Forum is held during even-numbered years, in conjunction with the Annual Conference on Sail Training and Tall Ships. The forum is designed to inform and inspire excellence in the development and delivery of educational experiences under sail, and overflows with creative exchanges among captains, crew, administrators, teachers, program developers, curriculum designers, and others.

ASTA's Maritime Heritage Forum

Also held in conjunction with the Annual Conference on Sail Training and Tall Ships, the ASTA Maritime Heritage Forum is designed to give participants insight into the role of maritime museums in preparing the public for tall ship visits, developing and delivering Tall Ships Are Coming!® activities, and recruiting and training volunteer Tall Ships® Ambassadors by exploring ways to link local museums and historic sites with sail training traditions and history.

ASTA's Annual Regional Meetings

Regional - Atlantic, Pacific, Great Lakes and Gulf Coast - meetings are held late winter/early spring. These meetings are less formal than our annual Conference, but like the Conference, we encourage our professional members to submit ideas for locations and topics. The regional meetings offer an opportunity for the host to showcase their facility and programs while providing an intimate setting for attendees to network. A typical regional meeting may include a tour, special presentation, safety demonstration, day sail, luncheon and reception. Planning usually starts in November with meetings held in February, March or April. If your organization would like to host a regional meeting, please send a letter of interest along with a proposed agenda to ASTA.

Recent Hosts have included:
Atlantic – Nauticus, the National Maritime Center and the Schooner Virgina Foundation, Norfolk, VA
Pacific – The Los Angeles Maritime Institute, San Pedro, CA
Great Lakes – The Mayor's Office of Special Events and Navy Pier, Chicago, IL
Gulf – Texas Seaport Museum/Galveston Historical Foundation and the Barque Elissa, Galveston, TX

The ASTA Sail Training Rally

In the 1980s, ASTA developed the concept of the Sail Training Rally; a competition among crews, both at sea and ashore. These rallies provide trainees with an opportunity to demonstrate their seamanship skills in a friendly but competitive format by participating in shoreside events such as knot tying, tug-of-war, bucket brigade, rowing, walk the plank, and heaving line toss/hawser pull. Most often held in conjunction with the TALL SHIP CHALLENGE® Race Series, Sail Training Rallies allow the general public to observe the sort of teamwork and maritime skills that are learned on board sail training vessels at sea.

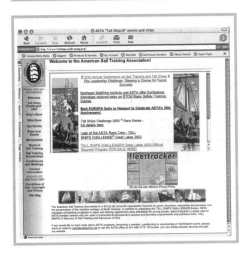

www.tallships.sailtraining.org is your portal to the world of sail training and tall ships. Links to ASTA member vessels and affiliates make it easy to learn more about opportunities under sail, the ships that can take you to sea, and shore-based programs. The ASTA Website also provides links to tall ship events such as the TALL SHIPS CHALLENGE® series and to international sail training associations and resources around the world. Information on upcoming ASTA events such as the Annual June Fundraiser, the Annual Conference on Sail Training and Tall Ships, regional meetings, and the Annual Appeal can also be found on the Website.

ASTA Scholarship and Grant criteria as well as printable application forms are available on the website - where you can also read first-hand accounts of the life-changing effects of sail training experiences in the form of essays and stories written by past scholarship recipients.

ASTA's Billet Bank

An on-line Billet Bank provides notice of positions available aboard ASTA member vessels. The Billet Bank is the most visited section of the ASTA website all year long and is the most effective service for matching professional sail trainers and open positions. ASTA Organizational Members are invited to post available positions using the standardized form found on the ASTA website. New information is added on a daily basis and billets remain posted for 90 days unless ASTA is otherwise advised. (ASTA does not endorse any specific

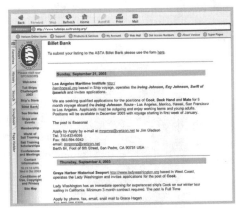

program or individual, but simply shares information as it becomes available.)
To learn more about the American Sail Training Association and how you can get involved, visit the ASTA Website today!

ASTA Publications

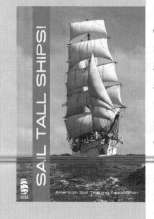

Sail Tall Ships! A Directory of Sail Training and Adventure at Sea first appeared in 1980, and is now in its sixteenth edition. The directory provides program and contact information for member vessels and sail training associations throughout the world. To help fulfill ASTA's mission, the directory is also distributed through maritime museums and their affiliated shops, marinas, maritime events, and sail training programs, as well as bookstores, libraries, high school guidance counselors, university career resource centers, and education conferences throughout the United States and Canada. US $14.95

Guidelines for Educational Programs Under Sail defines ASTA standards for sail training and sea education within the framework of the Sailing School Vessels Act. This manual defines criteria and indicators of effectiveness for the design, delivery, and evaluation of curricula, instruction, and program administration. In addition to the core of safe seamanship education, the guidelines apply to all aspects of sail training: adventure, education, environmental science, maritime heritage, and leadership development. US $12.00

The ASTA Training Logbook enables trainees to keep a personal log of their sea time and to document their progress in sail training, and records a progression of skill-building activities in nautical science, safety, seamanship, and navigation. Completion of course work and sea time must be certified by either the instructor or the ship's master. US $5.00 (Quantity discounts available)

Tall Ships® Fun! The Tall Ships® Fun! activity book is ASTA's newest product developed to spread the fun and adventure of sail training to future sailors. The 32-page book is designed to entertain the eager minds of 5 to 10 year old children. Unlike normal coloring books, this book provides cutout craft projects, stories and songs from the sea, charts, and various fun activities to connect youth with maritime culture and the tall ships. The Tall Ships® Fun! activity book is a great addition to your sail training program. A wonderful compliment to your educational resources, it encourages young people to further what they have learned from your programs and activities. Not only does it provide individual entertainment, but it can be used as a tool in your organization's youth and education departments too. US $6.95 (Quantity discounts available)

Tall Ships The Fleet for the 21st Century by Thad Koza, published by TideMark Press and now in it's third edition, includes a foreword by ASTA's Executive Director, Peter A. Mello, and is available through the ASTA Ship's Store. This beautiful book features four-color photographs of 150 sail training vessels in the international fleet. US $24.95

Tall Ships Calendar Few things on the high seas are more dramatic than the great clouds of sail raised by traditional full-rigged ships. This Tall Ships calendar features some of the world's most magnificent tall ships in photographs by Thad Koza. Sales benefit the American Sail Training Association, Wall hanging, full color, 14 by 11 inches. US $11.95

ASTA Publications can be purchased by calling the ASTA office at 401-846-1775.

ASTA SCHOLARSHIPS AND GRANTS

The Henry H. Anderson, Jr. Sail Training Scholarship was established in 1999 and the Ernestine Bennett Memorial Sail Training Scholarship added in 2003. Both are designed to assist people to achieve a sail training experience aboard USCG or national equivalent-inspected ASTA member vessels. The Henry H. Anderson, Jr. Scholarship is available to young people between the ages of 14 and 19 and is available to both individuals and groups. The Ernestine Bennett Memorial Sail Training Scholarship is available to people ages 14 and above with special consideration going to female applicants

from the Pacific Northwest. The ASTA Sailing Vessel Assistance Grant is designed to assist ASTA member vessels, which may not be USCG inspected, in maintenance and improvement projects that will better enable them to further ASTA's mission. The ASTA Crew Development Grant program is designed to help keep motivated crewmembers in the ASTA fleet by assisting them in upgrading their professional qualifications through training. Information about ASTA scholarship and grant programs, criteria and application forms are available through the ASTA Web site www.tallships.sailtraining.org or by calling the ASTA office 401-846-1775.

The ASTA Newsletter

RUNNING FREE is the American Sail Training Association's semi-annual newsletter providing in depth coverage of ASTA events including the TALL SHIPS CHALLENGE® Series, the Annual Conference the International Safety Forum, the ASTA Education under Sail Forum and the ASTA Maritime Heritage Forum.

e-RUNNING FREE is a monthly email newsletter guiding you to what's new at ASTA and in the sail training world In addition to current topics, check out the regular features like the Highlighted Program and TALL SHIPS CHALLENGE® News, To subscribe or to offer feedback, send an email newsletter@sailtraining.org.

Indices

Advertisers Index

We would like to thank our advertisers whose support makes the production of this directory possible.

Geographical Index

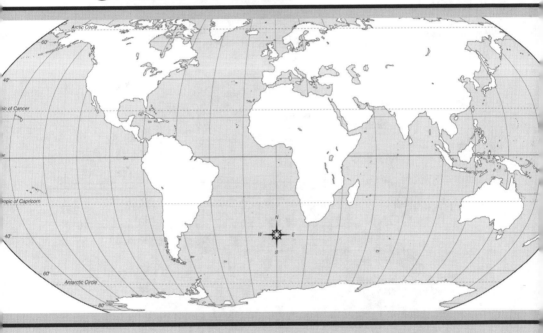

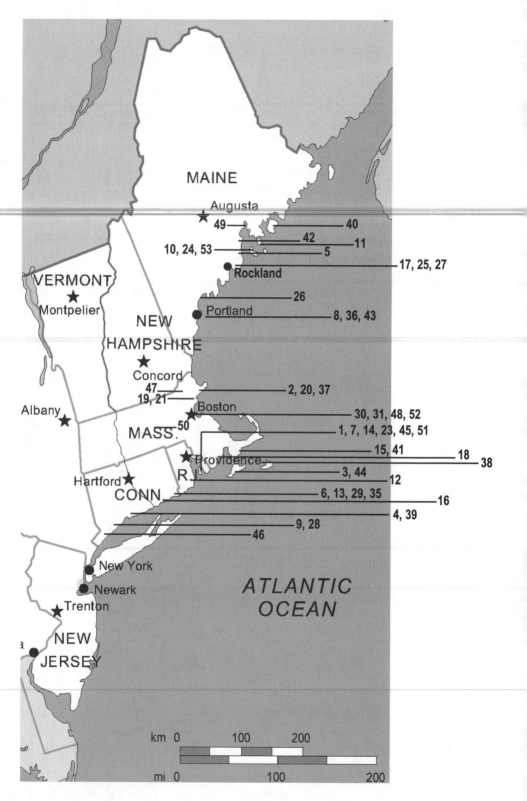

MAINE

Augusta ★

49 —

40

42

11

10, 24, 53 —

5

Rockland ●

17, 25, 27

26

VERMONT

Montpelier ★

Portland ●

8, 36, 43

NEW
HAMPSHIRE

★
Concord

47 —

2, 20, 37

19, 21 —

Boston

Albany ★

30, 31, 48, 52

MASS. 50

1, 7, 14, 23, 45, 51

15, 41

18

38

Hartford ★

Providence ★

R.I.

3, 44

12

CONN.

6, 13, 29, 35

16

4, 39

9, 28

46

New York ●

Newark ●

ATLANTIC
OCEAN

★ Trenton

NEW
JERSEY

●

km 0   100   200

mi 0   100   200

	Vessel	Organization	Homeport
1	ADIRONDACK II	Sailing Excursions, Inc.,	Newport, RI
2	ADVENTURE	Gloucester Adventure, Inc.	Gloucester, MA
3	ALABAMA	Coastwise Packet Co., Inc.	Vineyard Haven, MA
4	AMISTAD	Amistad America, Inc.	New Haven, CT
5	APPLEDORE II	Schooner Exploration Associates, Ltd.	Camden, ME
6	ARGIA	Voyager Cruises	Mystic, CT
7	AURORA	IDC Charters, Inc.	Newport, RI
8	BAGHEERA	Portland Schooner Company	Portland, ME
9	BLACK PEARL	The Aquaculture Foundation	Bridgeport, CT
10	BONNIE LYNN		Islesboro, ME
11	BOWDOIN	Maine Maritime Academy	Castine, ME
12	BRANDARIS	Friends of Brandaris	Wickford, RI
13	BRILLIANT	Mystic Seaport - Museum Education Dept.	Mystic, CT
14	CORONET	International Yacht Restoration School	Newport, RI
15	CORWITH CRAMER	Sea Education Association, Inc.	Woods Hole, MA
16	EAGLE (WIX 327)	U.S. Coast Guard Academy	New London, CT
17	ELLIDA	Maine Classic Schooners	Rockland, ME
18	ERNESTINA	Schooner Ernestina Commission	New Bedford, MA
19	FAME	Pennant Enterprises, Inc.	Salem, MA
20	FORMIDABLE		Gloucester, MA
21	FRIENDSHIP	Salem Maritime National Historic Site	Salem, MA
22	FRITHA	Sea Me.Sail	Mackeral Cove, ME
23	GERONIMO	St. George's School	Newport, RI
24	HARVEY GAMAGE	Ocean Classroom Foundation, Inc.	Islesboro, ME
25	HURRICANE	Hurricane Island Outward Bound School	Rockland, ME
26	ISLAND ROVER	Island Rover Foundation	Freeport, ME
27	J. & E. RIGGIN	Schooner J & E Riggin	Rockland, ME
28	JOHN E. PFRIEM	Aquaculture Foundation	Bridgeport, CT
29	JOSEPH CONRAD	Mystic Seaport-Museum Education Dept.	Mystic, CT
30	LIBERTY	The Liberty Fleet of Tall Ships	Boston, MA
31	LIBERTY CLIPPER	The Liberty Fleet of Tall Ships	Boston, MA
32	LOIS McCLURE		Burlington, VT
33	MABEL	Vineyard Voyagers, Inc.	Vineyard Haven, MA
34	MARY DAY	Penobscot Windjammer Co.	Camden, ME
35	MYSTIC WHALER	Mystic Whaler Cruises	Mystic, CT
36	PALAWAN	Palawan Services, Inc.	Portland, ME
37	POINCARE		Gloucester, MA
38	PROVIDENCE	Providence Maritime Heritage Foundation	Providence, RI
39	QUINNIPIACK	Schooner Sound Learning	New Haven, CT
40	RACHEL B JACKSON	Downeast Sailing Adventures, LLC	Southwest Harbor, ME
41	ROBERT C. SEAMANS	Sea Education Association, Inc.	Woods Hole, MA
42	ROSEWAY	World Ocean School	Belfast, ME
43	SAMANA	School of Ocean Sailing	Portland, ME
44	SHENANDOAH	Coastwise Packet Co., Inc.	Vineyard Haven, MA
45	SIGHTSAILER	Sightsailing, Inc.	Newport, RI
46	SOUNDWATERS	Soundwaters, Inc.	Stamford, CT
47	SPIRIT OF LARINDA	Wolverine Motorworks Shipyqard, LLC	North Reading, MA
48	SPIRIT OF MASSACHUSETTS	Ocean Classroom Foundation, Inc.	Boston, MA
49	STEPHEN TABER		Penobscot Bay, ME
50	TABOR BOY	Tabor Academy	Marion, MA
51	TREE OF LIFE		Newport, RI
52	USS CONSTITUTION	Navy of the United States of America	Charlestown, MA
53	WESTWARD	Ocean Classroom Foundation, Inc.	Islesboro, ME
54	WILLIAM H. THORNDIKE		Maine

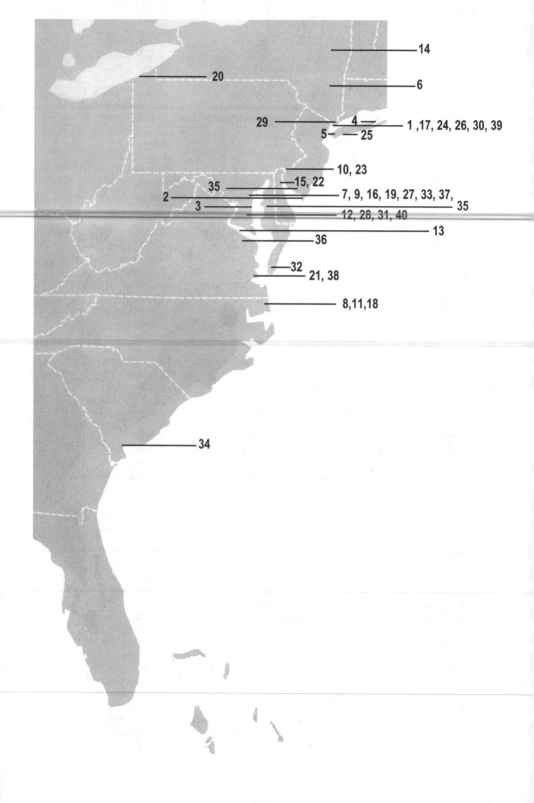

14

20

6

29   4

1 ,17, 24, 26, 30, 39

5   25

10, 23

35   15, 22

2

7, 9, 16, 19, 27, 33, 37,

3

35

12, 28, 31, 40

13

36

32

21, 38

8,11,18

34

Mid Atlantic

	Vessel	Organization	Homeport
1	ADIRONDACK	Sailing Excursions, Inc.	New York, NY
2	AJ MEERWALD	Bayshore Discovery Project	Bivalve, NJ
3	AMERICAN SPIRIT	National Maritme Heritage Foundation	Washington, DC
4	BOUNTY	HMS Bounty Organization, LLC	Greenport, NY
5	CHRISTEEN	The Waterfront Center	Oyster Bay, NY
6	CLEARWATER	Hudson River Sloop Clearwater, Inc.	Poughkeepsie, NY
7	CLIPPER CITY	Clipper City, Inc.	Baltimore, MD
8	ELIZABETH II	Roanoke Island Festival Park	Manteo, NC
9	FAREWELL		Dundalk, MD
10	GAZELA PHILADELPHIA	Philadelphia Ship Preservation Guild	Philadelphia, PA
11	GRAND NELLIE	Schooner Grand Nellie	Oriental, NC
12	GYRFALCON	The Longship Company, Ltd.	Oakley, MD
13	H. M. KRENTZ	Chesapeake Skipjack Sailing Tours, LLC	Potomoc River, MD
14	HALF MOON	New Netherland Museum	Albany, NY
15	KALMAR NYCKEL	Kalmar Nyckel Foundation	Wilmington, DE
16	LADY MARYLAND	Living Classrooms Foundation	Baltimore, MD
17	LETTIE G. HOWARD	South Street Seaport Museum	New York, NY
18	MEKA II	Pirate Pivateer	Beaufort, NC
19	MINNIE V.	Living Classrooms Foundation	Baltimore, MD
20	NIAGARA	Erie Maritime Museum	Erie, PA
21	NIGHTHAWK	Siren's Song Ltd.	Beaufort, NC
22	NORFOLK REBEL	Rebel Marine Service, Inc.	Norfolk, VA
23	NORSEMAN	Leif Ericson Viking Ship, Inc.	Wilminton, DE
24	NORTH WIND		Philadelphia, PA
25	PEKING	South Street Seaport Museum	New York, NY
26	PHOENIX	Coastal Ecology Learning Program	Glen Cove, NY
27	PIONEER	South Street Seaport Museum	New York, NY
28	PRIDE OF BALTIMORE II	"Pride of Baltimore, Inc."	Baltimore, MD
29	RESOLUTION II	Ship's Company	Londontown, MD
30	RICHARD ROBBINS	Classic Sail Windjammer Co., Inc.	Weehauken, NJ
31	Rocking the Boat		Bronx, NY
32	SAE HRAFN	The Longship Company, Ltd.	Oakley, MD
33	SERENITY	Low Sea Company	Cape Charles, VA
34	SIGSBEE	Living Classrooms Foundation	Baltimore, MD
35	SPIRIT OF SOUTH CAROLINA		Charleston, SC
36	SULTANA	Schooner Sultana Project	Chestertown, MD
37	SUSAN CONSTANT	Jamestown-Yorktown Foundation	Jamestown Settlement, VA
38	USS CONSTELLATION	Living Classrooms Foundation	Baltimore, MD
39	VIRGINIA	Virginia Maritime Heritage Foundation	Norfolk, VA
40	WAVERTREE	South Street Seaport Museum	New York, NY
41	WOODWIND and WOODWIND II	Running Free Inc.	Annapolis, MD

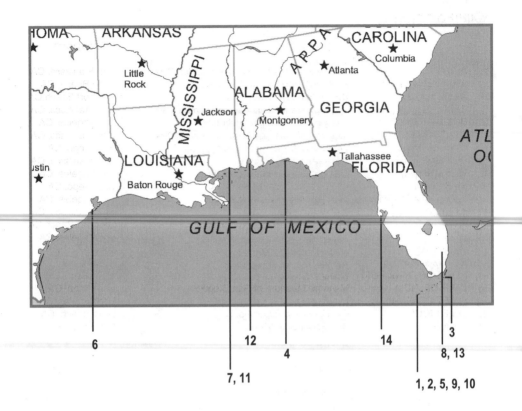

Florida and the Gulf

	Vessel	Organization	Homeport
1	ADASTRA	National Boat Owner's Association	Key West, FL
2	AMERICA	Historic Tours, Inc	Key West, FL
3	CALYPSO	Calypso Watersports and Charters	Key Largo, FL
4	DANIEL WEBSTER CLEMENTS	Sailing South Charters	Destin, FL
5	DREAM CATCHER	Coastal Sailing Adventures, Inc.	Key West, FL
6	ELISSA	Texas Seaport Museum	Galveston, TX
7	GLENN L. SWETMAN	Maritime & Seafood Industry Museum, Inc.	Biloxi, MS
8	HERITAGE OF MIAMI II	Heritage Schooner Cruises, Inc.	Miami, FL
9	LIBERTY	The Liberty Fleet of Tall Ships	Key West, FL
10	LIBERTY CLIPPER	The Liberty Fleet of Tall Ships	Key West, FL
11	MIKE SEKUL	Maritme and Seafood Industry Museum	Biloxi, MS
12	ST CHRISTOPHER	St. Christopher Services LLC	Mobile, AL
13	WILLIAM H. ALBURY		Miami, FL
14	YANKEE	Yankee Charter	St. Petersburg, FL

California

	Vessel	Organization	Homeport
1	ALMA	San Francisco Maritime National Historical Park	San Francisco, CA
2	AMERICAN PRIDE	American Heritage Marine Institute	Long Beach, CA
3	ARGUS	Boy Scout Sea Base	Newport Beach,CA
4	BALCLUTHA	San Francisco Maritime National Historical Park	San Francisco, CA
5	BILL OF RIGHTS	Los Angeles Maritime Institute	Los Angeles, CA
6	C.A.THAYER	San Francisco Maritime National Historical Park	San Francisco, CA
7	CALIFORNIAN	San Diego Maritime Museum	San Diego, CA
8	CORSAIR	Sea Scout Ship Viking	San Francisco, CA
9	EXY JOHNSON	Los Angeles Maritime Institute	Los Angeles, CA
10	HMS SURPRISE	Maritime Museum of San Diego	San Diego, CA
11	IRVING JOHNSON	Los Angeles Maritime Institute	Los Angeles, CA
12	KA'IULANI	Call of the Sea	San Francisco, CA
13	LYNX	Defense of Freedom Foundation	Newport Beach,CA
14	PETER PUGET		Los Angeles, CA
15	PILGRIM	Ocean Institute	Dana Point, CA
16	ROYALISTE	Privateer, Inc.	San Francisco, CA
17	SPIRIT OF DANA POINT	Ocean Institute	Dana Point, CA
18	STAR OF INDIA	Maritime Museum of San Diego	San Diego, CA
19	SWIFT OF IPSWICH	Los Angeles Maritime Institute	Los Angeles, CA
20	TOLE MOUR	CIMI Tall Ship Expeditions	Long Beach, CA
21	VIKING	Sea Scout Ship Viking	San Francisco, CA

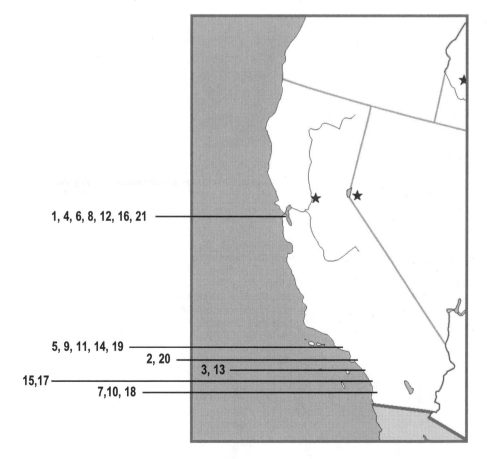

1, 4, 6, 8, 12, 16, 21

5, 9, 11, 14, 19

2, 20

3, 13

15,17

7,10, 18

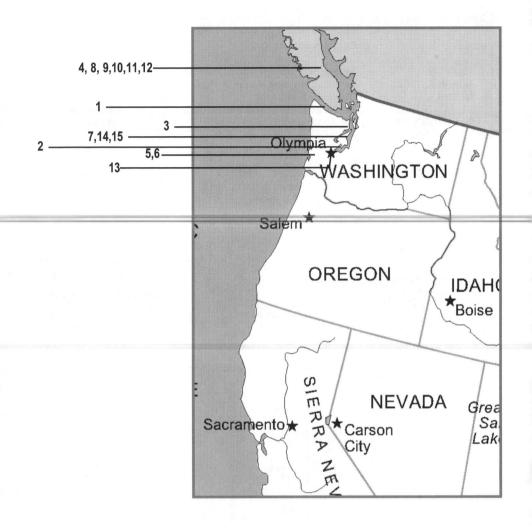

4, 8, 9,10,11,12

1

3

7,14,15

2

5,6

13

Olympia

WASHINGTON

Salem

OREGON

IDAH

Boise

NEVADA

Grea
Sa
Lak

SIERRA NEVA

Sacramento

Carson
City

Pacific Northwest

	Vessel	Organization	Homeport
1	ADVENTURESS	Sound Experience	Port Townsend, WA
2	BOUNTY OF KRISTER	Vashon-Maury Island Maritime Heritage Society	Vashon Island, WA
3	CUTTY SARK		Coupeville, WA
4	GAIA	Time of Yore	Vancouver, British Columbia,Canada
5	HEWITT R. JACKSON	Grays HarborHistorical Seaport Association	Aberdeen, WA
6	LADY WASHINGTON	Grays Harbor Historical Seaport Association	Aberdeen, WA
7	MALLORY TODD	Sailing Heritage Society	Seattle, WA
8	MAPLELEAF	Maple leaf Adventures	Victoria, British Columbia, Canada
9	MARY DARE	Pacific Sail Training Association	Victoria, British Columbia,Canada
10	ORIOLE	Royal Canadian Navy	Esquimalt, British Columbia,Canada
11	PACIFIC GRACE	S.A.L.T.S.	Victoria, British Columbia, Canada
12	PACIFIC SWIFT	S.A.L.T.S.	Victoria, British Columbia, Canada
13	RESOLUTE	Resolute Sailing Foundation	Olympia, WA
14	SUVA	Drayton Harbor Maritime	Seattle, WA
15	ZODIAC	Vessel ZODIAC Corporation	Seattle, WA

Great Lakes USA and Canada

	Vessel	Organization	Homeport
1	APPLEDORE IV	BaySail	Bay City, M
2	APPLEDORE V	BaySail	Bay City, MI
3	DENIS SULLIVAN	Pier Wisconsin	Milwaukee, WI
4	FRIENDS GOOD WILL	Michigan Maritime Museum	South Haven, MI
5	HIGHLANDER SEA	Highlander Sea, Inc	Port Huron, MI
6	INLAND SEAS	Inland Seas Education Assn.	Suttons Bay, MI
7	JULIANNA	Polish Yachting Assn	Chicago, IL
8	MADELINE	Maritime Heritage Alliance	Traverse City, MI
9	MANITOU	Traverse Tall Ship Company	Traverse City, MI
10	R. H. LEDBETTER	Culver Summer Camps	Culver, IN
11	RED WITCH		Chicago, IL
12	WELCOME	Maritime Heritage Alliance	Traverse City, MI
13	WINDY and WINDY II	WINDY of Chicago Ltd.	Chicago, IL
14	BLACK JACK	Bytown Brigantine, Inc	Ottawa, Ontario, Canada
15	FAIR JEANNE	Bytown Brigantine, Inc	Ottawa, Ontario, Canada
16	MIST OF AVALON		Ivy Lea, Ontario, Canada
17	NISKA		Midland, Ontario, Canada
18	PATHFINDER	Toronto Brigantines	Toronto, Ontario, Canada
19	PLAYFAIR	Toronto Brigantines	Toronto, Ontario, Canada
20	ST LAWRENCE II	Brigantine, Inc.	Kingston, Ontario, Canada

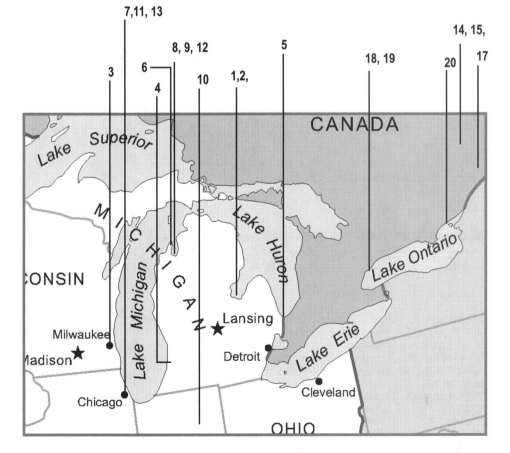

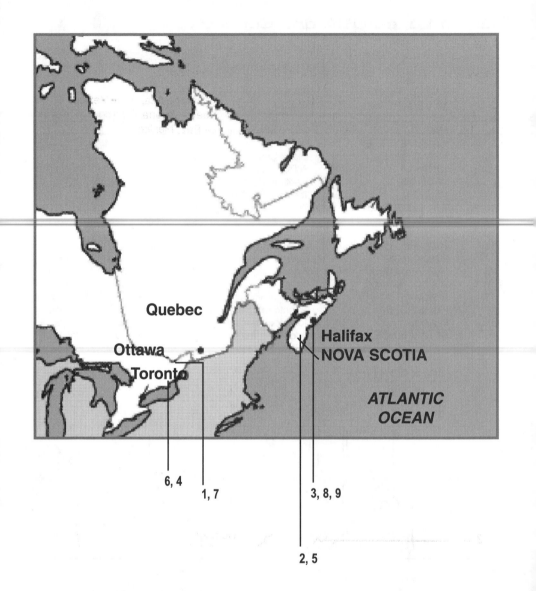

Canadian Maritimes
and the St. Lawrence Seaway

Vessel	Organization	Homeport
1 BLACKJACK	Bytown Brigantine, Inc	Ottawa, Ontario, Canada
2 BLUENOSE II	Bluenose II Preservation Trust	Lunenburg, Nova Scotia, Canada
3 CALEDONIA	Canadian Sailing Expeditions	Halifax, Nova Scotia, Canada
4 PATHFINDER	Toronto Brigantines	Toronto, Ontario, Canada
5 PICTON CASTLE	Windward Isles Sailing Ship Co.	Lunenburg, Nova Scotia, Canada
6 PLAYFAIR	Toronto Brigantines	Toronto, Ontario, Canada
7 FAIR JEANNE	Bytown Brigantine, Inc	Ottawa, Ontario, Canada
8 SILVA	Canadian Sailing Expeditions	Halifax, Nova Scotia, Canada
9 UNICORN		Halifax, Nova Scotia, Canada

Mexico

Vessel	Organization	Homeport
1 CUAUHTEMOC	Navy of Mexico	Puerto de Acapulco, Mexico
2 NINA	Columbus Foundation	Nuevo Vallarta, Mexico
3 TALOFA	Baja Schooner Cruises	La Paz, Mexico

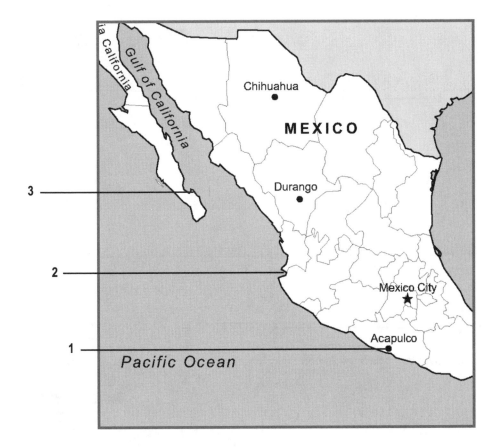

South America and the Caribbean

Vessel		Organization	Homeport
1	CAPITAN MIRANDA	Navy of Uruguay	Montevideo, Uruguay
2	CISNE BRANCO	Navy of Brazil	Rio de Janeiro, Brazil
3	CONCORDIA	Class Afloat	Bridgetown, Barbados
4	ESMERALDA	Navy of Chile	Valparaiso, Chile
5	GLORIA	Navy of Columbia	Cartegena, Columbia
6	GUAYAS	Navy of Ecuador	Guayquil, Ecuador
7	LIBERTAD	Navy of Argentia	Buenos Aires, Argentina
8	SIMON BOLIVAR	Navy of Venezuela	La Guaira, Venezuela

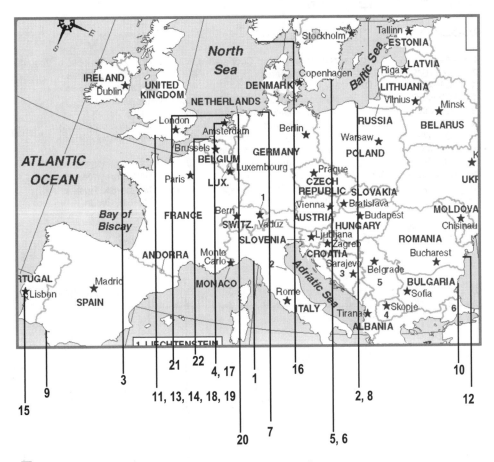

Europe

#			
1	AMERIGO VESPUCCI	Navy of Italy	La Spezia, Italy
2	DAR MLODZIEZY	Gdynia Maritime University	Gdynia, Poland
3	ETOILE and LA BELLE POULE	Navy of France	Brest, France
4	EUROPA	Rederij Bark Europa B.V.	Amsterdam, The Netherlands
5	FALKEN	Swedish Royal Navy	Karlskrona, Sweden
6	GLADAN	Swedish Royal Navy	Karlskrona, Sweden
7	GORCH FOCK II	Navy of Germany	Kiel, Germany
8	ISKRA	Navy of Poland	Gdynia, Poland
9	JUAN SEBASTION DE ELCANO	Navy of Spain	Cadiz, Spain
10	KALIAKRA	Navy of Bulgaria	Varna, Bulgaria
11	KRUZENSHTEN	Tall Ships Friends	Kalingrad, Russia
12	LORD NELSON	Jubilee Sailing Trust Ltd.	Southampton, United Kingdom
13	MIRCEA	Navy of Romania	Constanta, Romania
14	PICKLE		United Kingdom
15	PRINCE WILLIAM	Tall Ships Youth Trust	Portsmouth, England, United Kingdom
16	SAGRES	Navy of Portugal	Lisbon, Portugal
17	SORLANDET		Kristiansand, Norway
18	STAD AMSTERDAM	Netherlands Maritime Museum	Amsterdam, The Netherlands
19	STAVROS S NIARCHOS	Tall Ships Youth Trust	Portsmouth, England, United Kingdom
20	TENACIOUS	Jubilee Sailing Trust Ltd.	Southampton, United Kingdom
21	URANIA	Royal Netherlands Naval College	Den Helder, The Netherlands
22	ZENOBE GRAMME	Belgian Navy	Zeebruge, Belgium

Asia and the South Pacific

	Vessel	Organization	Homeport
1	ALVEI	Alvei Sail Training Cooperative	Port Vila, Republic of Vanuatu
2	ARUNG SAMUDRA	Navy of Indonesia	Jakarta, Indonesia
3	DEWARUCI	Navy of Indonesia	Surabaya, Indonesia
4	KAIWO MARU	National Institute for Sea Training	Tokyo, Japan
5	NIPPON MARU	National Institute for Sea Training	Tokyo, Japan
6	MIR	Tall Ship Friends	St. Petersburg, Russia
7	NADEZHDA		Vladivostock, Russia
8	PALLADA	Far Eastern State Technical Fisheries University	Vladivostock, Russia
9	R. TUCKER THOMPSON		Whangarei, New Zealand
10	SEDOV	Murmansk State Technical University	Murmansk, Russia
11	SHABAB OF OMAN	Sultanate of Oman	Muscat, Oman
12	SOREN LARSEN	Squaresail Pacific	Auckland, New Zealand
13	TARANGINI	Navy of India	Kochi, India
14	YOUNG ENDEAVOR	Royal Australian Navy	Sydney, Australia

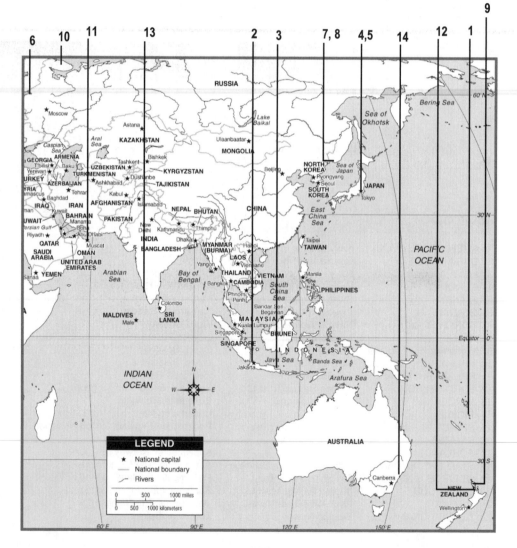

Alphabetical Index

A

I

J

K

L

385

386

T

Photo by Adria Lande

Photo by Adria Lande

Membership Opportunities

Membership Opportunities

In 2003, the American Sail Training Association celebrated the 30th anniversary of its founding. A lot has happened over that period, including growing the organization from a handful of vessels that sailed in the Northeastern United States to now nearly 250 tall ships and sail training vessels that navigate the world's lakes, bays, seas and oceans providing character building experiences and lifelong memories for thousands of youth of all ages each year.

A very important factor in ASTA's development over the years has been the strength of our membership. Without the support of our members, many of the education and scholarship programs that we offer such as the Henry H. Anderson, Jr. Sail Training Scholarship, the Ernestine Bennett Memorial Sail Training Scholarship, the ASTA Professional Crew Development Grants and the ASTA Vessel Assistance Grants would not be possible.

We offer several levels of membership:

Associate Membership

Individual - $50 per year
Benefits:
- Complimentary copy of Sail Tall Ships! A Directory of Sail Training and Adventure at Sea.
- Subscription to Running Free, our semi-annual newletter covering tall ships news and events.
- Subscription to e-RUNNING FREE our new monthly email newsletter.
- Discounts to attend ASTA Annual Conference
- Discounts to attend ASTA's Regional Meetings, Education and Safety Forums
- Invitations to attend ASTA special events and friendraisers

Junior - $25 per year
Open to sailors 22 years of age or younger
Benefits:
- All of the benefits of Individual Membership above

Family - $75 per year
Open to two members at the same address
Benefits:
- All of the benefits of Individual Membership above

Supporting - $250 per year
Benefits:

All of the benefits of Family Membership above

• An autographed copy of Tall Ships – The Fleet for the 21st Century by Thad Koza, a beautiful coffee table book featuring color photographs of 150 sail training vessels in the international fleet. (New members only)

Patron - $1,000 per year
For individuals wishing to express a greater commitment to ASTA's mission

Benefits:

• All of the benefits of Supporting Membership above

Organizational Memberships
Dues are based on a calendar year January 1 – December 31

Business Partners - $400 per year
For ports, businesses, and associates of sail training and tall ships.

Corporate - $1000 per year
For ports, businesses and associates of sail training and tall ships wishing to express a greater commitment to ASTA's mission.

Affiliate Membership - $250 per year
Open to non-profit organizations which do not operate their own sail training vessel, but do offer sail training, sea education or maritime history programs (Scouts, schools, colleges, etc.)

Benefits:
• A 150-word listing in the ASTA directory Sail Tall Ships!
• A listing of your Organization on the ASTA website. We provide a hot link to your website and appreciate reciprocity.
• The opportunity to post help wanted ads in the very popular Billet Bank on the ASTA website. The Billet Bank is the most visited section of the ASTA website all year long and is the most effective service for matching professional sail trainers and open positions.
• 10 complimentary copies of Sail Tall Ships for your staff and volunteers
• A subscription to Running Free, ASTA's newsletter to be published in June and October
• Discounts for staff to attend ASTA's Annual Conference on Sail Training and Tall Ships
• Discounts to attend ASTA Regional Meetings, educational and safety forums
• Invitations to attend ASTA special events and friendraisers

- 15% discount on display advertising in Sail Tall Ships!
- Additional copies of Sail Tall Ships! at production cost (plus shipping) for resale. We anticipate production cost to be less than $4.00 per book. Therefore, when you sell them at the suggested retail price of $14.95 you will not only be raising revenue for your program but equally important, you will be assisting us in spreading the word about the power of sail training.
- A subscription to our monthly email newsletter, e-RUNNING FREE, which covers a wide range of useful and news breaking topics. Additionally, your membership makes you eligible for the Highlighted Program section.

Sail Training Organizations/ Historic/Educational Vessels

Open to those organizations operating vessels. Membership dues are based on the organization's annual budget. **STO1:** Less than $250,000 / $375 per year, **STO2:** $250,000-$500,000 / $500 per year, **STO3:** Over $500,000 / $600 per year.

Benefits:
- A full page listing, including a photo of your vessel, in the ASTA directory Sail Tall Ships! (additional vessel listings are available for additional charges.) Distribution is 10,000 copies.
- Eligibility for the Henry H. Anderson, Jr. Sail Training Scholarship Program and the Ernestine Bennett Memorial Sail Training Scholarship Program.
- Eligibility for the ASTA Professional Crew Development Grant Program.
- Eligibility for the ASTA Vessel Assistance Grant Program.
- The opportunity to post help wanted ads in the very popular Billet Bank on the ASTA website. The Billet Bank is the most visited section of the ASTA website all year long and is the most effective service for matching professional sail trainers and open positions.
- A listing of your Organization on the ASTA website. We provide a hot link to your we site and appreciate reciprocity.
- 10 complimentary copies of Sail Tall Ships for your staff and volunteers;
- A subscription to Running Free, ASTA's newsletter to be published in June and October.
- Discounts for staff to attend ASTA's Annual Conference on Sail Training and Tall Ships.
- Discounts to attend ASTA Regional Meetings, educational and safety forums.
- Invitations to attend ASTA special events and friendraisers.
- 15% discount on display advertising in Sail Tall Ships!
- Additional copies of Sail Tall Ships! at production cost (plus shipping) for resale. We anticipate production cost to be less than $4.00 per book. Therefore, when you sell them at the suggested retail price of $14.95 you will not only be raising revenue for your program but equally important, you will be assisting us in spreading the word about the power of sail training.

• A subscription to our monthly email newsletter, e-RUNNING FREE, which covers
  a wide range of useful and news breaking topics. Additionally, your membership makes
  you eligible for the Highlighted Program section.

In addition to the above direct benefits, ASTA works on a regular basis with the Coast
Guard, Customs and Immigration and other government agencies on behalf of the sail
training industry.

We are also working on several additional projects that will bring added benefits in the
upcoming year to you as an ASTA member. We are exploring an ASTA member discount
program for STCW training courses and we are working on providing a member's
section to our website which will allow you to communicate with other ASTA members
on topics that you face as professional sail trainers.

We look forward to having you come aboard and join the ASTA Crew with the above
membership that best suits your interest and budget! Not only will you become a
member of the largest sail training association in the world, but you will be supporting
the youth education and leadership development programs that can help shape young
people's lives!

To become a member please mail or fax the form on the following page to:

ASTA
PO Box 1459
Newport, RI 02840 USA
Fax: +1 401.849.5400

Yes! I/We want to join the American Sail Training Association!

Name: _____

Organization: _____

Vessel(s): _____

Mailing Address: _____

City: _____ State/Province: _____ Postal/Zip: _____

Country: _____ *

Phone: _____ Fax: _____

E-Mail: _____

Website: _____

Please enroll me/us in the following membership category:

Associate Memberships *
Associate memberships are renewable on date of anniversary.

_____	Individual $50		_____	Supporting $250
_____	Junior $25		_____	Patron $1,000
_____	Family $75			

* For all addresses in Canada or Mexico, please add US $16 to cover the additional postage and handling costs. For addresses outside of North America, please add US $24.

Organizational Memberships **
Organizational Memberships are for calendar year (January 1 through December 31).

_____	Corporate $1000		_____	Business Partner $400
_____	Affiliate $250			

Sail Training Organizations/Historic/Educational Vessels:

_____	Budget less than $250,000	$375
_____	Budget between $250,000 and $500,000	$500
_____	Budget greater than $500,000	$600

** For all addresses in Canada or Mexico, please add US $25 to cover the additional postage and handling costs. For addresses outside of North America, please add US $40.

Payment of dues:

_____ Check or money order enclosed (US dollars please)

_____ Visa or MasterCard

Card number: _____ Expires: _____

Name on card: _____ Signature: _____